BUILDING CONSTRUCTION ESTIMATING

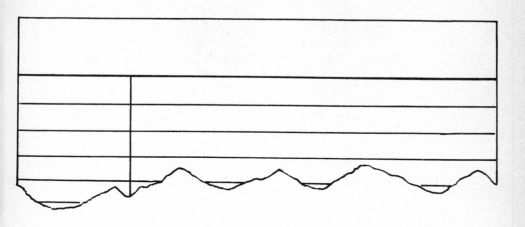

BUILDING CONSTRUCTION ESTIMATING
THIRD EDITION

GEORGE H. COOPER
Late Instructor
Mechanics Institute, New York

STANLEY BADZINSKI, JR.
Instructor
Milwaukee Area Technical College

McGraw-Hill Book Company
New York   St. Louis   San Francisco   Düsseldorf
Johannesburg   Kuala Lumpur   London   Mexico
Montreal   New Delhi   Panama   Rio de Janeiro
Singapore   Sydney   Toronto

This book was set in News Gothic by The Maple Press Company, and printed on permanent paper and bound by The Maple Press Company. The designer was Edward Zytko; the drawings were done by John Cordes, J. & R. Technical Services, Inc. The editors were Cary F. Baker, Jr., and David Dunham. Sally Ellyson supervised production.

BUILDING CONSTRUCTION ESTIMATING

Library of Congress Catalog Card Number 70-154221

07-012931-2

3456789 KPKP 79876543

CONTENTS

PREFACE

This is the third edition of a textbook originally written by the late George H. Cooper. He wrote the earlier editions as texts for standard courses in building construction estimating in vocational and technical schools. This edition is also intended to be a standard text for a building estimating course in technical and vocational schools. It is written to lead the student through a method of estimating, but does not cover methods of construction in detail. It is expected that the student will have obtained a working knowledge of construction details and blueprint reading.

As in the earlier editions, the practical requirements of the classroom have been given consideration throughout. The book forms a complete working plan for the instructor and includes some background material on each of the topics covered, specimen estimates, and essential reference data.

Chapters 1 to 9 discuss contracting as a business, building codes, plans, specifications, contracts, and the general technique of estimating. This material might constitute the first half of the course. Chapters 10 to 23 deal with the estimating of work performed by subcontractors and by the general contractor's own men.

The aim is to present in orderly sequence a well-rounded course covering the everyday work of the building contractor's estimator. The final chapter, Are You an Estimator?, deals with the terminal aspect of the course. The challenge should provide the student with a strong motive for learning. The comprehensive examination suggested by this chapter should be based on a set of selected blueprints available to the student in the classroom.

A full set of specifications, as for a modern business building, would require many pages and might confuse the student. For these reasons, only the essential extract of specifications for a residential building were included, and may be elaborated upon as desired by the instructor.

Several complete sets of plans and specifications should be available in the classroom for drill and test purposes. Complete estimates for several types of buildings should be available to show their general form and arrangement.

It is also suggested that full-size samples of many building materials be on display in the classroom, where students may see them and handle them to get a better understanding of these materials, especially if they are not provided in concurrent classes.

STANLEY BADZINSKI, JR.

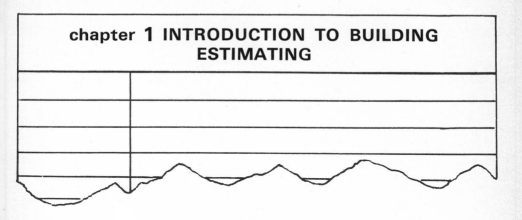

chapter 1 INTRODUCTION TO BUILDING ESTIMATING

INTRODUCTION

Building construction estimating requires a working knowledge of all phases of building work. The serious student of estimating may therefore be said to have an excellent opportunity to make a good general study of building work. Since nearly every man will find this knowledge useful at some time or other, whether or not he is directly connected with the building industry, it will readily be seen that the practicality of a course in estimating can hardly be overemphasized.

THE ESTIMATOR

In a well-organized contractor's office, the estimator is usually in the center of activity. From the time the office makes the first contact regarding a proposed building until the job is well under way, the estimator is deeply involved in the project. He may even have to make the contacts. His first duties include quantity surveying, interviewing subcontractors, obtaining quotations on materials, and preparing the estimate. After approval from company management, he submits the bid and follows through to help secure the contract. He has to make adjustments quickly; he must therefore have his records in good order and his wits about

1

him at all times. His role is important at every stage of the work.

Before the work on the job can begin, the estimator prepares the working estimate and the material lists and helps prepare the construction schedule. He is in constant touch with sources of supply, because it is often his duty to award the subcontracts and to supervise the purchasing of materials. Unless these are properly and promptly taken care of, there is much wasted energy all along the line afterward. The saying "A job well begun is half done" applies aptly here, for many a job has been bungled merely because it was turned over to the superintendent before it had been properly started in the office.

When the job gets under way, the general superintendent has control, and the estimator gradually relinquishes his hold, in order that he may put his time to use in securing other contracts. A good estimator will see that complete plans and specifications, copies of all subcontracts, and all other required data are given to the superintendent. He will make sure that every adjustment has been made in the records up to the time that he turns them over to the superintendent. He will clarify all points about which he thinks there may be any question or which may tend to slow up the progress of the job. He will insist upon his records being so complete at the time of their final release by him that nobody can hold him responsible for a mishap afterward.

PURPOSE OF THE COURSE

This course is for the practical purpose of training students in the everyday work of the building contractor's estimator. It is planned to cover the entire ground as thoroughly as possible in the time given to the subject. The textbook, which contains all the material required for a complete presentation of the principles underlying this subject, is planned both for classroom use and for home study.

A complete set of plans is included and will be referred to in the text. This plan illustrates many kinds of materials and several areas of construction.

Specimen estimate sheets will be found in all the chapters dealing with the estimates. These illustrate the recommended method of making the entries required in each of the various lines of work. Each student individually should do all the actual measuring of the plans, and each should make all the entries in the estimates. In this way he will gain familiarity with plan indications, units of measure, and methods of scaling the plans.

The hundreds of construction terms treated in the text are those commonly used by architects, contractors, and others concerned with building work everywhere. The student should realize that these constitute the construction man's basic language. As the terms are tied in with the text and the estimating work throughout the course, every serious student will have an opportunity to enrich his vocabulary by acquiring these new words and expressions. They will probably be of more practical value than the same number of words learned in a class in English literature.

The exercises given at the end of each chapter are based upon the work of the chapter. They should therefore be worked out thoroughly by every student while the chapter is being studied. In this way the weak points of the instruction or of the study will become apparent and can be reviewed before the next chapter is started. The last chapter in the book contains suggestions for final examinations and estimating problems, and represents the goal of the course.

Many unit costs are given in the text and in the specimen estimates. These are for the purpose of making the work more realistic and may be employed for pricing the estimates. However, it should be borne in mind that costs vary, for many reasons, which will be discussed in the text; these unit costs should therefore not be treated as permanent references for actual pricing of work.

This is a practical course, and the students should react by asking questions and looking up information to satisfy their interest in the practical nature of the work. Thus the conditions that facilitate the acquisition of knowledge will be fulfilled: a determination to know, an active mind, and an effective method of study. As the student increases his own power, imitation must gradually give way, and reason play an ever-larger role. The students are urged to discuss the work among themselves as well as with the teacher; in fact, they should work in pairs, if possible, always making sure, however, that each member of the pair goes through all the steps of the estimating process individually.

EXERCISES

1 Briefly, what are the duties of an estimator?

2 Up to what point is an estimator in control of a building operation?

3 What should the estimator do for the good of the job and for his own safety when relinquishing control?

4 Look over some of the books on estimating, such as those listed in the Bibliography. Write at least 100 words of notes on an introduction to estimating. Name the books that you have used for this purpose.

5 Prepare an annotated bibliography of books on estimating.

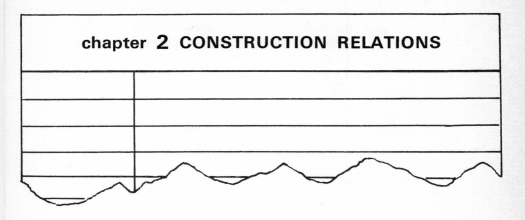

chapter 2 CONSTRUCTION RELATIONS

INTRODUCTION

The construction of a building involves many kinds of administrative and technical skills. This fact is not often fully appreciated by the general public or even by businessmen in other lines of work. They see a building going up, but seldom have an opportunity to look behind the scenes and observe the working of the system that makes possible the construction of the building—the activity in the various departments of the architect's, the contractor's, and the subcontractors' offices.

In a contractor's office much careful planning and scheduling must be done, equipment must be arranged for, and materials must be purchased and coordinated as to sequence of delivery. The field working force must be organized anew for each project, and definite arrangements must be made for payrolls, accounting, insurance, and tax records, in connection with this floating population of workers on the job.

It is the contractor's skill and the use of his business and technical organization that the owner buys when he signs a construction contract. A contractor who attempts to enter the field without proper skill and without a proper business and technical organization is operating under a great handicap.

Figure 2-1 shows the usual relationship that exists between the men who are concerned with the design and the construction of an average building job. This study is presented from the general contractor's viewpoint, and therefore the main line of action is shown running through the contractor's organization, as the chart indicates. The contractor looks to the owner as the man who pays him and as the one he wants to satisfy regarding the particular job.

THE ARCHITECT

The man who makes the plans is the *architect*. He also writes the specifications that accompany the plans and that

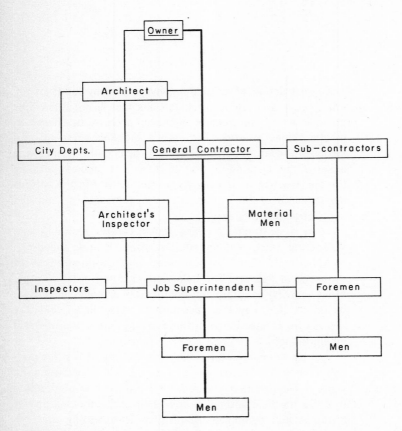

FIGURE 2-1 Construction relations.

further describe the work. He is engaged and paid by the owner to do this planning and to look after the owner's interests in connection with the building work.

At the beginning, the architect has dealings with the owner alone, preparing preliminary sketches and then making the regular plans and writing the specifications. After this is done, the *general contractor* enters the negotiations. He is asked to submit a bid for the job of constructing the building. Usually, the architect invites the contractors to bid, although sometimes it is the owner who does so.

Contractors are very likely to know about the job before it is time for bidding, because they follow up trade reports and other leads to jobs and are constantly in touch with a number of architects and others who frequently have work to be estimated. Since public contracts have to be legally advertised, one can always know about this class of work at least ten days before the bids are due.

The architect lends each invited contractor a set of plans and specifications, in order that he may prepare his estimates on which to base his bid. After the contract between the owner and the successful contractor is signed, this contractor looks to the architect for further information regarding the work to be done and for detail plans. He soon finds that he has both the owner and the architect to satisfy.

The architect sends a man from his office to act as his inspector on the job. This man is sometimes referred to as the *architect's superintendent*. The contractor has his own superintendent on the job to handle the various trades and to lay out the work, to order material as required, to manage the subcontract work, etc. The contractor's superintendent has continual contact with the architect's man and with the inspectors from the municipal departments that have jurisdiction over the work of constructing buildings.

MUNICIPAL DEPARTMENTS

The municipal departments are visited by the architect, because he has to file applications and plans in order to enable the contractor to secure a permit for the erection of the building. The contractor also visits them to get this and various other permits that contractors are required to have. After the job starts, the building site will be visited by the inspectors from these departments—and the contractor will have them to satisfy too!

Local laws always include regulations governing building work, which are generally referred to as *building codes*. The building code states the minimum requirements regarding the design, construction, and use of buildings and other structures. Safe and sanitary buildings are required. The minimum requirements for the size and quality of materials for walls, floors, roofs, plumbing, etc., are stated in the code.

SUBCONTRACTORS

Men or firms who do work for the general contractors are called *subcontractors*. This may be work that the general contractor does not wish to do, or work that he has not the facilities to do with his own men, or perhaps work for which he has not the required license. Steel, iron, roofing, sheet-metal, plumbing, heating, and electrical work are some of the lines that are commonly sublet in this way. The subcontractors send their men, equipment, and materials for the work they do on the job. The general contractor's superintendent sees that they do their work on time and in harmony with the other lines of work.

In small towns, where there are very few inspectors from the municipal departments, often one man acts for the building department. Similarly, in small places there are fewer subcontractors than in cities. In such cases the general contractors employ men directly for most of the trades, instead of giving the work to subcontractor specialists. In very large cities there seem to be subcontractors without end—for wood flooring, for scraping and finishing wood floors, for doing the cement finish work, for caulking, and for many other items of work that would ordinarily be done by the general contractor's own men in a smaller community.

Separate contracts are sometimes awarded by the architect or the owner, especially for the plumbing, heating, and electrical work, and on large jobs also for the structural steel, air conditioning, and elevators. The general contractor usually has no jurisdiction over such work but is expected to cooperate with the men who do the work. This cooperation may involve considerable expense to the general contractor, and it must be considered by his estimator in preparing the estimate. The owner who makes the separate awards saves on the general contractor's supervision costs, overhead expense, and profit on subcontracts but at the same time is burdening himself with the supervision and overhead expense connected with handling matters he may not be organized to handle. Furthermore, dividing the work in this manner may result in confusion on the job because the general contractor, who is experienced in coordinating the work of all trades, no longer has the power over these separate branches that would enable him to control the work properly.

Realizing all these factors, architects usually try to persuade the owner to make one complete contract for the entire job. Architects may even charge the owner an additional fee for having to deal with more than one contractor, because they are, in effect, acting as general contractors and are put to additional expense in the office and on the job.

MATERIAL MEN

Material man is the term used to denote any of the men or concerns that merely sell the materials used in building work. The lumber dealer is a material man. He sends the lumber to the job but does not send the carpenters who install it. The mason supply yard, the sand and gravel company, the hardware dealer, and all others from whom materials are bought are called material men and are thus distinguished from subcontractors, who do actual work on the jobs.

The subcontractors themselves use the material men, for supplying their own men with materials. Thus it may happen that occasionally the same material men will send material to the same job, both for the general contractor's use and for use by one or more of his subcontractors.

The same mason supply man may send bricks and cement for the general contractor's masonwork, and plastering materials for the subcontractor who is doing the plastering.

MECHANICS

The *mechanics* are the men who work with tools on the job. Helpers or apprentices also are employed in some trades. *Laborer* is a broad term, used to apply not only to the men who do the ordinary heavy work about the job, but also to helpers and apprentices. A bricklayer's helper, for example, is often referred to as a laborer.

A list of the employee classifications found on large jobs, together with their rates of wages, is shown in Table 2-1. The rates are given here merely so that the student

Table 2-1   Employee Classifications

Classification	Rate per Hour*	Classification	Rate per Hour*
Asbestos worker	5.83	Plasterer	4.82
Boilermaker	5.10	Plasterer's helper	4.69
Bricklayer	5.71	Plumber	5.57
Bricklayer's helper	4.48	Plumber's helper	4.63
Carpenter	5.21	Sheet-metal worker	5.41
Cement and concrete worker	5.25	Slate and tile roofer	5.17
Cement finisher	5.25	Steamfitter	5.77
Composition roofers	5.02	Steamfitter's helper	4.63
Composition roofer's helper	3.77	Stonemason	5.71
Electrician	5.46	Structural ironworker	5.36
Elevator constructor	5.29	Tile layer	5.30
Elevator constructor's helper	3.70	Tile layer's helper	4.52
Glazier	4.61	Operators of Equipment:	
Laborer, common	4.48	Air compressor	5.00
Marble setter	5.22	Hoist	5.65
Marble setter's helper	4.52	Concrete mixer	5.22
Metal lather	4.82	Tractor	5.44
Terrazzo worker	5.22	Truck	4.48
Terrazzo worker's helper	4.50	Bulldozer	5.44
Painter	5.11	Shovel	5.65

*Payments for employee insurance, pension, and vacation plans must be added to the hourly rate.

may become somewhat familiar with them; naturally, they do not apply in all parts of the country. The whole field of industrial relations and business economics is undergoing a change. Workmen on construction jobs are being unionized in practically every part of the country. The rates shown are union rates per hour that apply in some localities.

In some areas plasterers and electricians may work only six hours per day; excavating workers, ironworkers, and plumbers eight hours per day; and some other trades only seven hours per day.

Most unions maintain funds which provide the men with various welfare benefits, such as sickness and vacation payments and pensions when they retire. These benefits are in addition to the workmen's compensation and unemployment insurance coverages required by state law and the social security payments required by the federal government.

Good contractors also carry public liability and property damage insurance and sometimes are required to pay other insurance and taxes which are based on the men's pay. Because of all these payroll costs, contractors frequently speak of all-inclusive costs per hour instead of merely the regular wage rate per hour. A man whose wage rate is $5 per hour might cost the contractor more than $6 per hour when all these added costs are included.

EXERCISES

1 Make a chart showing the relationship between men on an average job or, if possible, on a job with which you are familiar.

2 State the relationship of subcontractors to a job and name at least six lines of work that are commonly sublet.

3 What is a material man? Name several kinds.

4 State what the term mechanic means as used in building work, and name six trade classifications of mechanics.

5 Name ten positions held by men on a building job who are not employed by the general contractor.

6 Write at least 100 words of notes on the men concerned with building work, taken from one or two of the books listed in the Bibliography. Name the books used.

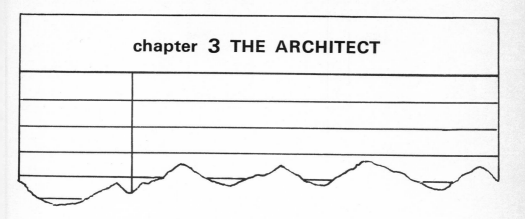

chapter 3 THE ARCHITECT

INTRODUCTION

The architect's duties have been partly set forth in Chapter 2, which shows his relations with the group of men concerned in a building operation. He furnishes the drawings and specifications necessary for the proper prosecution of the work and also any additional drawings, details, and directions required as the work proceeds, except the shop drawings.

Shop drawing is the general term applied to all plans and details prepared by the contractor and his subcontractors and material men. The millwork details submitted by the material man for the millwork are shop drawings. The fabrication details and setting plans prepared by the subcontractors for the structural steel work and miscellaneous ironwork are shop drawings.

The architect inspects and passes upon the work and determines whether it accords with the contract and with his plans and specifications. He usually has the power to make decisions relating to all the contracting parties and all controversies arising under the contract.

The architect has the power to determine allowances for changes in the work ordered by the owner. He has the power to act as the owner's agent in emergencies affecting the safety of limb or property and to order any work necessary to meet such emergencies. If he thinks such action is necessary for the proper execution of the contract or for safeguarding the work from unfavorable weather conditions, he may suspend the work until the offending causes have been removed. He certifies as to the amount owing to the contractor and has the power to withhold payments to protect the owner from loss that is due to failure on the part of the contractor to meet obligations under the contract.

THE OFFICE

The architect's office personnel usually consists of a head draftsman, several other draftsmen, and a secretary. The head draftsman works in close conjunction with the architect in preparing the preliminary sketches and in studying the client's requirements, as well as in the general designing and planning. The other draftsmen complete the drawings and make the tracings.

In architectural offices there is always ample provision for drafting work. Even a small office will have several drafting tables. In addition, there are plan files, sample cabinets, bookcases, and other special equipment, as well as the usual desks, files, typewriters, etc., that are common to all offices. (See Figure 3-1.)

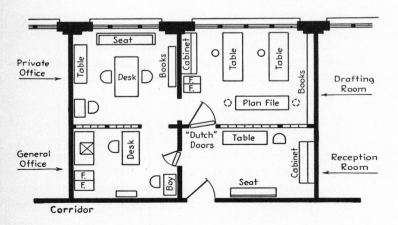

FIGURE 3-1 An architect's office.

Generally, either the architect or his head draftsman does all the specification writing. This is a sort of one-man specialty, involving not only continual contact with manufacturers' representatives, but also the coordinating of all the building work described under the different specification headings.

In large architectural offices there are designers, squad leaders, draftsmen, tracers, detailers, engineers, structural draftsmen, mechanical draftsmen, checkers, etc. Such offices are often highly organized. Figure 3-2 shows the layout of offices for a firm of architects and engineers that handles the design of large industrial plants as well as the general run of architectural work.

LICENSES

In practically all states it is unlawful for any person to practice or to offer to practice architecture unless he has been duly licensed as an architect. Engineers, as such, may also obtain licenses, and they then have almost the same powers and duties as architects in connection with building work.

In New York State, licenses are issued by the State Education Department. To secure a license as architect the applicant must submit evidence that he is at least twenty-five years of age and a citizen of the United States. Besides, he must have completed an approved four-year high school course or its equivalent, as determined by the State Education Department, plus the completion of two years in an institution registered as maintaining satisfactory standards, conferring the degree of bachelor of arts or science or the equivalent.

The applicant must submit satisfactory evidence to the Board of Regents of at least five years' practical experience in the office of a reputable architect, commencing after the completion of the high school course of study. The law in New York also provides that, notwithstanding all else, every applicant shall establish by written examination his competency to plan, structurally design, and supervise construction. Each complete year of study in a registered school or college may be accepted in lieu of one

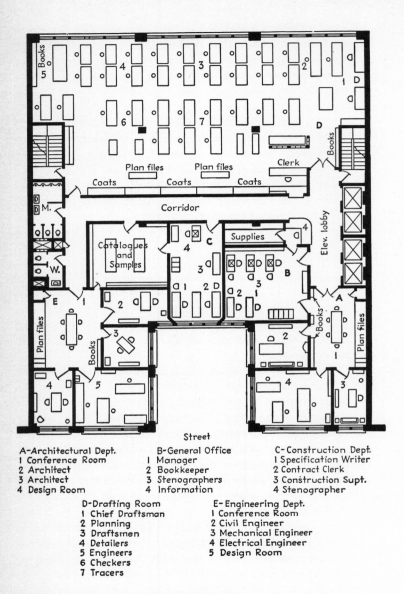

FIGURE 3-2 A firm of architects and engineers.

A—Architectural Dept.
1 Conference Room
2 Architect
3 Architect
4 Design Room

B—General Office
1 Manager
2 Bookkeeper
3 Stenographers
4 Information

C—Construction Dept.
1 Specification Writer
2 Contract Clerk
3 Construction Supt.
4 Stenographer

D—Drafting Room
1 Chief Draftsman
2 Planning
3 Draftsmen
4 Detailers
5 Engineers
6 Checkers
7 Tracers

E—Engineering Dept.
1 Conference Room
2 Civil Engineer
3 Mechanical Engineer
4 Electrical Engineer
5 Design Room

year of experience; in this case, the applicant must submit evidence of sufficient additional experience to give him a total of eight years.

The examination in New York State is based on the four following subjects or groups:

History of Architecture

The candidate gives evidence in the examination, by means of clear descriptions, analyses of plan, construction, general expression, and ornament, that he understands the essentials that give character to the various historic styles of architecture.

Architectural Composition

The candidate must show that he understands the broad principles underlying the subject of architectural planning by the application of those principles to specific problems stated in the examination. The social, economic, and physical requirements of several architectural problems are outlined, and the candidate is asked to state the principal considerations that would guide him in the choice of an arrangement of plan that would most adequately express and fulfill the conditions suggested.

Architectural Engineering

In this subject the candidate's handling of the examination must give evidence that he has a thorough understanding of the appropriate use of the various materials used in buildings. He is required also to solve certain technical problems, such as the calculation of the proper economic dimensions of various structural members common to buildings in the several materials noted. The use of handbooks is permitted. Questions are asked relating to structural design, use of materials, heating and ventilating, electric equipment, plumbing and fire-protection equipment, and elevators.

Architectural Practice

In the examination the candidate must give evidence that he understands the moral and legal responsibilities of the architect in the proper performance of his duties. He is required to outline or draft clauses of contracts and to show that he understands the major provisions of state, county, and municipal laws and ordinances and the way they affect the different classes of buildings. Questions under this heading will be asked relative to the following topics:

Business and professional functions of architects. Professional relation of clients and contractors. Responsibilities of architects and methods of conducting their business.

Building Laws. State, county, and municipal. Filing plans and specifications. Obtaining permits.

Contracts. Drawings, specifications, and agreement, as essential parts of the customary contract between owner and builder. Provisions as to bids, letting contracts, requisitions, certificates, and payments.

Specifications. General conditions, purposes, and scope Principles that should be observed in writing specifications.

Drawings. Purposes, use, and limitations of preliminary drawings. Essentials that should be embodied in contract drawings.

THE INSPECTOR

The architect's *inspector* watches the men while they work and reports back to his office as to what is going on at the job day by day. If he is a practical and experienced construction man, his worth is appreciated on the job. His presence there is equal to that of an additional superintendent or engineer. He will be able to offer practical suggestions that will help in making the worker contented on the job.

No honest contractor objects to this sort of inspection or supervision on behalf of the architect or the owner. Some architects, however, send young draftsmen to the job to act as their inspectors, perhaps only occasionally if it is not a large job. Since these young men have not had much to do with construction work and do not keep in close contact with the work, they can merely act as messengers between the architect and the job. If they fill just that function, the contractor's men are usually satisfied. There is trouble sometimes, however, because a young man of this type becomes overambitious and makes a nuisance of himself in many ways; yet he must be treated courteously, even when there is the feeling that he deserves to be "thrown off the job."

Specifications are usually based on average conditions. These may not foresee unexpected circumstances that can

---

JOHN T. BARTHOLOMEW, ARCHITECT

INSPECTOR'S DAILY REPORT

JOB _Morgan Residence_

WORK DAY _16_   DATE _April 2, '71_

GENERAL CONTRACTOR	WORK
4 Supt. T.K.	Watch. Casp. Fore.
6 Bricklayers ⎫	S. & E. walls. To 2nd
4 Laborers ⎭	floor tonight
3 "	Moving scaffolds
2 "	Grading rear lawn
4 Carpenters	N. & W. window frames
4 "	Started 2nd fl. beams
SUBCONTRACTORS	WORK
4 Plbg.	Roughing 1st floor
3 Elect.	Leaders, 1st floor

CAUSES OF DELAY _Much water from storm yesterday. No pump on job – expect one tomorrow._

INFORMATION NEEDED _Please send the revised 2nd floor plan at once_

(Put Remarks on Other Side)   SIGN _Wm. Smith_

FIGURE 3-3 An architect's inspector's report.

arise as the work progresses. Sometimes it is impossible or impractical to meet the specification requirements in every detail. In such cases an experienced inspector can work out a compromise.

Figure 3-3 shows a typical daily report sent by an architect's inspector, employed full time at the job, to his home office. The contractor's superintendent daily sends to his office a somewhat similar report.

SPECIFICATIONS

Specification writing involves a knowledge of the materials and methods of construction in detail and of the various customs that apply in all the trades. This implies that the specification writer must have experience in all these matters. Renderings for the client and well-prepared working drawings for the contractor should be followed by specifications that are as complete as the work warrants. The specifications are what guide the whole work in regard to the quality of materials and workmanship and the relations between the many parties concerned with the job. Specifications are legal documents as well as technical treatises and should always be written with these facts in mind.

Many specifications include a set of general conditions as established by AIA Document A-201. The entire document with its forty-four articles may be made a part of the actual specifications and contract, or it may be adapted to the specifications by reference. The estimator should be familiar with these general conditions because they define the responsibilities of the concerned parties and, when understood and followed, help to avoid disputes.

Following the section devoted to the general conditions, a good specification is written in the same sequence, generally speaking, as the order in which the trades commence work on the job. Thus the first work heading would be Demolition, Clearing Site, or Excavating, depending upon which of these would be appropriate in the particular case. Suitable headings for the rough and finish trades would follow. The so-called mechanical trades, however, are generally placed at the end of the specifications. These mechanical lines are plumbing, heating, electrical work, elevator work, and other piping, wiring, and machinery work.

The specifications are, theoretically, supposed to take precedence over the plans; what is described in the specifications is used in place of a differing plan indication for the same item. Similarly, large-scale drawings take precedence over small-scale drawings; therefore estimators should always study all the detail drawings that are supplied with the general plans. Specifications, contracts, and plans must be studied with great care; often a single sentence in a specification or a contract or a simple note or symbol on a plan will mean the loss of profit on a job.

Estimators like a specification so arranged that they can follow its order in their own work and use the specification as a complete check on the items required. It must be said, however, that nearly all specifications show an overlapping of items. The estimator is expected, perhaps unfairly, to see that every item is provided for in the estimate, to ascertain whether all items are specified, and to straighten out any duplications in the specifications or in the estimate.

Contractors and estimators learn to beware of loose phrases in specifications, especially if they have not had previous experience with the architect. Someone has described specifications as an architect's dream, a contractor's nightmare, and a material man's dilemma. Such phrases as "to the satisfaction of the architect," "as directed," "in the opinion of the architect," "as approved by the architect," "if required," etc., depend for their meaning upon the character and the whim of the architect and his inspector on the job and are therefore obviously unfair to the contractor. The estimator is at a loss as to what prices to put on items so worded, because the architect does not specify just what is wanted.

An estimator should make a list of all vague wording found in specifications, especially if the indications are that his firm is to be awarded the contract, and then, if possible, should have a clarification put into the contract before it is signed. At the least, he should have all such items discussed before the contract is signed, and notes kept of the clarifications.

THE ARCHITECT'S ATTITUDE

Some architects set themselves up as a kind of court of last resort in regard to the judgment of quality of material, even going so far as to overrule the official grade markings of lumber inspectors, who are supposed to be unbiased. An estimator is forewarned by a specification in which an architect deliberately states that the architect's decision will be final. This usually means that he will be hard to please and will probably act as if he were paying for the building himself rather than serving as architect, or third party, to the contract. Despite the so-called ethics of the architectural profession, which claim that architects are fair-minded men, contractors know that many among them are very hard to please and inflexible and far from what is generally regarded as fair-minded. Fortunately, very few have the reputation of "breaking" the contractor or of "rubbing it in" on every job.

GROUNDS FOR DISPUTE

Most of the disputes in connection with building work arise when too little care has been given to the writing of the specifications. These disputes often lead to expensive lawsuits and arbitrations, which, although final, are unsatisfactory to all parties. It should be a duty of the architect to take care, when a contract is entered into, that no dispute will arise about the amount of work the builder has to perform, the quality of that work, and how much the owner must pay for it.

EXERCISES

1 Briefly, what are the functions of an architect? (80 to 100 words)

2 Describe the work of an architect's office personnel.

3 What is a shop drawing? Name some types.

4 What are the four subjects or groups upon which the New York State architects' license law examination is based?

5 What is the general form and arrangement of a specification?

6   What lines of work are commonly referred to as the mechanical trades?

7   What is the order of precedence of specifications, general scale plans, and detail drawings?

8   What should an estimator do regarding vague phrases that he knows may bring about disputes if they are not clarified?

9   What are four vague phrases often used in specifications?

10   Write at least 100 words of notes on the architect and his work, from one or two of the books listed in the Bibliography. Name the books used.

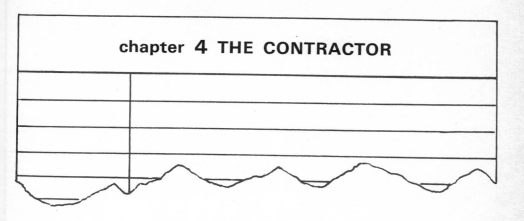

chapter 4 THE CONTRACTOR

THE CONTRACTOR'S DUTIES

The contractor (general contractor) organizes and is responsible for the entire job. He supplies the tools, equipment, and material for doing the work that is to be done by his own men and he makes subcontracts for the work that he does not intend to have done by his own men. He establishes the job office and provides the superintendent, job clerks, layout engineers, and watchmen. He usually has to obtain the building permits and to provide the temporary safeguards, temporary toilet facilities, and water supply. He builds the architect's office on the job (when one is called for), and on large operations he provides telephone service, heat, and water supply in it. The contractor pays all the bills and payrolls for his own work on the job, and he also pays the subcontractors. He has to satisfy a great number of federal, state, and local laws, which call for taxes and insurance of many kinds, and he must make the whole job comply with the requirements of labor department, building department, and other public inspectors.

The term *contractor*, as used in building work, generally refers to the man (or firm) who undertakes to construct a complete building or to make a complete alteration of an existing building for an owner. The chart in Figure 2-1 shows this relationship. He is sometimes called the *general contractor* or the *builder,* to distinguish him more clearly from the subcontractors. Subcontractors may be called contractors also, in their own special lines of work. Thus there are plumbing contractors, heating contractors, painting contractors, etc. Material men are occasionally referred to as contractors or subcontractors, too—millwork contractors, hardware contractors, etc., for example.

The building business is romantic and challenging, but it becomes increasingly complex with the passing years. No longer can the bright young foreman blossom out into a contractor by merely having a sign painted with his name on it. At least, this is not one of the important steps. Now,

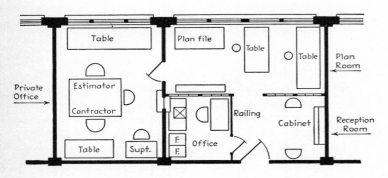

FIGURE 4-1   A contractor's office.

he must first organize to suit many laws and regulations, union requirements, financial arrangements, etc. Modern contracting is a business to be learned well before one undertakes it. It is not a poker game where the inexperienced may think they can jump in occasionally and win. Sometimes even an experienced contractor errs in thinking that he will be a wizard at anything he attempts. Only a small proportion of the men who start in business as contractors ever become really successful. Many of those who fail are expert mechanics, some are good foremen, and others are estimators who are lacking in experience. Perhaps the main reason for all failures is a lack of the understanding that the expert estimator possesses. Such an estimator is the logical man to start a building business; yet—by virtue of his deep insight into the many problems that are involved—he knows the importance of being organized for efficient management of every detail of the business, in addition to being strongly organized financially.

Figure 4-1 shows a plan of a typical contractor's office. The staff organization in such an office consists of the contractor, the estimator (or "office man"), the superintendent (or "outside man"), and the bookkeeper-stenographer. Where there is enough work, a regular bookkeeper and a timekeeper are employed. If the jobs handled are large enough in size, a superintendent is placed on each one and the so-called outside man becomes the general superintendent.

JOB MANAGEMENT

Some men are peculiarly fitted for the planning and planting of construction work. Other men, who are deficient in this faculty, are capable of managing and executing plans. It almost goes without saying that unless a job is well planned, even the most conscientious management will all too frequently not be able to save it from loss. One is beaten from the start. Time could not be spent more wisely than in making a close study at the beginning to discover the best possible way of doing everything on the job. Obviously, hit-or-miss, slovenly ways of working should be avoided. Economy and savings usually follow in the wake of method and orderliness. In addition, the morale and interest of employees are raised by an atmosphere of order and method. Construction men like clean-cut, decisive instructions, but only with a well-thought-out program can such instruction be given with confidence.

A job is on comparatively safe ground when it is under the direction of a real superintendent, when it has a sensible but simple cost system, and when it has been properly planned and coordinated before being started. Good men cannot be held for such purposes in an organization, however, unless loyalty, ability, and earnest interest are rewarded. "Cheap" men are often very expensive in the end. A real superintendent is a man with experience, judgment, alertness, and a disdain for carping criticism. He is considerate and tactful in handling men, although he demands results from them. He avoids all favoritism. He is thick-skinned but always fair. He keeps informed as to new methods and equipment.

Jobs are affected by dissatisfaction among subcontractors. Too close bargaining or poor supervision on the job on the part of the general contractor's men may cause this. When a contractor holds the subcontractors down to the last cent, things seldom go along as smoothly as they otherwise would. Bargains can be too close, and there is no tonic so stimulating to subcontractors as making money. If they are squeezed too tight, by and by the general contractor himself gets squeezed, often in most unexpected ways. The law of compensation seems to bring this about.

A *progress schedule* should be made out for every job. This shows the approximate working periods assigned to each branch of work. In this way, control is better and the work of the various trades is less likely to conflict. The foundation, the rough superstructure, and the work of the finishing trades are the three general divisions of the schedule. Each of these divisions is subdivided to include the work of every different group of men that will be required on the job. The progress schedule is made out by the contractor's estimator, after consultation with those subcontractors upon whose work the progress of the job will mainly depend. Copies of the schedule are given to the architect and to all the main subcontractors. The other subcontractors and material men are notified as to when they will be required. Figure 4-2 shows a typical progress schedule.

This type of progress schedule is a traditional method of scheduling and is usually referred to as a bar chart, or Gantt chart. To make this type of chart, the contractor must use his knowledge of construction to arrange the proper sequence of work, but often conditions which were unknown or unthought of cause difficulties in getting work done according to the schedule. To overcome this problem, more and more contractors are turning to the critical path method of job scheduling.

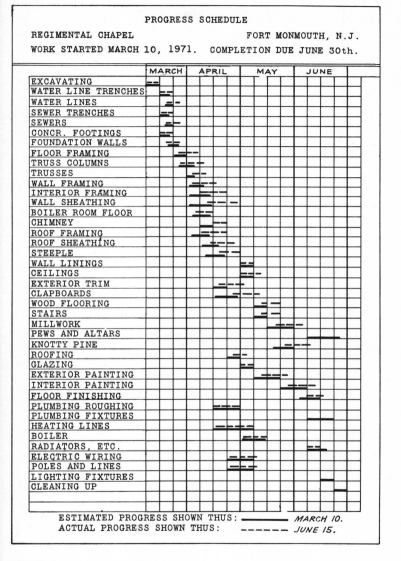

FIGURE 4-2   A progress schedule.

CRITICAL PATH METHOD

The *critical path method*, or CPM, may be referred to as a method of planning a construction job. It involves a line diagram or chart which depicts the various parts of the job in the order they must be performed. Figure 4-3 shows a critical path diagram for the job named in Figure 4-2. In this model the work to be performed is shown by lines with the starting point at the tail and completion at the head of the arrow. The construction of this model requires the contractor to think the job through from beginning to end before even starting actual work, and in so doing, reveals situations which may have gone unnoticed until encountered on the job. CPM is also used to allocate resources (men, equipment, and materials) to the various jobs, and perhaps most important, CPM is used to control the construction job.

Because construction costs for labor, materials, and financing are rising each year, it is very important that the contractor control the job so as to avoid slowdowns in the work, inefficient use of equipment, delays in material delivery, and other conditions which add to the overall cost of construction. In using CPM to control a job, the contractor checks to see that work is following the CPM schedule. If it falls behind at any point, action is taken to bring the work back on schedule. If this is not possible, the work is rescheduled to make the best use of time and resources.

The estimator should be familiar with CPM because of its increasing use in construction and its effect on job time and job costs. Many contractors are including a CPM diagram or model in their bids, and in some cases it is required by the specifications.

Historical Background CPM was developed in the period 1956 to 1958 for the E. I. du Pont de Nemours & Company. Its purpose was to provide the company with a means of making accurate time and cost estimates for the construction of several chemical plants.

In 1958 the U.S. Navy was concerned with the control of a large number of contracts and contractors involved

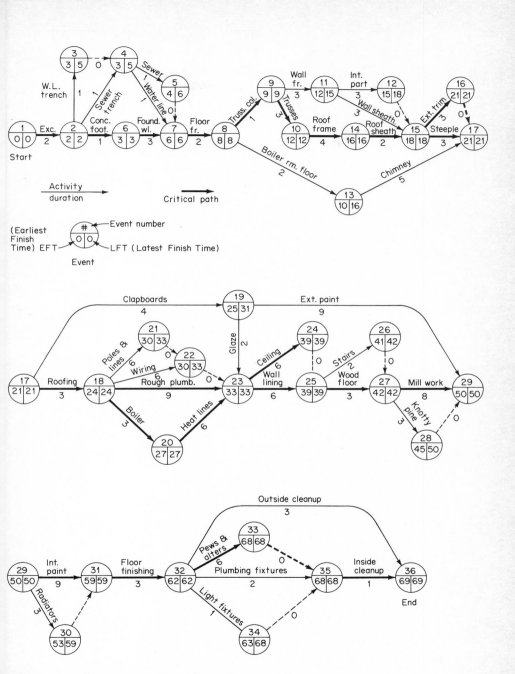

FIGURE 4-3 CPM network—regimental chapel.

in the development and manufactur of its Polaris Missile program. Because time and costs could not be accurately estimated, they had to be based on mathematical probability. The procedure employed by the Navy was referred to as *program evaluation and review technique* and has become known as PERT. Because PERT systems involve a probability approach, they are best suited to jobs which involve many uncertainties.

Both PERT and CPM use the arrow diagram model, and both have computer application. CPM, however, can be used without computers, and there is little need for math other than arithmetic.

Advantages of CPM On some jobs CPM is said to have reduced completion time by as much as 20 percent over similar jobs which did not employ CPM. The cost of a job will vary with the time required to complete it, and with CPM the time-and-cost relationship may be analyzed.

Job costs will vary with the time spent on the job. Direct costs (labor and materials) tend to decrease if more time is available for the job. These costs will increase if the job is speeded up to require overtime, additional material, and additional equipment. Indirect costs and overhead tend to increase if more time is available for the job but will decrease if the time is shortened. Therefore CPM can be used with certainty to get the proper balance of time and cost, thereby reducing the time needed for the job as well as its cost.

The use of CPM requires construction managers and planners (and estimators, too) to think their way through a job from beginning to end even before it is started. In so doing they use all their knowledge in a logical manner to construct the critical path model. As this model is constructed it reveals relationships unthought of before the planning began and helps the contractor to use all his resources to best advantage. It also provides a means for preparing plans with different approaches. The graphic representation of the relationships between different activities aids in determining which activities can be speeded up to ensure early completion and which activities have no need for increased speed.

The CPM model, a graphic representation of the contractor's scheduling ability, allows the contractor to establish starting and completion dates for all the activities on a construction job and to determine when and where rescheduling is needed.

All the advantages of CPM have not yet been completely realized. However, several of the advantages of CPM can be summarized as follows:

1 CPM enforces planning and scheduling in detail not accomplished by other methods.

2 CPM allows and encourages communication among different departments of an organization.

3 CPM can make planners more competent by forcing them to look at the job objectively.

4 CPM provides for closer communication among subcontractors working on the project.

5 CPM accurately predicts project duration and indicates which activities must be kept on time to maintain the planned schedule.

Preparing a CPM Network   There are many applications for CPM. In construction work the three major objectives of the system are to determine (1) the completion time of the project, (2) which activities establish and control the completion time, and (3) the amount of leeway, or float time, there is in noncritical activities.

One of the first steps in preparing a CPM network is to define all the operations needed to complete the project. This step requires the construction planner to use his knowledge, skill, and experience in construction. After he has defined the operations and listed them in tabular form, he is able to start his CPM network. In originally defining the operations or activities, the planner may list them more or less in the order in which he expects them to occur in construction. As he prepares the network, however, he may find a real need to rearrange the operations. This, of course, is one of the advantages of CPM.

Activities or operations are indicated by arrows on the network. The ends of the arrows terminate at nodes, the tail of the arrow representing the start of an activity and the head representing completion. Before an activity can be placed on the network, the planner must answer three questions concerning the activity:

1 Which activities must be accomplished before this activity?
2 Which activities must follow this activity?
3 Which activities may be performed at the same time as this activity?

As these questions are answered the activities are placed on the network. To avoid confusion, no two operations should have the same starting and stopping point on the network. This is avoided by use of a dummy operation, which is indicated by a broken line as shown in Figure 4-4. This indicates that activities 2-3 and 2-4 must be com-

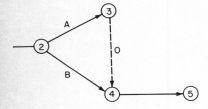

FIGURE 4-4 Activities with common starting and completion events.

pleted before activity 4-5 may be started. The entire arrow network defines the sequence for performing all the activities.

Following the completion of the network, the duration of each activity is estimated and placed on the network near the center of the corresponding arrow. The duration of the activity is obtained from the time-cost estimate for the job.

After the duration of each activity is listed on the network, the earliest event time (EET), or earliest possible occurrence, or node, is calculated. This time is the maximum amount of time a series of activities takes to lead to an event. It follows then that the earliest starting time (EST) for an activity is the EET of its preceding activities. The earliest finish time (EFT) for this activity is its EST plus the duration of the activity. The determination of the EET for the last event is also the determination of the total length of time needed for the project.

Some of the activities which are carried out concurrently will not require all the time available. This extra time is referred to as free float (FF) in CPM planning. Free float of an activity is determined by subtracting the EFT of the activity from its EET. Using the free float time of an activity to advantage will not affect the total job time.

The latest event time (LET) for the last event, the completion of the project, is equal to its earliest finish time. This is also the latest finish time (LFT) for the event. The latest starting time is calculated from the latest finish time of the job. Starting with the last event, the planner subtracts the duration of the activity from its latest finish time (LFT). The result is the latest starting time (LST) for this activity. By determining the LST of each activity, the planner also determines the latest event time, that is, the latest finish time for all activities which terminate at that event. Total float times may be calculated after the latest starting time and latest finish time are known.

Total float (TF) of an operation or activity is equal to the latest starting time of the activity minus the earliest starting time of the same activity. This is the length of time an activity may be delayed without affecting the completion time of the project. Although delaying an activity within its free float did not affect any event, the same cannot be said for total float. Delaying an activity to the extent of the total float may alter the position of some intermediate events.

Any activity which has zero TF is on the critical path. Delaying any of these activities will delay the entire project.

To organize the various data for the critical path it is advantageous to prepare a chart with all the activities listed in a single column more or less in the order in which they occur (see Figure 4-5). Additional columns are provided for duration, EST, EFT, LST, LFT, TF, and FF.

The steps in preparing a CPM schedule are as follows:

1 Make a list of activities for the project.

2 Estimate the duration of each activity.

Operation Name	Oper. Number	Duration (days)	Earliest Start (EST)	Earliest Finish (EFT)	Latest Start (LST)	Latest Finish (LFT)	Float Total (TF)	Float Free (FF)
Excavating	1-2	2	0	2	0	2	0	0
Water Line Trench	2-3	1	2	3	4	5	2	0
Sewer Trenches	2-4	1	2	4	4	5	1	0
Conc. Footings	2-6	1	2	3	2	3	0	0
Dummy	3-4	0	3	3	5	5	2	0
Sewers	4-5	1	3	4	5	6	2	0
Water Lines	4-7	1	3	4	5	6	2	2
Dummy	5-7	0	4	4	6	6	2	2
Foundation Walls	6-7	3	3	6	3	6	0	0
Floor Framing	7-8	2	6	8	6	8	0	0
Truss Columns	8-9	1	8	9	8	9	0	0
Boiler Room Floor	8-13	2	8	10	14	16	6	0
Trusses	9-10	3	9	12	9	12	0	0
Wall Framing	9-11	3	9	12	9	12	0	0
Roof Framing	10-14	4	12	16	12	16	0	0
Int. Partition Framing	11-12	3	12	15	15	18	3	0
Wall Sheathing	11-15	3	12	15	15	18	3	3
Dummy	12-15	0	15	15	18	18	3	3
Chimney	13-17	5	10	15	16	21	6	6
Roof Sheathing	14-15	2	16	18	16	18	0	0
Exterior Trim	15-16	3	18	21	18	21	0	0
Steeple	15-17	3	18	21	18	21	0	0
Dummy	16-17	0	21	21	21	21	0	0
Roofing	17-18	3	21	24	21	24	0	0
Clapboards	17-19	4	21	25	27	31	6	0
Boiler	18-20	3	24	27	24	27	0	0
Poles & Lines	18-21	6	24	30	27	33	3	0
Wiring	18-22	6	24	30	27	33	3	0
Rough Plumbing	18-23	9	24	33	24	33	0	0
Glazing	19-23	2	25	27	31	33	6	6
Exterior Painting	19-29	9	25	34	41	50	16	16
Heating Lines	20-23	6	27	33	27	33	0	0
Dummy	21-22	0	30	30	33	33	3	0
Dummy	22-23	0	30	30	33	33	3	3
Ceiling	23-24	6	33	39	33	39	0	0
Wall Lining	23-25	6	33	39	33	39	0	0
Dummy	24-25	0	39	39	39	39	0	0
Stairs	25-26	2	39	41	39	41	0	1
Wood Floor	25-27	3	39	42	39	42	0	0
Dummy	26-27	0	41	41	42	42	1	1
Knotty Pine	27-28	3	42	45	47	50	5	5
Millwork	27-29	8	42	50	42	50	0	0
Dummy	28-29	0	45	45	50	50	5	5
Radiators	29-30	3	50	53	56	59	6	0
Interior Painting	29-31	9	50	59	50	59	0	0
Floor Finishing	31-32	3	59	62	59	62	0	0
Pews & Altars	32-33	6	62	68	62	68	0	0
Light Fixtures	32-34	1	62	63	67	68	5	0
Plumbing Fixtures	32-35	2	62	64	66	68	4	4
Outside Clean-up	32-36	3	62	65	66	69	4	4
Dummy	33-35	0	68	68	68	68	0	0
Dummy	34-35	0	63	63	68	68	5	5
Inside Clean-up	35-36	1	68	69	68	69	0	0

FIGURE 4-5 CPM data—regimental chapel.

3 Determine which activities must be accomplished before each activity.

4 Determine which activities follow each activity.

5 Determine which activities may be performed simultaneously.

6 Make the CPM network.

7 Number the events, or nodes, on the network.

8 Prepare a chart and determine duration, EST, EFT, LST, LFT, TF, and FF.

9 Determine the critical path.

The foregoing discussion of CPM was intended merely to introduce the estimator to the critical path method of job planning and scheduling, not to make him proficient in CPM. Now that the estimator has become familiar with some of the terms of CPM, he will at least be able to discuss the method with some degree of confidence. However, it is recommended that texts which deal entirely with CPM be consulted so that it will be more completely understood and utilized.

COST RECORDS

Cost records should show all the items on the job—at least all those in any given main division—and not just a sample day's work or a single item of work. The cost books should preferably be made to balance, just as an accountant's ledgers are balanced and closed. In this way, the incidental costs of foreman, hoisting, handling materials, insurance, etc., will not be ignored. The final analysis of the job-cost records should be carefully compared with the estimate, and every possible lesson should be learned from this comparison for future estimating. Figures 4-6 to 4-8 present typical labor cost records. Nothing quite takes the place of one's own records when the matter of costs is concerned. Actual detailed accounts and analysis of work done under a contractor's own supervision give him a keen insight into the cost of the work performed that will develop in him (and in his estimator) the confidence required to estimate future items of the same kind.

CONSTRUCTION COMPANIES

The construction company is simply an enlargement of the building contractor. There are many varieties and sizes of these companies. Some are national or even international as to the territory in which they operate. Some offer to build any kind of structure, while others specialize in certain types of structures or in certain kinds of construction. Often they maintain complete designing and drafting departments

LABOR DISTRIBUTION											

Job _PS #148_   Sheet No. _12_

Class of Work _PLACING CONCRETE_   Foundation Week Ending _APRIL 26, 1970_   Job No. _148_

OCCUPATION	M	T	W	T	F	S	S	HOURS	RATE	AMOUNT	
1 LABORERS	—	16	16	96	16	—	—	144	4.48	645	12
2 ENGINEER	—	2	8	8	—	—	—	18	7.80	140	40
3											
4											
5											
6											
7											
8											
Total										785	52

	Quantity Work in Place	Pay Roll Costs	Labor Average Unit Cost	Average Quantity Per 8 Hour Day	Quantity Work in Place	Pay Roll Costs	Labor Average Unit Cost	Average Quantity Per 8 Hour Day
Previous	—	—	PER CU. YD.	—				
This Week	114 cu yd	785.52	6.90	6.33 cu yd				
Total	114 cu yd	785.52	6.90	6.33 cu yd				

FORM C-105   MFD. IN U.S.A.   FRANK R. WALKER CO. PUBLISHERS, CHICAGO   (Over)

COST ANALYSIS RECORD								
TOTAL LABOR HOURS					UNIT			
	1 LAB	2 ENG	3	4	5	6	7	8
Previous	—	—						
This Week	144	18						
Total	144	18						
LABOR HOURS PER UNIT				UNIT	CUBIC YARD			
	1 LAB	2 ENG	3	4	5	6	7	8
Previous	—	—						
This Week	1.27	.18						
Total	1.27	.18						

REMARKS

Ready mix concrete wheeled into place with buggies

PRACTICAL
FORM C-105   MFD. IN U.S.A.   FRANK R. WALKER CO. PUBLISHERS, CHICAGO

FIGURE 4-6   A cost record for concrete work.

and may go so far as to have financing departments as well. A few companies have no workmen on their own pay-rolls and sublet all the various lines to other contractors. A few, at the other extreme, have all the workmen on their own payrolls and sublet nothing. The majority, however, do all the laying out and superintending and some of the work with their own men. Figure 4-9 shows the plan of one construction company's home office. Figure 4-10 is the organization chart of the same company.

Job J.C. RESIDENCE	LABOR DISTRIBUTION								Sheet No. 14		
Class of Work ROUGH CARPENTRY				Week Ending MAY 3, 1970				Job No. 152			
OCCUPATION	M	T	W	T	F	S	S	HOURS	RATE	AMOUNT	
1 CARPENTERS	24	24	24	24	24	–	–	120	5.91	709	20
2 " APPRENTICE	8	8	8	8	8	–	–	40	2.96	118	40
3											
4											
5											
6											
7											
8											
Total										827	60

	Quantity Work in Place	Pay Roll Costs	Labor Average Unit Cost	Average Quantity Per 8 Hour Day	Quantity Work in Place	Pay Roll Costs	Labor Average Unit Cost	Average Quantity Per 8 Hour Day
Previous	900 FBM	141.84	152.60/m	300 FBM				
This Week	5400 FBM	827.60	153.26/m	270 FBM				
Total	6300 FBM	969.44	153.88/m	274 FBM				

FORM C-105   MFD. IN U.S.A.   FRANK R. WALKER CO. PUBLISHERS, CHICAGO   (Over)

	COST ANALYSIS RECORD							
TOTAL LABOR HOURS			UNIT					
	1 CARP	2 CARP APPR	3	4	5	6	7	8
Previous	24	—						
This Week	120	40						
Total	144	40						
LABOR HOURS PER UNIT			UNIT PER 1000 BD. FT.					
	1 CARP	2 CARP APPR	3	4	5	6	7	8
Previous	26.66	—						
This Week	22.22	7.41						
Total	22.86	7.41						
REMARKS								

INTERSECTING HIP ROOFS
RAFTERS - 2×6 - ½" plywood sheathing

PRACTICAL
FORM C-105   MFD. IN U.S.A.   FRANK R. WALKER CO. PUBLISHERS, CHICAGO

FIGURE 4-7 A cost record for carpentry.

Very large operations are usually organized with full business facilities in the job office itself. The job office then becomes really a branch office of the company. Figure

4-11 shows the organization of a large and important job, employing about 4,000 men. Chapter 9, dealing with the cost of job expense and office expense, explains some of the various costs involved in a construction project and

Job PS-148	LABOR DISTRIBUTION							Sheet No. 13		
Class of Work 8" CONC. BLK WALL			Week Ending MAY 3, 1970					Job No. 148		
OCCUPATION	M	T	W	T	F	S	S	HOURS	RATE	AMOUNT
1 MASONS	32	32	32	—	—	—	—	96	5.71	548 16
2 LABORERS	16	16	16	—	—	—	—	48	4.48	215 04
3										
4										
5										
6										
7										
8										
Total										763 20

	Quantity Work in Place	Pay Roll Costs	Labor Average Unit Cost	Average Quantity Per 8 Hour Day	Quantity Work in Place	Pay Roll Costs	Labor Average Unit Cost	Average Quantity Per 8 Hour Day
Previous	1900	763.20	.402/blk.	158				
This Week	1900	763.20	.402/blk.	158				
Total	3800	1526.40	.402/blk.	158				

FORM C-105   MFD. IN U.S.A.   FRANK R. WALKER CO. PUBLISHERS, CHICAGO   (Over)

	COST ANALYSIS RECORD							
TOTAL LABOR HOURS			UNIT					
	1 MASONS	2 LABORER	3	4	5	6	7	8
Previous	96	48						
This Week	96	48						
Total	192	96						

LABOR HOURS PER UNIT			UNIT PER 100 BLOCKS					
	1 MASONS	2 LABORER	3	4	5	6	7	8
Previous	5.05	2.53						
This Week	5.05	2.53						
Total	5.05	2.53						

REMARKS

8" CONC. BLOCK — CONCAVE TOOLED JOINTS
NO HOISTING
4' HIGH SCAFFOLD BUILT BY LABORERS

FORM C-105   MFD. IN U.S.A.   FRANK R. WALKER CO. PUBLISHERS, CHICAGO

FIGURE 4-8   A cost record for masonwork.

will help the student to understand non-production costs directly connected with the project. A careful study of the various cost items mentioned there will aid in understanding the items that go into general divisions such as Job Expense and Overhead. Job Expense may have a number of subdivisions, and Overhead may be divided into general expense, office expense, and job overhead.

This chapter has discussed points that are of interest to everybody concerned with building work. They are of interest to students of estimating because of their effect on estimates. The general contractor's own personality,

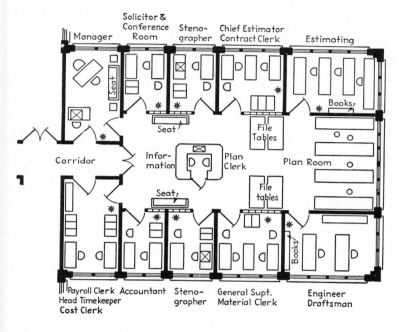

FIGURE 4-9 A construction company.

training, and character are important factors that must be kept in mind by the estimator. The contractor's personality has a psychological bearing on the office organization, on the job management, and on the subcontractors. His training, if it is thorough and practical with respect to building work, can be turned to advantage in a very beneficial way; but if it is not based upon practical experience, it must be seriously considered in connection with the pricing of

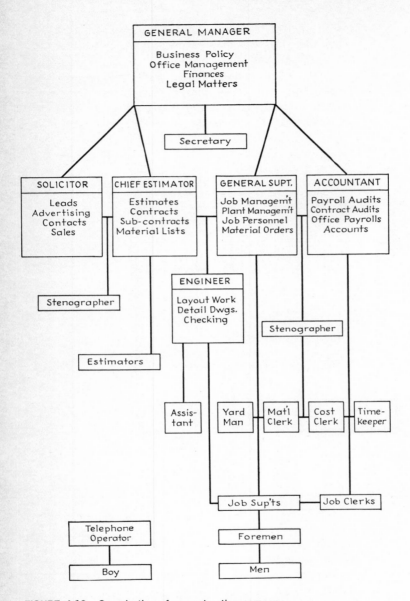

FIGURE 4-10 Organization of a construction company.

estimates. His character, as is the case in that of any businessman, is of prime importance. If he is honest and has a good reputation among his own employees and among subcontractors and architects, then the whole work in the office and on the job runs along in a pleasant way, without undue friction. If he is of poor character, it would be better to dispense with him as soon as possible, for fear of becoming contaminated. Character and reputation—both more valuable than many young men realize—can make for happi-

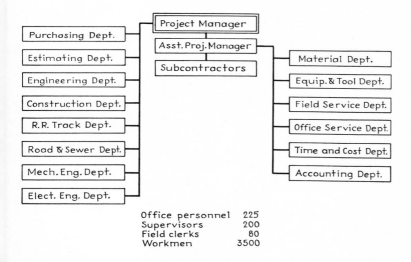

Office personnel   225
Supervisors   200
Field clerks   80
Workmen   3500

FIGURE 4-11   A large-job organization.

ness. As a rule of conduct: Keep your character and your reputation *clean.*

EXERCISES

1   Briefly, what are the functions of a general contractor in connection with building work? (80 to 100 words)

2   What are the qualities of a good superintendent of construction?

3   Make a progress schedule for an imaginary job.

4 What is CPM? PERT?

5 What are some advantages of using CPM?

6 Define:

Earliest possible occurrence

Activity

Event, or node

Earliest starting time

Earliest finish time

Free float

Latest possible occurrence

Latest starting time

Total float

7 What questions must be answered before an activity or operation can be placed on the CPM network.

8 Make a CPM network for an imaginary job.

9 Name the departments that might be found in a highly organized job.

10 Write at least 300 words of notes on the contractor and the business of contracting, taken from two or three of the books listed in the Bibliography. Name the books used.

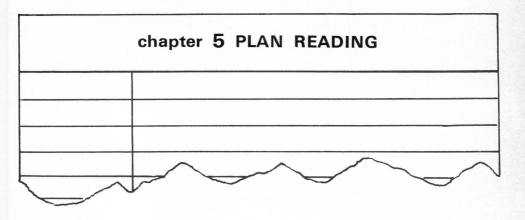

chapter 5 PLAN READING

INTRODUCTION

Blueprints are copies of drawings made by placing a tracing over sensitized photographic paper and exposing it to a strong light. The exposed paper is then passed through a developing solution which causes the exposed area to turn blue, leaving white lines and markings where light could not penetrate the lines and markings on the tracing. The prints are the same size as the original drawing from which the tracing was made; thus, in reading a blueprint, one is really reading the architect's drawing. Other kinds of prints are also used, some with blue or black lines on white paper. As many prints as are desired can be made from one tracing. Usually, about eight sets of the regular plans are required to provide enough for the contractor's office, for the subcontractors, and for other purposes.

The term *building plans* is generally understood to mean those plans which are prepared by an architect. These, together with the accompanying specifications, are intended to show or to describe all the work. What is not shown on the plans should be fully described in the specifications, and what is not described fully in the specifications should be plainly shown on the plans. In general, dimensions, shapes, and other items of information that can best be shown graphically are put on the plans. Long descriptions of the way the work is to be handled and other matters that are best treated in written form are covered in the specifications. In some ways, the specifications are more important than the plans. Realizing this, a good architect takes as much care in the writing of the specification as he does in the preparation of the plans. Specification writing involves a detailed knowledge of the materials and methods of construction and of the various customs that apply in building work.

READING BUILDING PLANS

Plan reading involves specification reading as well, for although plans may be complete in every respect, the materials to be used and the workmanship desired are generally found only in the specifications. To understand properly what is shown on the plans, therefore, it is usually necessary to read the specifications, too. Even the plans and the specifications together do not give every little detail of building work. It is assumed that the builder knows how buildings are constructed, and for this reason he and the estimator must have training in the practical use of plans and specifications. They should also have had considerable experience with actual building work of the general nature of that shown on the plans being used.

A logical system to follow when preparing an estimate is to examine the entire set of plans in order to become familiar with the overall job. This would involve study in a general manner of the plot plan, each of the plan views, sectional drawings, and special details. With a general knowledge of the proposed structure, the builder and the estimator will go to the specifications and study each part carefully as the estimate is prepared for each type of work.

Figures 5-4 to 5-13 comprise a complete set of architectural plans, except that the borders, titles, etc., have been omitted in order to make use of the entire area of the textbook page to show the drawings to better advantage. Figure 5-1 shows two typical title boxes, etc.

Besides architectural plans, sometimes separate structural plans and sometimes separate mechanical plans are furnished. Structural plans, or framing plans, as they are often called, show the columns, girders, beams, and other framing members more clearly than they could be shown on the general architectural plans. These plans are used when the framework of the building is to be of the skeleton-steel type or when the portions of the structure of the

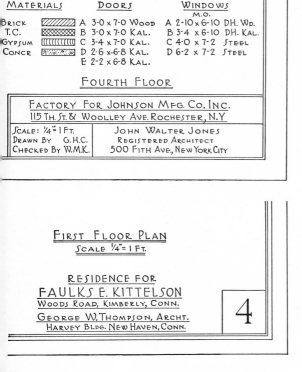

FIGURE 5-1 Title boxes, etc., on drawings.

building are so complicated in design that a large amount of information is required on the plans. In like manner, mechanical plans are used when it is desired to show the plumbing, heating, and other branches of the mechanical equipment better than they could be represented on the regular plans. Special plans, such as these, may be prepared in the architect's own office or they may be made by outside engineers. The latter is usually the case when the special problems involved are very intricate and require the services of a specialist. Figure 5-2 shows a portion of a structural plan, and Figure 5-3 a portion of a mechanical plan.

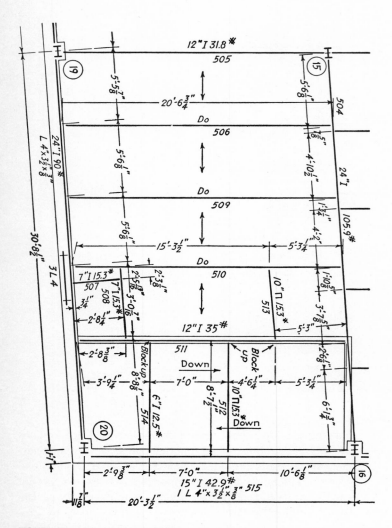

FIGURE 5-2   Portion of a structural plan.

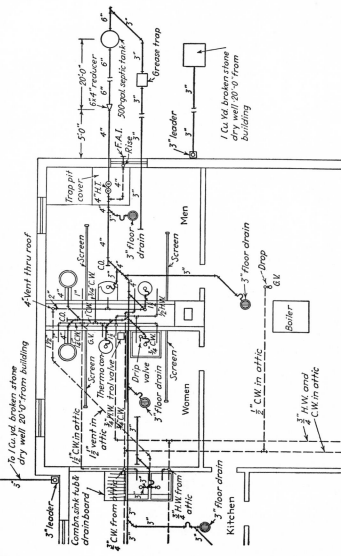

FIGURE 5-3 Portion of a mechanical plan.

49

Symbols are used on plans to save time in making the plans and in reading them. Unfortunately, like the conventional ways of indicating materials, etc., they are not absolutely established as to use. Good architects do indicate brickwork, terra-cotta blocks, and other regularly used forms of construction by crosshatching lines that are all but accepted as the standard method of indicating them. Doors, casements, and double-hung windows are generally shown on plans in such ways that persons familiar with plan reading seldom have trouble discovering what is intended. National trade associations have endeavored to standardize the electrical and plumbing symbols. Despite all this, however, the estimator and all other men using plans have to be careful not to jump to conclusions regarding the symbols and other indications they see on plans. What seems to be meant for gypsum blocks may mean terra-cotta, instead, and what looks like brickwork may be concrete, just to mention two examples. Figure 5-1 shows a typical key to the symbols used on a plan.

Abbreviations are used to a considerable extent on plans, and less frequently in specifications. There is usually no difficulty about them, although at times it is hard to interpret some of them, and there are often two possible meanings that could be applied to one abbreviation. It is recommended that as few as possible be used and that those that are used be made easy to understand. Specifications should describe all work fully, with only the most common abbreviations, in order that disputes may be minimized.

TYPES OF DRAWINGS

The term *plans* is used loosely to refer to all the drawings, including floor plans, elevations, sections, and other drawings as well.

Most architects prefix the page numbers of the plans with letters designating the type of drawings found on that page. The letter designations are usually listed on the first page of a set of plans and are identified there. Some examples of letter prefixes commonly used are given in Table 5-1.

Most building plans are drawn to the scale of a quarter inch to the foot. This means that every quarter inch measured on the plans represents 1 foot, or 12 inches, at the building. The scale rules are intended to save time in measuring the plans, although, of course, an ordinary rule can be used, and the number of quarter inches measured can be counted. Other scales in common use for regular architectural drawings are $\frac{1}{2}$ inch to the foot and, particularly for details, $\frac{1}{2}$, $\frac{3}{4}$, and 3 inches to the foot. Full-size and half-full-size details are occasionally made for special features of buildings.

Table 5-1   Prefixes Used to Identify Types of Drawings

Prefix	Classification
SK	Sketches
A	Architectural drawings
T	Topographical drawings
S	Structural drawings
E	Electrical drawings
M*	Metal equipment drawings
P	Plumbing drawings
H	Heating drawings
H-V	Heating and ventilating drawings

*M is also used for mechanical drawings.

Some draftsmen have a bad habit of using several different scales in a single set of plans where one scale could be used, or of using different scales for several drawings that appear on one sheet. They may even indicate one scale in the corner of a sheet and then make all the work or part of the work on the sheet at a different scale. Estimators learn to be very careful to apply the proper scale to each drawing separately, regardless of the scale that may have been indicated.

Floor plans, generally speaking, are pictures of the floors of buildings, such as one would get were he to imagine a building cut through on a horizontal plane, just above the windowsill level, and the upper part of the building removed. This view of the building shows the arrangement of the rooms and the location of the doorways, halls, stairs, etc., and gives the thickness of the walls and partitions and the size of the various parts of the building as measured horizontally. In making a floor plan, the draftsman uses conventional symbols or ways of indicating objects. These conventional indications are fairly well established, but there is no law making it necessary for any particular form of indication to be used. It should be noted, also, that draftsmen take liberties, so to speak, and show on floor plans items that would not be seen in a strict interpretation of the floor plan as a picture. Electric ceiling outlets, wall brackets, and kitchen wall cabinets, for example, are shown on the floor plans of a building. Other ceiling and wall features, also, are frequently included on floor plans. Figures 5-9 to 5-11 show floor plans.

Elevations are views of the exterior of a building. The front elevation shows the outside of the front wall as one would see it when standing across the street. Note, however, that it is not a perspective or photographic view of the building. This is because the draftsman assumes that every point is directly opposite him or that he is always directly in front of every feature or point shown on the drawing. This is necessary in order that the drawing may be measured correctly with the scale rule. Figures 5-5 to 5-8 show elevations.

Sections show the interior of a building. A floor plan is really a section—a horizontal section, showing the floor layout, etc.—but the term *plan* is always applied in this case. Sectional views are those obtained by imagining a building cut through the other way—in a vertical plane instead of a horizontal plane—with one section of it removed. The picture thus presented shows the various floors, one above another, and the roof at the top. It shows the thickness of the floors and the heights of the basement and other stories, as well as their relation to the ground level at the building. Figure 5-12 shows a section. Other types of sections are used to show construction details of a building.

Detail drawings are made of the parts of the building that require to be developed in this way in order that the exact construction or shape of the parts may be seen more readily. This is done when these details cannot be shown well enough on the regular plans or when they cannot be readily described in the specifications. Details are thus made of doors, windows, cabinetwork, cornices, etc., when these are to be made up specially instead of in stock patterns. Special details of floor construction and of decorative work are often furnished along with the regular plans or are made up afterward. These details are made up in the form of sections, elevations, and even plan view of small portions of the building. The scale used for this type of drawing will depend on the amount of detail which must be shown. A greater amount of detail requires a larger scale drawing. Figure 5-13 is a sheet of details made up of sections and elevations.

LAWS AND REGULATIONS

There are many laws and regulations pertaining to building work. The national labor laws and the social security and old-age pension laws have to be considered, both in the preparation of estimates and in the actual work of erection of buildings. State laws directly affect the design and construction of buildings and the use of buildings after they have been completed. A thorough study of the state labor laws and the local building code would constitute an excellent review of the whole field of building design, materials, methods of construction, and the proper care and use of buildings of all kinds. However, an understanding of the more involved parts of these laws requires a background of technical training and experience in building work. Union regulations are becoming more definite and understandable, and these also will have to be considered by the estimator.

Building codes originated out of the desire for fire protection. Later, there was concern for safety of life and health, and the present-day codes cover the design, construction, equipment, and occupancy of structures of all kinds. Codes are intended to be schedules of minimum requirements and should never be used as specifications of good design and construction. In many instances, they certainly fall far short of describing the best.

A building code is a technical treatise on a highly involved subject and is not readily understandable by the layman. The purpose of the New York City code, as stated in it, is to provide standards, provisions, and requirements for safe design, methods of construction, and sufficiency of materials in structures and to regulate the equipment use, and occupancy of all structures and premises. It deals with the heating and ventilating of buildings. Stairways and other means of egress are given consideration. The important subject of sanitation is treated in a separate section and fire-resistive construction, fire sprinklers, and stand pipes for fire fighting are provided for. Elevators, in which many thousands of people travel every day, are governed by what is probably the longest and most elaborate set of elevator regulations ever produced anywhere.

Codes generally give definitions of the terms used in them. One should keep in mind that terms in a code are not always the same as those used in trade language or as used among real estate dealers and others having to do with property. For example, the terms basement, cellar, fire wall, penthouse, and others given in the code may have different meanings when used in other connections. Therefore, when there is any doubt as to the meaning of terms used in the code, reference should be made to the code's section on definitions.

READING A SET OF PLANS

For a beginner, reading a set of building plans may seem a near-impossibility because of all the details to coordinate among the various pages. The task usually seems more difficult as the number of pages in the set increases. However, as more plans are looked at and worked on, the difficulty diminishes and reading plans becomes almost routine. To aid the beginner, a complete set of architectural plans for a house is included in Figures 5-4 to 5-13. These will serve for further drill in plan reading and will also be used in the discussion of construction work and the study of estimating.

It should be pointed out here that the procedure followed in examining plans for a residence can readily be applied to a complex commercial building.

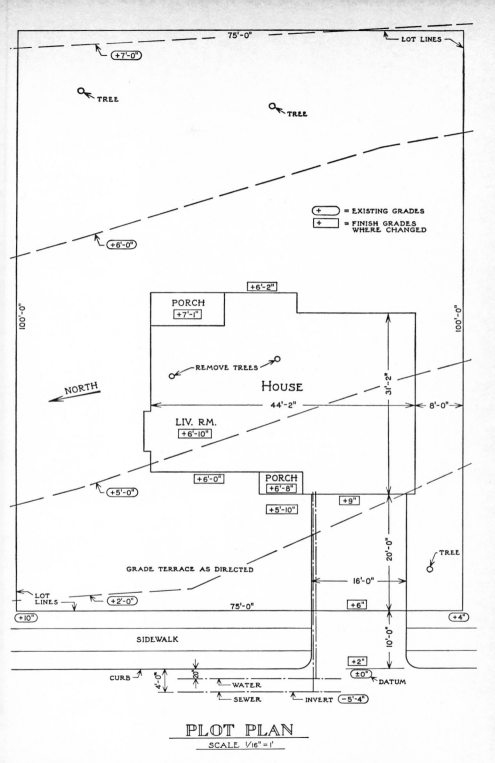

FIGURE 5-4 A plot plan.

55

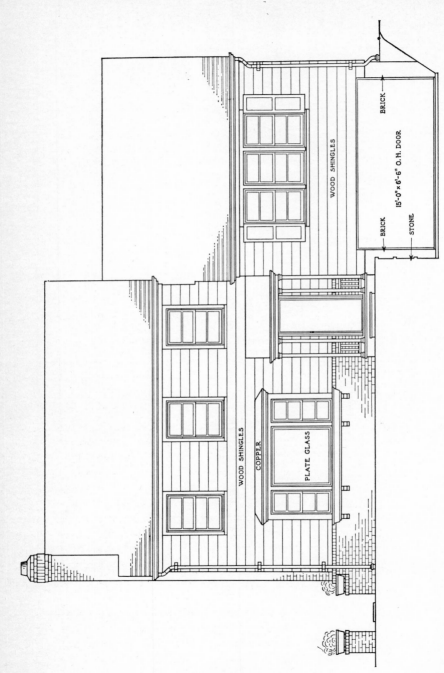

FIGURE 5-5 Front elevation.

56

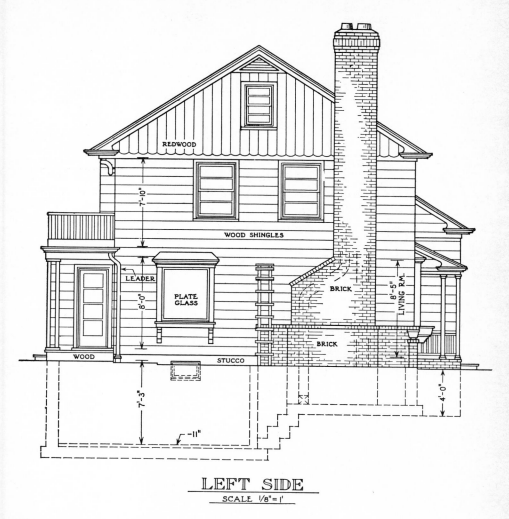

LEFT SIDE
SCALE 1/8"=1'

FIGURE 5-6 Left-side elevation.

READING THE PLOT PLAN

A plot plan is shown in Figure 5-4. This one indicates the location of the house on the property and also gives the ground grades and the relation of the floor levels to these grades.

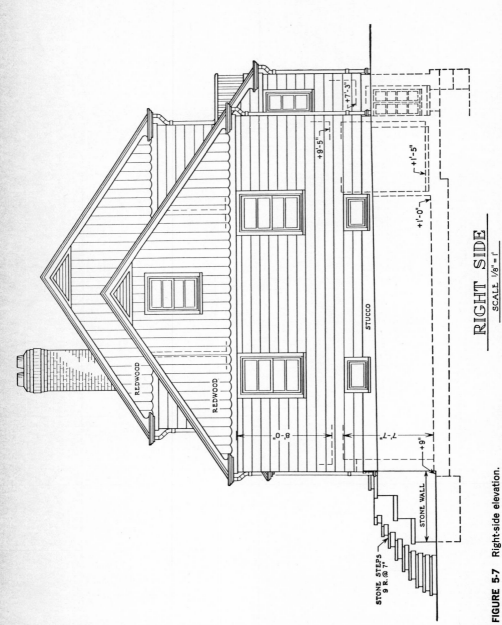

FIGURE 5-7 Right-side elevation.

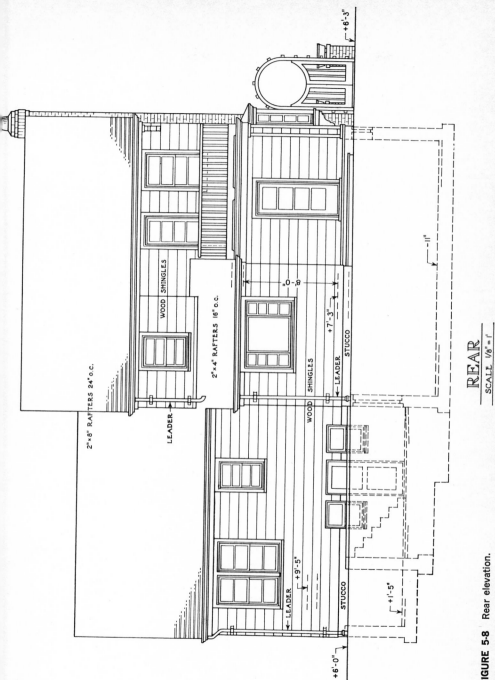

FIGURE 5-8 Rear elevation.

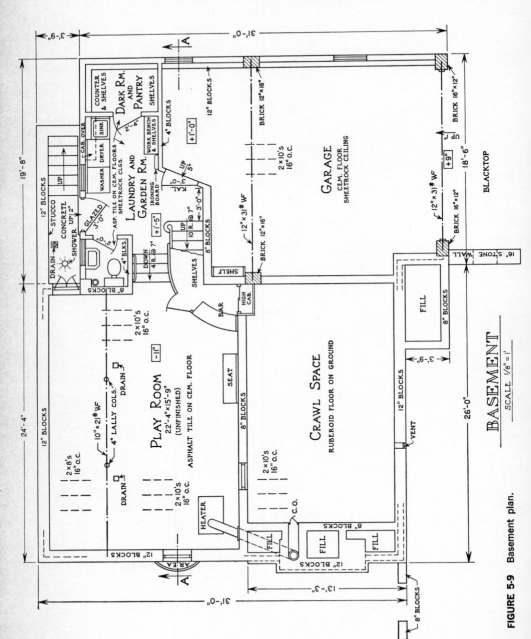

FIGURE 5-9 Basement plan.

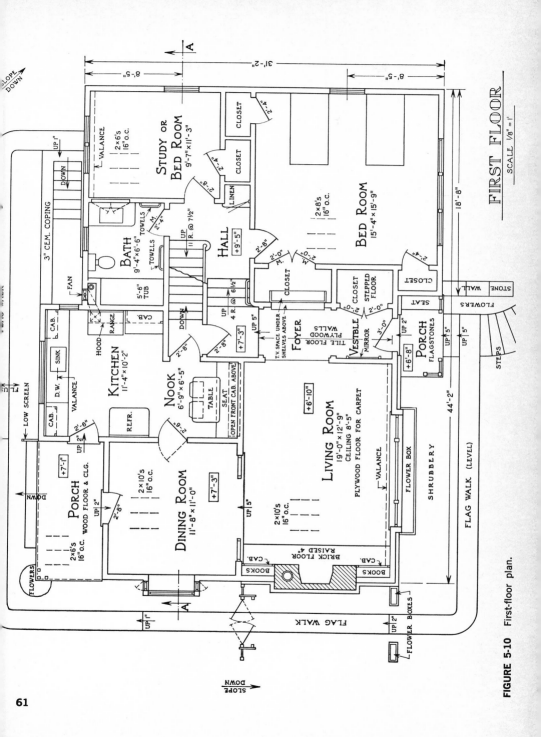

FIGURE 5-10 First-floor plan.

61

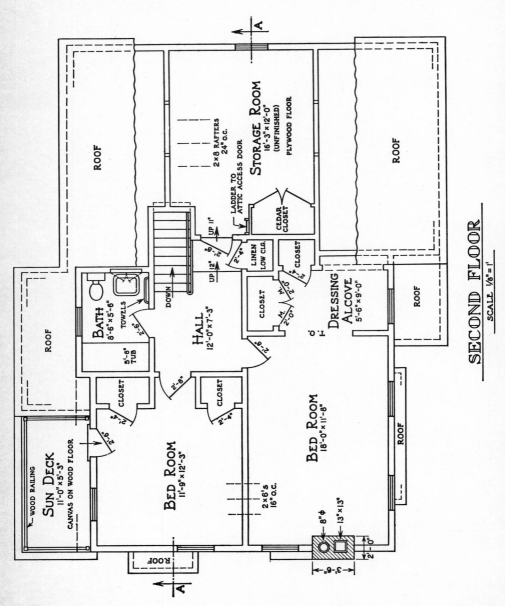

SECOND FLOOR

SCALE 1/6" = 1'

ROOF

STORAGE ROOM
16'-3" × 12'-0"
(UNFINISHED)
PLYWOOD FLOOR

2×8 RAFTERS
24" O.C.

LADDER TO
ATTIC ACCESS DOOR

UP 11"

CEDAR
CLOSET

ROOF

LINEN
LOW CLG.

UP 12"

2'-4"

CLOSET

BATH
8'-6" × 5'-6"

5'-6"
TUB

TOWELS

2'-6"

DOWN

HALL
12'-0" × 7'-3"

CLOSET

M
2'-0"

CLOSET

ROOF

CLOSET

ROOF

2'-8"

2'-4"

2'-6"

M
2'-0"

DRESSING
ALCOVE
5'-6" × 9'-0"

WOOD RAILING

SUN DECK
11'-0" × 5'-3"

CANVAS ON WOOD FLOOR

2'-6"

CLOSET

2'-4"

BED ROOM
11'-9" × 12'-3"

2×6's
16" O.C.

BED ROOM
18'-0" × 11'-8"

ROOF

ROOF

8" φ

13" × 13"

2'-0"

3'-6"

A

A

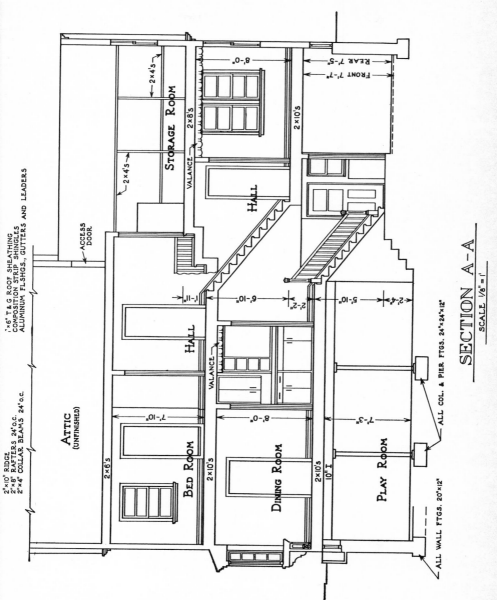

FIGURE 5-12 Section A-A.

63

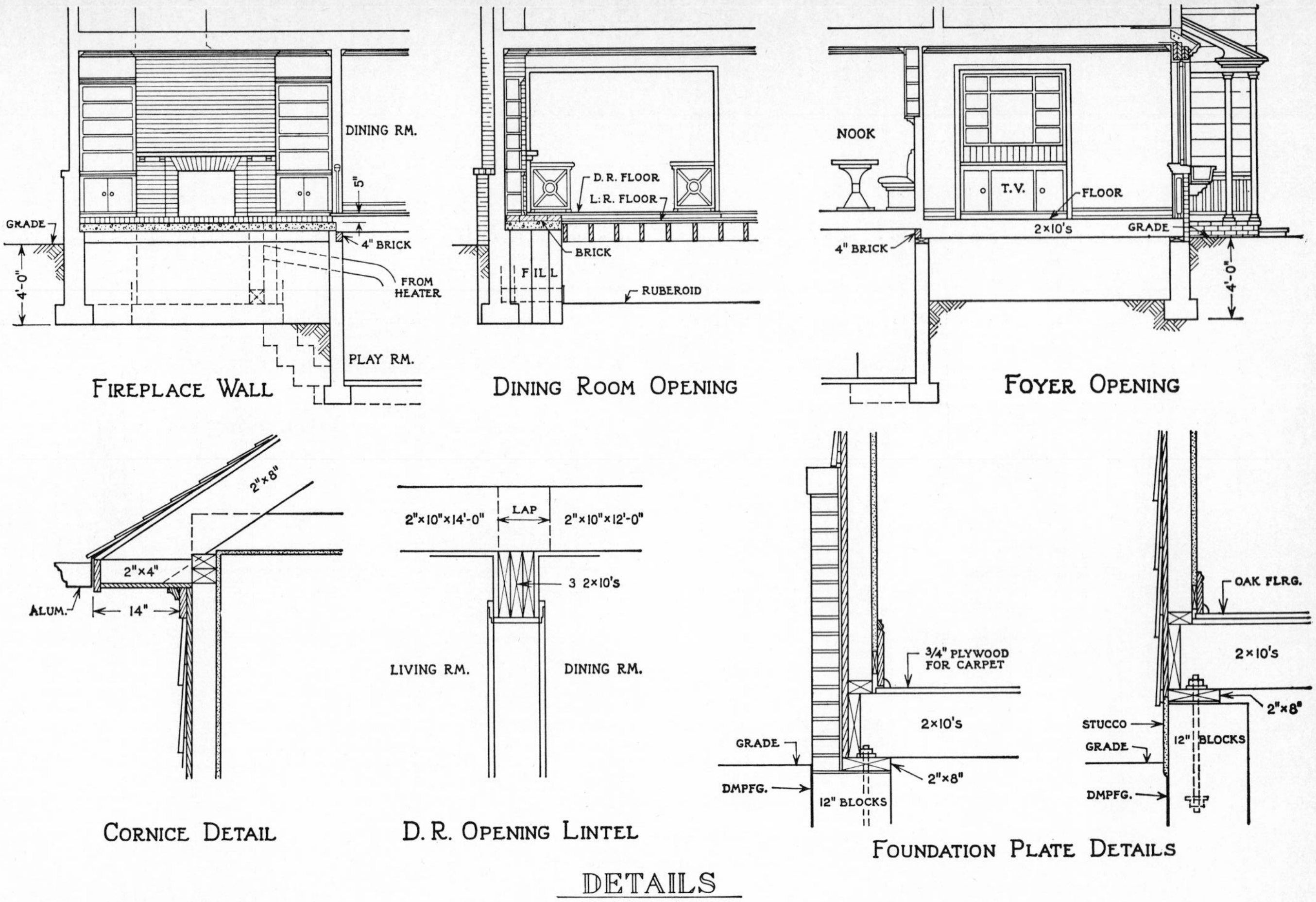

FOYER OPENING

DINING ROOM OPENING

FIREPLACE WALL

FOUNDATION PLATE DETAILS

D. R. OPENING LINTEL

CORNICE DETAIL

DETAILS

FIGURE 5-13   Detail drawings.

64

The term *existing grade,* or *present grade,* means the ground surface before any change is made in it. The term *finish grade,* or *final grade,* means the surface that is to be produced by the changes. In this case the street surface at the driveway has been established as datum, which is the reference grade, or bench mark, from which the other grades are taken. The architect has marked this zero on his plot plan.

Five trees are shown, and two of these are to be removed because they are in the way of the house. The existing ground levels, or grades, are to remain for the most part. However, the specifications for the job require that 9 inches of topsoil, from the entire width of the property and for a distance of 60 feet back from the sidewalk, is to be removed, piled at the rear of the property, and finally spread over the front lawn and terrace and elsewhere on the property as directed by the architect. None of this material is to be removed from the premises. Topsoil is the rich soil usually found at the surface of the ground, sometimes as much as 18 inches deep.

The *excavation* for the house will be about 4 feet deep below the removed topsoil, and most of this excavated material will have to be hauled away. The removed topsoil will be ample for any terrace grading required. *Grading* means lowering or raising the ground surface to bring it to the desired level or slope.

Lot lines, or *property lines,* define the extent of the property, but the driveway extends out to the street. The front-lot line is often referred to as the *building line.* This is a legal term meaning the line between public and private property. A corner plot would have a building line on each street. Local laws and regulations generally state how close to this line one may build. In sections zoned by the authorities for business use, one may build out to this line and, within specified limits, construct steps, areaways, and cornices which extend into the public property. In residential sections, however, it is likely that not only zoning restrictions but also setback restrictions are established by law, and possibly deed restrictions, established by the present or former owners of the property, may apply.

The house shown in Figure 5-4 is required by law

to be set back at least 20 feet from the building line and at least 5 feet from the side-lot lines and to be on a plot at least 7,000 square feet in area. The deed restrictions require that the house be a one-family house, two stories high.

Surveys are often used as plot plans, or information taken from a survey may be incorporated in the plot plan. Surveys are generally made by licensed surveyors. On them are accurately shown the property lines and the angles and directions of these lines; also streets, curbs, lampposts, sewers, and other pertinent information. Frequently, the contractor is required to furnish the owner, for his records, a survey showing the exact position of the building after it has been built.

READING THE FRONT ELEVATION

Figure 5-5 shows the front of the house and is referred to as the *front elevation.*

Elevations are sometimes named according to the way they face. This one could be called the west elevation because it faces west, as can be verified on the plot plan.

This is a frame house having a portion of the front and left side walls veneered with brick. The piers, or pedestals, under the flower boxes at the left side, and the chimney are also of brick on concrete-block foundations.

The *other elevations* show that other brickwork is involved. The left side, which shows the brick veneer and the brick chimney, also shows brick walls under the front porch. The basement plan shows four brick piers in the garage. The first-floor plan shows a brick floor, or hearth, in front of the fireplace. The detail drawing shows the brick veneer and also the fireplace wall and brick at the top of the wall between the crawl space and the playroom. This will point out the need to refer to all the drawings when looking for one material or one kind of work, in this case, the brickwork. All the drawings must be examined and the specifications carefully read to obtain complete information.

The *garage door* is the overhead type, swinging up on tracks suspended below the ceiling of the garage. Sufficient space must be provided above the door opening for the door clearance.

The *main-entrance door* is 3 feet 0 inches wide, as shown on the first-floor plan. The specifications describe it and state further that it is $1\frac{3}{4}$ inches thick and 7 feet 0 inches high and is of white pine. The frame for this door is also described in the specifications, and of course the hardware and glass would be found noted under proper headings in the specifications.

The *living-room window* is a triple window consisting of a plate-glass stationary picture window flanked on either side by a regular double-hung window. All three are contained in a special frame which projects out about 6 inches and has a copper-covered roof. The term *double-hung* means the commonly used type of window in which a lower and an upper sash slide past each other. The other front windows are regular double-hung windows, the one over the garage door being a triple window.

The *exterior walls* are faced for the most part with wood shingles, but reference to the two side elevations will show that the gable areas have redwood siding set vertically. Also note that the portions of the foundation walls which extend above the ground are indicated on the side and rear elevations to be stuccoed.

The *specifications* must always be used in conjunction with the drawings. It will usually be found that some items are specified but are not shown on the drawings, and in many instances the specifications give important additional information regarding what the drawings do show.

The specifications for this house will be found in Appendix A.

READING THE LEFT ELEVATION

The left elevation is shown in Figure 5-6. This can also be referred to as the north elevation because it faces north.

The *brick chimney* and the brick veneer on either side of it may be seen here. Two terra-cotta (TC) flues project from the top of the chimney, one leading from the boiler and the other from the fireplace. These flue linings are clay pipes and come in 2-foot lengths which are built in as the chimney construction progresses. The one serving the boiler in this house is round and has an inside diameter of 8 inches. The fireplace flue is larger, 13 by 13 inches on the outside, to provide a better draft, which is required for fireplaces. Flues are obtainable in round and rectangular shapes of various sizes. The outside dimensions are used for rectangular flues, and the inside diameter for round flues. The chimney is broader at the bottom to accommodate the fireplace and is shaped above this to relieve the appearance.

One *gable end* of the house appears on this side. The gable is faced with redwood vertical siding and contains a double-hung window, a triangular gable louver, and false (decorative) rafters. The slope of the roof may be seen in this drawing. This is called a gable roof, to distinguish it from a hip roof and a flat roof.

There are two *porches* shown on the left elevation. The front-porch floor is of flagstones (see first-floor plan), supported on a concrete slab and brick walls. The other portions of it are wood with asphalt shingles on the roof and an aluminum gutter along the front with a short spout at one end. The rear porch is all of wood, including the floor and the roof-deck and railing. The roof-deck is covered with heavy canvas for a walking surface.

The *dining-room window* is a box window composed of a stationary picture window with an outswinging casement window at each side. It projects out about 18 inches and has a window seat on the inside. The projecting portion is supported on two wooden brackets, and the roof over it is covered with copper. See the rear elevation, the first- and second-floor plans, and the cross section for other views of this box window, or bay window, as it might be called, and the roof over it.

Subsurface conditions are sometimes shown on elevations. This one shows, in dotted lines, the wall footings and foundation walls at this side of the house and the foundation under the front porch. All foundations in northern climates should extend down far enough to escape the heaving action of frost. The law in these areas, through the state or municipal building code, generally requires a minimum depth of 4 feet for all foundations except those under steps and other minor parts.

The wall footing shown in Figure 5-6 is "stepped" where the levels change between the playroom and the crawl space. This stepping is carefully constructed to provide level surfaces on which to construct the wall. Furthermore, if the excavation here or under any other footings is cut deeper than the plans show, it is required that the excess depth be filled with concrete, not with dirt.

Note that no footings are called for under the front-porch foundation walls nor under the foundation for the stone wall at the driveway.

All the foundation walls for this house are of hollow concrete blocks on 20-inch-wide concrete footings. The blocks under the chimney and the top course of all the other foundation walls are specified to be filled in solid with concrete. Brick piers are used to support the concentrated loads of the steel girders in the garage. See the basement plan for the thicknesses of the walls and the size of the piers.

READING THE RIGHT ELEVATION

The right elevation, or south elevation, is seen in Figure 5-7. Stone steps and a stone wall are shown at the front of the house. The steps are curved, and the specifications call for them to be carefully constructed over rough-concrete steps, the concrete to be reinforced with $\frac{3}{8}$-inch steel rods placed 6 inches on centers in both directions. This means that the rods run crosswise every 6 inches and longitudinally every 6 inches and thus form a steel grid embedded in the concrete. The steps are specified to have rough-local-stone risers and $1\frac{1}{2}$-inch-thick one-piece bluestone treads, all laid in cement mortar. The wall, which is at the north side of the driveway, is also of local stone, in random-ashlar formation, with one-piece bluestone copings $1\frac{1}{2}$ inches thick. The wall rests on a foundation of hollow concrete blocks filled with concrete and extending down 24 inches.

At the right side of the drawing may be seen the portion of the kitchen which extends at the back of the house and, above this, the sun deck over the rear porch, which is beyond the kitchen extension. One of the kitchen windows, a casement, is shown. The window below the kitchen window is also a casement, or more precisely, a pair of casements. This opening is in the areaway at the back of the house and provides ventilation and some light for the playroom. The two garage windows have single top-hinged outswinging sash.

The rain gutters are "returned" on the side walls about 24 inches to improve the appearance. These are molded aluminum gutters which, with the fascia boards, soffit, and wood moldings, form the cornice of the house. See the cornice detail in Figure 5-13. The gable trim, or rake cornice, is composed of a false beam with shaped pieces at the lower ends and a molding under the edge of the roof shingles.

Louvers are installed in the peaks of the gable ends for attic ventilation. The size and type of these louvers, when not indicated on the plan, may be found in the specifications.

The upper gable is on the two-story portion of the house. The lower gable is on the south-end wall at the storage room. As indicated in the specifications, the headroom is only 6 feet 8 inches under the rafter collar beams in the storage room.

Collar beams are ties between rafters on opposite sides of a roof. They are installed in accordance with the local building code and the requirements of the plans and specifications. In this building, collar beams are required on every pair of rafters, as indicated in the specifications. The placement of collar beams is sometimes noted on a wall section.

Sometimes, as a supposed aid in tying the building together, collar beams are introduced partway up on the slope of the rafters. They should never be depended upon as ties unless the rafters are quite steep, because the nearer the tie is to the top, the greater the leverage action upon it, with a consequent tendency to pull out the collar-beam nails, and also to bend the rafters. The proper function of collar beams is to stiffen the roof.

If the action of a collar beam is analyzed, it will be seen that it probably acts as a strut rather than a tie. When secured against spreading at the base, rafters tend to sag. The collar beam will therefore act as a strut or prop, which, to be most effective, should be at the halfway point. Sagging of a rafter on one side tends to push out the one opposite. This reinforcement will prevent both from sagging.

The collar beams over the storage room in this house are placed high to provide headroom under them. Additional support for the rafters is provided by 2- by 4-inch stud walls as shown in Figures 5-11 and 5-12. Collar beams at the midpoint of the rafters, and also similar stud bracing, are specified for the attic over the main portion of the building.

READING THE REAR ELEVATION

The rear elevation is shown in Figure 5-8. The pair of windows near the left-hand side are spoken of together and called a *mullion window*. The dividing member between them is called the *mullion*. Three windows, placed with mullions between them, are also taken together and termed a *triple window*. The narrow members dividing the glass are called *muntin bars*.

Areawey steps are indicated by dotted lines on the drawing. The areaway door leads to the laundry and garden room in the basement. It has glass in the upper part and is flanked on either side by a small double-hung window. The kitchen window is a unit containing a stationary window with an outswinging casement at each side.

At the right side of the drawing is a rose arbor with a pair of gates, and beyond this, the brick piers and flower boxes at the front of the house may be seen.

READING THE BASEMENT PLAN

The floor plans are shown in Figures 5-9 to 5-11, Figure 5-9 being the basement plan.

Basement is used broadly to denote any space below the main floor. Building laws generally define the term to mean a floor space which is more than one-half below outside grade level.

The *foundation walls* (or basement walls) in this house are of hollow concrete blocks, some of which are filled with concrete. They are 12 inches thick in the main walls and 8 inches in the other walls, and all rest on concrete footings. The 4-inch cinder-concrete-block partitions start on the concrete basement floor.

The heights of the walls vary. It is necessary to examine carefully this drawing and the elevations and cross section and detail drawings to determine these heights. Obviously, all those enclosing the playroom will be the highest walls because they start at the lowest level in the basement, and the beams over this room are 7 feet 3 inches above the finish-floor level. However, the 8-inch block wall between the playroom and the crawl space extends up only to the underside of the living-room floor joists and is therefore about 10 inches less in height than the exterior walls of the playroom.

Steel girders are shown in the playroom and in the garage. The ends of those in the playroom rest on the block walls, and they are also supported by two Lally columns. *Lally column* is a term commonly used to designate a column composed of a steel pipe filled with concrete. The name derives from its originator, but many other manufacturers now make similar columns. The girders in the garage are carried on brick piers. The one at the front may be called a *lintel*. A lintel is any member placed over an opening in this fashion to carry the load above it.

The floor joists indicated on this drawing are those over the basement, and they support the first floor. These are all 2 by 10's except under the back porch, where 2 by 8's are shown. The dash lines indicate the direction in which the joists run.

This house has a back areaway in which steps lead up to the rear walk. Full advantage of the areaway is taken for windows in the laundry, toilet, and playroom and for a glazed door.

The laundry is planned to serve also as a garden workroom and as a passage between the stairway and the various rooms in the basement. All the rooms, except the garage, have asphalt tile on the cement floors, and the concrete steps to the playroom have rubber treads.

However carefully a building may be framed, or however rugged it may be built, inadequate foundations will result in uneven settlement, cracking of plaster or tile, ill-fitting doors and windows, and other difficulties, which will offset, to some extent, the advantages of good work in the superstructure.

Pier and column footings under girders of the average building carry loads much greater per square foot than do those under foundation walls. Such a footing may often carry ten times the weight per square foot that is carried by the wall footing. The load on these footings should be figured, and they should be made large enough to carry the load that will be placed upon them.

READING THE FIRST-FLOOR PLAN

The first-floor plan is given in Figure 5-10. This floor has three levels. The vestibule, foyer, and living room are on one level. The dining room, kitchen, and nook are up one step, and the other rooms are four steps higher. These are all "easy" steps, each one being more than an inch lower than usual in height.

The *vestibule* and foyer have quarry-tile floors laid on *deafening*. This is cinder concrete 4 inches thick placed on wood subflooring. The floor beams here are set 4 inches lower for this purpose. The floor in the coat closet is stepped up to provide clearance, or headroom, in the garage below it. All the wide closets in this house have pairs of hinged doors, and those in the bedrooms are fitted with full-length mirrors. Some people prefer wood or metal sliding doors or accordion-type doors.

The front-porch floor is of flagstones laid on a concrete slab. The posts, railing, and seat are wood.

The *living room* has a fireplace, and the brick hearth extends also in front of the bookshelves. The balance of the living-room floor is ¾-inch-thick plywood which is planned to be entirely covered with carpeting. Interior elevations of the living room are shown in Figure 5-13, where the cabinets here and in the foyer may also be seen.

The *dining room* is one step up from the living room, and the opening between the two rooms requires a strong lintel, or header, over it. This is composed of three 2 by 10's spiked together. A detail of this is shown in Figure 5-13. This room will have oak flooring, and there is a glazed door to the back porch and a double-acting door to the kitchen.

The *kitchen and dining nook* will have vinyl-tile flooring, plastic table and counter tops and splashbacks, and enameled steel cabinets. The seat in the nook will have a leather-covered foam-rubber cushion and back and, above it, an open-front cabinet with plastic shelves. A door shuts off the kitchen from the hall and the basement stairway.

The *other rooms* on this floor are set apart and at a higher level for privacy. The bathroom will have tile flooring and wainscoting, and the other spaces oak flooring. The bathroom has a recess tub with a shower curtain, a lavatory contained in a plastic-topped cabinet, and a large medicine cabinet with a pair of doors. The small room is intended to be used as a study, a den, a guest room, or a child's bedroom.

READING THE SECOND-FLOOR PLAN

The second-floor plan is shown in Figure 5-11. The storage room on this floor is at a higher level than the other rooms. It is entered by stepping up on a ledge in the hall and then up one step at the door to the room. The room has a single plywood floor and is otherwise unfinished. This means that the wood studs and rafters will be exposed to view. No flooring is provided in the low-roof spaces adjoining the storage room, and therefore the ceiling beams over the rooms below will be exposed. The attic space above the main portion of the house is also unfinished, and it is reached by way of a ladder which leads to an access door above the linen closet. The specifications call for a catwalk, 24 inches wide, in this upper attic, from the access door to the north wall.

The chimney flues are shown on this drawing. The flue linings have shells about $\frac{3}{4}$ inch thick. Larger flue linings have thicker shells. All come in 2-foot lengths.

The roof is "broken" over the storage-room portion in order to show the interior construction. The roof over the main portion is not shown on this drawing. There is a canvas-covered flat roof, or sun deck, over the rear porch. The roof over the living-room windows is of sheet copper, as noted on the front elevation. The other three small roofs are covered with composition-asphalt-strip shingles the same as on the main roofs.

Doors of various widths are noted on the plans. Those leading from the bedrooms are 2 feet 8 inches wide to provide access for large pieces of furniture. The wide closets have pairs of doors, each leaf opening independently, to give full and easy access to the entire closet, and some are provided with mirrors.

Note the way the various parts of the building are drawn. The walls and partitions are represented by two parallel lines scaling about 6 inches apart. The walls are constructed of 2- by 4-inch studs covered on the outside with insulating sheathing board and wood shingles and on the inside with plasterboard and plaster, the whole thickness being about 6 inches. However, the 4-inch studs actually measure only $3\frac{5}{8}$ inches. The partitions are constructed of 2- by 4-inch studs with plasterboard and plaster on both sides.

For partitions, the common practice is to provide a double-top plate. It might be mentioned here, however, that inasmuch as a plate is usually supported every 16 inches and no weight is ordinarily imposed upon the plate between the studs, one 2 by 4 would be sufficient in most cases. Good practice, however, suggests that a double plate be used in the case of bearing partitions, and it is desirable to use double plates on walls to secure a good lap joint at corners and at partition intersections.

The best of materials and workmanship for plaster and interior trim will fail to give satisfactory results unless the underlying framework of a building is strong and rigid. Durability and wind resistance, freedom from cracks and settlement, all depend in part on good framework.

READING SECTIONS

Section A-A is shown in Figure 5-12. Reference lines A-A, indicating where the section occurs, will be found on the basement and first-floor plans, with arrows giving the direction of the sectional view.

This drawing is sometimes referred to as a cross section, but it is really a longitudinal section because it is taken through the length of the building. Other section drawings are sometimes provided by the architect, and the detail drawings in Figure 5-13 may be referred to as sections.

The floor levels may be seen in this drawing. The playroom is at the lowest level, 11 inches below datum, which, on these plans, is the street level at the driveway. This is shown on the plot plan in Figure 5-4. The floor at the back of the garage is 12 inches above the street level.

The stairs have $1\frac{1}{8}$-inch-thick oak treads and $\frac{7}{8}$-inch-thick white pine risers, all housed and wedged together.

Dimensions given on this drawing, as well as those on the other drawings, are nominal and will vary slightly, depending upon actual sizes of the floor joists and actual thickness of flooring, etc. The 2 by 8's are made from 2- by 8-inch rough lumber but actually measure only $1\frac{5}{8}$ by $7\frac{1}{2}$ inches after they are planed smooth. This is done in the mill before the lumber is shipped. The 1 by 3 oak flooring is made from 1- by 3-inch rough stock but actually measures only $\frac{25}{32}$ or $\frac{13}{16}$ inch thick. This flooring is tongued and grooved, and while being laid, the tongued edge of one piece locks into the grooved edge of the next piece. Thus the effective covering width is only $2\frac{1}{4}$ instead of 3 inches.

The permissible minimum live load for purposes of design given in most building codes for residential occupancy in 40 pounds per square foot. There are occasional instances where codes permit 30 pounds per square foot on upper floors of single-family dwellings, and the same figure has been advocated by some authorities for general use throughout dwellings.

The permissible minimum live load given in building codes for business occupancy varies to some extent. If office space in buildings is taken as an example, the range in building codes recommended by various organizations for national or regional use in building-code standards is from 50 to 80 pounds per square foot.

The term *mercantile occupancy* is not used in all codes,

but it covers such occupancies as stores, salesrooms, and markets. For these, the permissible minimum live load recommended ranges from 75 to 125 pounds per square foot.

Obviously, the industrial classification will contain widely varying examples of floor loading since it includes occupancies involved in manufacturing, fabrication, and assembly of all kinds of industrial products. For heavy manufacturing, some codes give values of from 125 to 150 pounds per square foot, and others do not assign any particular value.

Safe building design requires the use of a combination of assumed loads and working stresses which will result in structures that will not be seriously overstressed in any part by the imposed loads. The first consideration, of course, is that there shall be ample strength. Often, however, a beam which is strong enough may still be limber enough to permit a noticeable bending or vibration from walking. This is not only annoying but may be sufficient to crack the plaster of the ceiling below. Stiffness, therefore, must also be considered as a factor.

READING DETAIL DRAWINGS

Detail drawings are given in Figure 5-13.

The *fireplace* and the wall above it are faced with brick, the portion immediately around the fireplace projecting 1 inch. The mantel shelf is a plain 1¾-inch-thick oak board only 4 inches wide and supported on four small oak brackets. The cabinet doors are of oak-faced plywood, and the shelves and moldings are also of oak.

Railings of ornamental wrought iron are provided in the opening between the living and dining rooms. This detail also shows the floor joists under the living room.

The *foyer-opening* detail shows the space for a television set and shelves and cabinets for a record player and record albums. All the exposed wood in the foyer is oak plywood. The detail also shows sections through the dining nook and the front window and flower box. The nook contains an open-front cabinet above the upholstered seat. There is a convector enclosure under the front window and a drapery valance which extends along this side of the living room.

The *main-cornice* section is shown in one of the details. The wall plate is a double 2 by 4. The ceiling joists or attic floor joists are 2 by 6 inches over the north portion of the building and 2 by 8 inches over the south portion, where they support the storage room. All the rafters in the main roofs are 2 by 8 inches. The cornice lookouts are 2 by 4 inches. All the exposed wood in the cornice is specified to be white pine, and all the gutters and leaders are aluminum.

The *lintel,* or header, over the dining-room opening is composed of three 2 by 10's spiked together, and the second-floor joists rest on this and are spiked together.

Box sills are shown in the foundation details. The sills, or foundation plates, are 2 by 8's fastened on the concrete-block walls with $\frac{5}{8}$- by 18-inch anchor bolts mortared into the blocks. The sill course on the brick veneer is a rowlock course of bricks cut to 5-inch length and tilted slightly to shed water.

The length of the sill is determined by the size of the building, and therefore the foundation should be laid out accordingly. Dimension lines for the outside of the building are generally figured from the outside face of the subsiding, or sheathing. Where high winds are at all probable, it is important that the building be thoroughly anchored to the foundation. In fact, anchoring is good practice in all localities. It is accomplished by setting, at intervals of 6 to 8 feet, bolts that extend at least 18 inches into the foundation. They should project sufficiently through the sill to receive a good-sized washer and nut.

Estimators do not like plans drawn at a scale as small as $\frac{1}{8}$ inch to the foot because this does not allow enough room for showing the work clearly, and they are thus forced to rely on the specifications, which, in turn, may not be very clear. Some architects always use $\frac{1}{8}$ inch for the regular plans and elevations but give also a number of large-scale drawings which show the important features properly.

Mechanical work is not shown on these drawings. Separate plans will be found in Chapters 19 and 21 for the plumbing and electrical work.

EXERCISES

1 Briefly, what is each of the following:

   $a.$ A floor plan

   $b.$ An elevation

   $c.$ A section

   $d.$ A detail drawing

2 Describe briefly architectural, structural, and mechanical plans, and state what each shows.

3 What are blueprints?

4 What is meant by $\frac{1}{4}$-inch scale? Give an example of its use.

5 What is a plot plan?

6 What do the terms present grade and finish grade mean?

7 What do the terms building line and lot line mean?

8 What are zoning restrictions and deed restrictions?

9 With what materials is the front all faced?

10 What is a double-hung window?

11 How many double-hung windows are there in the front wall?

12 What material is used for the front-porch flooring? For the rear-porch flooring?

13 Using a scale rule, what is the total height of the chimney for the top of the footing to the top of the brickwork?

14 What is meant by the platform-frame type of house framing?

15 What material is used for the basement and other foundation walls? What thicknesses?

16 How many steel columns are there? How many steel girders?

17 What kind of flooring is used in the living room? Dining room? Kitchen?

18 How long are the steel columns?

19 What size rafters are used in the main roofs? At what spacing are they?

20 Describe the main-cornice construction.

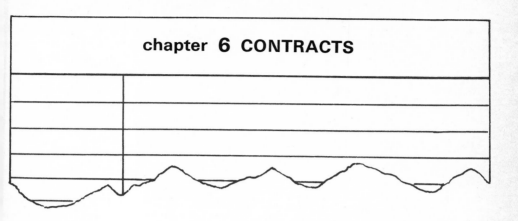

chapter 6 CONTRACTS

INTRODUCTION

In doing business in the construction industry it is necessary to enter into various types of agreements for work to be done, materials to be used, equipment installation, etc. To maintain order in the operation of the business, written contracts are used to indicate to the contractor and building owner the amount and type of work to be done for the specified compensation.

A *contract* may be defined as an agreement between two or more competent parties to perform or not to perform some lawful act for compensation. Although it is not necessary that every contract be written in order to be enforceable, enforcement, in case of dispute, is easier if the agreement is in written form.

REQUIREMENTS OF A CONTRACT

Competent parties to a construction contract will generally mean parties legally competent to make that type of contract. Generally, they may not be minors or persons of unsound mind, persons in the state of intoxication, or persons under legal guardianship. Persons making contracts for a corporation must have authority to do so as regulated by the corporation's articles of incorporation and the board of directors.

For the contract to be valid it is essential that the parties to the contract mutually agree to the subject matter of that document. Where there is clear evidence of misunderstanding as to the scope of the contract on the part of both parties, the agreement may be set aside. To avoid such misunderstanding, it is essential that the parties to a contract discuss its contents and thoroughly comprehend its meaning before signing the document.

There must be valuable consideration as a part of the contract to make it enforceable. That is, there must be something of value: money, property, or services, transferred from one party to the other for items covered by the contract. Generally, the amount of valuable consideration transferred is not important in enforcing a contract unless the question of fraud is raised. Underbidding on a job is not sufficient reason for setting aside the terms of the contract unless it can be proved that the bidder was intentionally misled.

Any contract, to be enforceable, must be for lawful acts and not contrary to public policy. A construction company in dealing with contracts for public works should, naturally, avoid any activity which would link it with obscure deals or unfair competition.

The written contract must be in proper form, cover all points required by law, and be executed according to the governing laws. In the construction business standard forms may be used on which pertinent information is filled in to complete the form. Building specifications may be made part of the contract, or the contract may be written to refer to the plans and specifications by title and description.

DISCHARGE OF A CONTRACT

There are a number of ways in which the responsibilities under a contract may be discharged. Perhaps the most common way is by performance of the work or service in accordance with the terms of the contract.

However, it may not be possible in some cases to

perform work covered by the contract. This situation might arise when the contract contained a clause on unknown conditions, such as owner's responsibility for added cost due to unstable soil conditions. If these conditions prevent building according to the plans and specifications, the contractor could be relieved of obligations under the contract because performance was impossible. It would be impossible for a builder to perform under terms of the contract if he were unable to obtain a building permit due to changes in zoning laws. In this case his obligation under the contract would be discharged.

Occasionally, a contractor's obligation under a contract may be discharged by *substantial performance*. Under substantial performance a contractor may have completed his work as near as possible to plans and specifications. Minor deviations from these plans and specifications might technically prevent discharge of obligation by performance but would not prevent discharge by substantial performance where the deviations did not adversely affect the quality of the finished product.

Obligations to a contract may be discharged by mutual agreement of the parties involved. That is, they can agree to cancel the contract without executing any part of it, or they can agree on terms for canceling remaining obligations under the contract.

There are a number of other ways to terminate a contract, but they will not be discussed here. A student interested in the rules governing contracts is encouraged to look for information in standard texts on contracts.

TYPES OF CONTRACTS

Most contracts in the construction field are made for a fixed price or lump sum on a given amount of work. Bidding on a job with this type of contract is entirely satisfactory as long as the plans and specifications are reasonably complete and there are no obscure factors which would introduce the possibility of unduly high risk in carrying out the terms of the contract. The possibility of high risk necessitates an increase in the bid price to ensure a reasonable return for the building contractor.

To avoid the element of risk to the contractor inherent in the fixed-price type of contract, a contract for actual construction cost plus a specified percentage for overhead and profit has been used. Although this removes the element of risk for the contractor, it may place an added burden on the building owner since increased building costs, whatever the reason, lead to greater profit for the building contractor at the owner's expense. When this type of contract is entered into, it becomes increasingly important that the owner deal with a contractor of highest reputation.

Contracts for cost plus a fixed price have been used to avoid the possibility of a contractor profiting from increased job costs. It does not, however, avoid increased costs from inefficient methods and unsatisfactory labor conditions.

Other types of contracts for actual cost plus a variable premium have been proposed and used. The scheme of payment in all of them strives to give the owner the lowest possible price for the work done, and the contractor a reasonable profit and a limited financial interest in seeing that the construction progresses efficiently.

ARBITRATION OF DISPUTES

Whatever the type of contract used, it should be written clearly, and both parties should fully understand its terms. However, even in the most simple, clearly written contracts, disputes do arise. It is therefore advisable that the contract contain a clause on *arbitration* of disputes.

This method of settling disputes chooses men who are familiar with the practical work and problems of building construction to take the place of courts and lawyers, who are likely to become entangled in legal technicalities and are often groping in their judgment because they have not sufficient practical knowledge. Estimators would do well to insist that an arbitration clause be provided in every contract. By this method, usually three men are chosen to settle any dispute arising out of the contract or plans or specifications. Each party to the contract selects one man, and these two select a third. Each side presents its case to this three-man board, and when two of the three agree on a basis for settlement of the dispute, the matter is ended (it should be thus stated in the contract) and their decision is binding on both parties to the contract. One of the main advantages of arbitration is that either party has the right to ask for an arbitration any time it wishes. Thus disputes may be quickly settled while matters are still fresh in the minds of those concerned. Law cases have a habit of dragging out for months and even years, and it is often impossible to find the records and witnesses that are necessary for properly presenting the case. Besides, law cases are notoriously expensive, while arbitrations may involve only a few hours of work on the part of the arbitrators. The fee to be paid to the arbitrators and the decision as to who is to pay it should be left to the arbitrators, or else each side should pay for the arbitrator it retains, and the payment of the third member decided by the three members acting together as a board.

Custom plays an important part in the interpretation of contracts and, to a lesser degree, of plans and specifications. If one can prove that a definitely established custom prevails in a matter under dispute, he has already won an advantage toward settlement in his favor.

All contracts, except those for very small amounts, should be reviewed by the contractor's lawyer before being signed. It is also advisable to have an insurance agent look over contracts that contain "hold harmless" clauses. In such cases, the contractor agrees to indemnify and save harmless the owner for injuries to persons and damage to property. He thereby assumes liabilities under which his insurance carrier is prevented from holding parties at fault in the event of a claim. Policies generally have a clause stating that "the insured shall not voluntarily assume any liability, settle any claim, nor incur any expense except at his own cost, nor interfere in any negotiation, settlement or legal proceeding without the consent of the company previously given in writing." If such a contract must be signed, the insurance carrier may give this consent, but will undoubtedly increase the premium to cover not only what may be reasonably expected to happen, but also what could possibly happen in the worst circumstances. It may be necessary for the contractor to charge the owner an additional amount to cover this extra expense.

Contracts must be honest. A party to a contract who

discovers that major misrepresentations were made to him may either continue and sue for damages or he may repudiate the contract and sue for damages. Courts have held that when a defrauded party repudiates a contract, he is entitled to recover damages incidental to the contract and caused directly by the fraud. One fraud that courts recognize is concealment by an owner of known adverse conditions or information, not disclosed in the plans or specifications; in such instances the contractor can sue the owner for damages. Many of these cases relate to subsoil conditions, but there are other types of concealment. An example may be found in the case of a contractor who undertook a job on which other separate contractors were also engaged and who was led to believe at the time of bidding that all contracts would be awarded together. The other contracts were not awarded for a long time, and this contractor was thereby forced to work for a considerably longer time than he had anticipated. The court held that he was entitled to recover for the increased cost of the work resulting from the failure of the owner to award all the contracts at the same time. Failure to disclose that the other contracts had not been let constituted constructive fraud. The court stated:

Silence by the defendant as to a change in plans so important to the timely performance of the work served to mislead the plaintiff into a false assurance that the work contemplated by his bid would progress and be integrated with the work of the other contractors. Silence may constitute fraud where one of the parties to a contract has notice that the other is acting upon a mistaken belief as to a material fact.

FINANCING CONTRACTS

Some contracts provide that the contractor shall pay all his bills every month before asking for a payment from the owner to cover them. Thus, if a contractor has ten jobs under way at one time and they average an expense for one month of $25,000 each, he would have to pay out $250,000 before sending in his bills to the various architects for approval. Then, before he received his payments from the owners, another half month would go by and he would have about $375,000 outstanding. On this basis, the contractor would have to be a very wealthy man, or else he would find himself in the banking business to a greater extent than in the contracting business. It is therefore part of the estimator's duties to warn the contractor against accepting contracts with such extreme wording regarding the method of making payments. If it is necessary to accept such a contract, the means of financing the undertaking should be worked out before the contract is signed, and proper interest and service charges should be included in the contract amount to take care of the unusual financing requirements. The more customary procedure is for the

Table 6-1

Month	Cost of Amount Done	15% Withheld
1	$ 18,000	$ 2,700
2	55,000	8,250
3	110,000	16,500
4	245,000	36,750
5	420,000	63,000
6	500,000	75,000

contractor to pay his bills immediately after receiving payments from the owner and, if necessary, to submit proof to the architect or the owner that he has actually paid these bills before his next payment is approved by the architect.

On an average job costing $500,000 and extending six months, the amount held back in the customary 15 percent that is retained is a large sum, as will be seen from Table 6-1.

By the time the fifth payment is made, and only about $40,000 of work remains to be done, the amount being withheld is about $70,000. Thus, instead of 15 percent, 175 percent is being withheld, based on the amount of work yet to be done.

The 15 percent is often referred to as the contractor's profit. It actually represents the cost of his office rent, the salaries of his estimators and general superintendent, general office salaries, and expenses. The salaries have to be paid every week, and the many other items involved, at least every month. Then, whatever may be left is profit! If contractors wrote out their bills to show general expense and office overhead and profit separately, the profit item might be only 2 or 3 percent instead of 15 percent.

The percentages and the time of payments often require thought on the part of the estimator. In some cases it may be necessary to refuse to figure a job or to accept a contract unless better terms of payment are offered. Architects seem to be forever guarding against overpayments to the contractors. Few of them are good businessmen, and this fact may account for their fear of granting more liberal terms. Contracts should be worded definitely as to how long the contractor must wait for each monthly payment. If twenty or more days are to elapse, he will not receive one payment until it is nearly time to apply for another. Meanwhile, his payrolls have had to be met every week with cash. Inasmuch as the partial payments are based on estimates of the work done and not on detail measurements, it should be possible for the contractor to submit requisitions three or four days before the end of the month and to expect these to be checked through so that he will receive payment by the fifth day of the following month, instead of having to wait several weeks, as is often the case.

TYPICAL LUMP-SUM CONTRACT

As stated earlier, there are a number of types of contracts which a contractor may enter into, each containing a different method of compensating the contractor for his services. The *lump-sum contract,* however, is the most commonly used and does offer the owner the advantage of a definite price on the work to be done. A typical lump-sum contract is reproduced here to introduce the student to its form.

MEMORANDUM OF AGREEMENT made this twentieth day of February 1970, by and between HENRY V. MALLIN, of 494 Fifth Avenue, New York City (hereinafter called the Owner), and RENISON CONSTRUCTION CO., INC., of 30 West 42nd Street, New York City (hereinafter called the Contractor).

WITNESSETH: That for and in consideration of the agreements herein contained, it is agreed by and between the parties hereto, as follows:

1   The Contractor agrees to furnish all the labor, materials, equipment, tools, and supplies for constructing and completing the hereinafter described house (hereinafter referred to as the work).

The Owner agrees to pay to the Contractor the sum of money hereinafter mentioned at the times and in the manner and upon the terms and conditions hereinafter set forth.

2   The house to be constructed under this contract is to be a one-family house constructed on the Owner's property at 110 Park Avenue in the Village of Florence, Nassau County, New York. The exact location, dimensions, and other characteristics of the house are given in the specifications and plans hereinafter mentioned.

3   The work is to be in strict accordance with the specifications dated February 5, 1970, prepared by John Edgar Smith, Architect, and the plans referred to therein, which specifications and plans have been signed by the parties hereto and are hereby made a part of this contract.

4   The Contractor will prosecute the work diligently at all times until completion and upon completion will leave the work complete and perfect. He will not have materials provided or obtained, nor will he have work performed or labor or means employed in the carrying out of this contract that would in any way cause or result in suspension or delay of, or strike upon the work.

5   The Owner will pay the Contractor for the work, subject to additions and deductions as hereinafter provided, the sum of FOURTEEN THOUSAND SIX HUNDRED DOLLARS ($14,600).

Payments to the Contractor will be made in current funds and in installments payable on the fifth day of each month in amounts not to exceed ninety percent (90%) of the value of the work done and materials substantially incorporated in said work on the last day of the month preceding. The other ten percent (10%) will be retained by the Owner as part security for the faithful performance of the work, this amount to be retained until thirty (30) days after the entire work has been completed and the Contractor has paid all claims for labor and material furnished on said work.

The right of the Contractor to receive any payment hereunder shall be evidenced by a certificate issued by the Architect. No payments made or certificates thereof will in any way be construed as an acceptance of any part of the work, nor will the same in any way lessen the total and final responsibility of the Contractor.

Prior to final payment and as a condition thereto, the Contractor will furnish the Owner with a verified statement that all bills and claims have been satisfied, and a release of all claims against the Owner, arising under and by virtue of this agreement.

6 This agreement, and the specifications and plans referred to herein, may be modified and changed from time to time, as may be previously agreed upon in writing between the parties hereto, in order to carry out and complete more fully and perfectly the work herein agreed to be done and performed.

The Contractor will submit a written proposal covering each modification or change, at the request of the Architect, within ten days after receipt of such request, and such proposal shall be accepted or rejected by the Owner within ten days. In the event of rejection because of the price quoted in the proposal, such modification or change may be paid for, at the option of the Owner, on the basis of cost of labor and materials and insurance, plus twenty percent (20%).

7 The Contractor will procure all necessary permits and licenses, abide by all applicable laws, regulations, ordinances, and other rules of the States or political subdivisions thereof, or any other duly constituted public authority. He will assume, pay, and be responsible for any and all taxes and contributions under Federal, State, and Municipal tax laws arising as a result of this agreement.

8 In case the parties hereto cannot agree as to the interpretation of any part of this agreement, the same shall be determined in accordance with the arbitration laws of the State of New York. One arbitrator will be chosen by the Owner, one by the Contractor, and the third by the two so selected, and the decision of a majority of the said three persons will be binding upon the parties hereto.

IN WITNESS WHEREOF, the parties hereto, for themselves and their respective heirs, executors, administrators, and assigns, executed this agreement the day and year first above written.

Attest: _____   _____
                John W. Randolph   Henry V. Mallin
                                                Renison Construction Co., Inc.

Attest: _____   by _____
                George H. Cabot   Robert T. Renison
                    Secretary   President

EXERCISES

1 What are the essential requirements of a building contract? (60 to 100 words)

2 How may responsibilities under a contract be discharged?

3 What is a lump-sum building contract? (50 to 75 words)

4 What is meant by arbitration? (50 to 75 words)

5 How does a builder finance contracts?

6 Write at least 200 words of notes on contracts, taken from one or two of the books listed in the Bibliography. Name the books used.

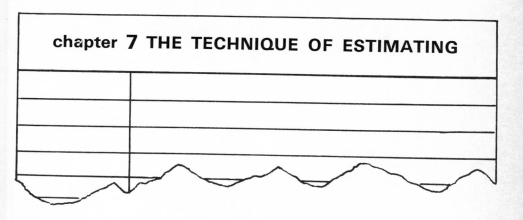

chapter 7 THE TECHNIQUE OF ESTIMATING

INTRODUCTION

When one speaks of an estimate in connection with building work, he generally refers to the regular estimate that is used for computing the amount of the contract price. This estimate lists all the materials, labor, and equipment costs for the job. Because it is a detailed estimate it is time-consuming and costly to make.

Preliminary, or budget, estimates are sometimes made up to find the approximate cost of a proposed building. These are usually made before the plans and specifications are complete, and may be based on unit costs from previous jobs of similar nature. These unit costs may be cost per square foot or cost per cubic foot or some other unit such as per desk in a classroom building or per bed in a hospital. Such an estimate enables the architect to gauge the extent to which he may go in developing the details of the work on the final plans and in the specifications. Financial arrangements also may require a preliminary approximation of the cost.

PRELIMINARY ESTIMATES

A preliminary estimate may be quite comprehensive in scope. If it is to be used as a guide for the owner in determining his total expense, a preliminary estimate may include such items as the cost of the property upon which the proposed building is to be built. The legal costs of transferring the ownership of the property from other parties may also be shown. The owner's cost of investigating into the proposition, his expense for architects' and engineers' fees, the interest on his money for temporary and permanent financing of the undertaking, and other items not commonly considered by builders' estimators may have to be included. Often a contractor is given a set of preliminary sketches that show the proposed building but do not include walks, roads, floor coverings, lighting fixtures, decorations, and other items that are obviously necessary to make the building complete and ready for use. If it is intended to serve for the owner's full guidance, an honest preliminary estimate should list all these items and all other possible items of expense. They should be listed by name without figures after them if no figures are available. Among the items that might be included are taxes and insurance to be borne by the owner, besides an allowance for additional work that may be ordered and for furnishings, the operation of the building, and maintenance costs.

When preliminary cost estimates are based on cost per cubic foot, or other unit, it must be remembered that this estimate is only an approximation of the actual cost because no two buildings are ever built under exactly the same conditions. Since preliminary estimates seem to have an annoying tendency not to agree with the final estimates, those to whom they are submitted should be advised that preliminary estimates are only rough approximations and that it is not safe to regard them as final.

REGULAR ESTIMATES

The regular estimates are made up by the general contractor's estimator; preliminary estimates are sometimes made up by the architect or by an agent of the owner, instead of in a contractor's office.

Working Estimates Some contractors make a habit of using what may be called working estimates. These are prepared by the estimator—or by the superintendent when another man's check is desired—after word has come that the contract is to be secured. They are made up in much the same style as the regular bidding estimates, but much more detail is included in them so that they form valuable aids in the management of the job. The plans and specifications are carefully checked over, and all adjustments are made up to this point. These working estimates form the basis for awarding the subcontracts and for preparing material lists, construction schedules, and other working data.

Regular printed forms for estimates and material lists are obtainable (see Appendix B), as well as standard forms for contracts of all kinds. Although some contractors use these, most either do their estimating on stock-type journal-ruled pads or have estimating sheets made up to suit their own ideas.

The main heading of the estimate includes the name or type of building, its location, the owner's name, and the architect's name. Some estimators give a brief description of the building, its size, the number of stories in height, the type of construction, the cubical contents, and other information.

The cost of doing different kinds of construction work under different conditions cannot be exactly determined, but if the plans and specifications are well prepared, there is no question that the costs can be approximated very closely. A great part of estimating, however, is done by very loose and unscientific methods; figures are based on limited rather than broad experience, and many factors of great importance are left out of consideration.

The first step in estimating any kind of building work is to determine in the simplest way possible, yet with a reasonable degree of accuracy, the number of units of work to be done. In some cases this may mean the amount of material required, but usually it is not so simple as that. In their effort to oversimplify the work, careless estimators are led into omissions.

Estimating, like accounting, is an established business routine and is an integral part of the business of constructing buildings. In a broad sense, it must be thought of as equal in importance to the preparation of the plans and the writing of the specifications. Estimating done by men not trained for it is usually based on hasty judgment or on guesses. Such estimators lack the thorough schooling in the analysis work that is necessary for the preparation of complete and reliable estimates. The methods used by some contractors in going over work preparatory to making bids are superficial almost beyond belief. In the main, these are responsible to a great degree for the losses later sustained by the contractors.

Organization   The estimate should be a complete story of the construction work—in builder's language. It should be so arranged and so worded that the man who made it or any other man familiar with building estimates will be able to obtain from it a clear mental picture of the proposed work in all its parts.

Estimates, schedules, and material lists are generally arranged in the same order as specifications, that is, in the sequence in which the trades commence work on the job. The mechanical lines, however, such as plumbing, heating, and electrical work, are more often put at the end.

The estimate is divided, in general, according to the branches of work that are required on the particular job under consideration. There is no definite arrangement to be followed. The divisions are made for convenience in pricing the work to be done. They do not conform to the divisions used in the architect's specifications; these may not suit the method of handling the various parts of the job from a construction standpoint.

The heading for the first part, or division, of the estimate is Excavating, because excavation is usually the first work to be done on the job. However, if there are on the property any old buildings or other structures that have to be removed, a preliminary heading Demolition, or Clearing Site, will be required.

A division of the estimate is not necessarily confined to the trade that the heading might indicate. The heading Concrete Work, for example, will very likely include some carpentry work (for installing temporary forms) and the work of installing reinforcing steel by the ironworkers as well as that of the concrete workers themselves. The heading Plastering nearly always includes lathing, since only established custom has made the name plastering the one commonly adopted. This heading is, in fact, sometimes extended to Lathing and Plastering. These are examples of divisions that embrace more than their names indicate.

Other headings may include less than the name indicates. Carpentry is one of these. Although under this heading are mentioned all the items that are customarily grouped there, not all work to be done by carpenters will usually be listed among these items. As has been mentioned before, the carpentry of installing the temporary forms used to support concrete is more often placed under the heading of Concrete Work. Another part of the job done by carpenters is the installation of kalamein work (metal-covered doors, etc.). This special branch of carpentry may be set up under a separate heading in specifications and estimates, or it may be included under Carpentry.

In spite of this apparent lack of definite rules, the experienced estimator finds little difficulty in arranging his estimate.

NEATNESS, ORDER, AND CHECKLISTS

Neatness and order in the form of the estimate will help to eliminate errors. Besides, the student should try to be systematic and to develop a uniform method of working, arranging the entries so that the result will have an attractive orderly appearance and be easy to read.

Some estimators use colored pencils to check off the items on the plans as they are listed on the estimating sheets. This is an aid in some lines of work and on some kinds of jobs. One danger in this practice lies in assuming that the check marks cover all the items required—in other words, in marking the items that were seen and listed and failing to look further for other items that may have been missed. Experienced estimators seldom mark plans.

Some estimators use separate sheets for pricing the quantities, which are first grouped on the takeoff sheets and then carried forward to these pricing sheets. This is desirable on large jobs, where many sheets are necessary for the takeoff for each line of work. In this case, an accurate check should be made to see that all the items are actually carried over to the pricing sheets. On smaller jobs it is perhaps better to price directly on the same sheets with the quantities, thus eliminating any possibility of failing to carry over all the items. This method also keeps all the work of an item in one place. Thus, if any corrections or adjustments are required, there is only one place, instead of two, in which to make the changes. For the same reasons, on the smaller jobs it is best to dispense with summaries and grand summaries.

Calculations should be made by the estimator and then checked by another person. In busy offices where adding machines and calculating machines are used, the process is reduced to a simple matter of mathematical checking, which can be done by any office assistant after a little practice. Every reasonable effort should be made to have the estimate entirely correct.

Checklists are helpful in catching items that may be omitted, but because of the vast number of possible items, it is impracticable to have complete lists. A standard job expense sheet is generally used, however. On this all the items that are expected to be encountered in this category are already enumerated and therefore serve as a check. Here the items of scaffolding, hoisting, temporary protection, temporary heat, and others that are likely to be omitted entirely are picked up. Even if an item is included on another sheet, there is no harm in having it appear here also; it can easily be crossed out if not needed. Many contractors, to make sure that their insurance costs are not overlooked, carry these costs on the job expense sheet, instead of including such large items on all the various sheets having to do with the divisions of the work.

It is impossible to use anything in the nature of standard costs for reference in the pricing of estimates. Even cost records kept by the contractor's own office are not reliable to the extent that they may be safely used for all estimates. So many factors enter into the actual cost of building work that each job is a problem in itself. However, accurate cost records should be kept of all work done, so that the estimator may keep abreast of actual costs as far as possible; also, they may serve the purpose of finding changes made in the work that may not have been properly charged to the owner. To ensure better estimating thereafter, cost records should also be used to bring out errors and omissions made in the original estimate. Figures 4-3 to 4-5 show typical cost record sheets.

PLANS AND SPECIFICATIONS

The plans and specifications are examined first by the estimator, so that he may become familiar with the job to be estimated. No definite procedure that will be applicable to all jobs can be given, but certain rules do apply. Generally speaking, in the arrangement of the estimate, the same order is followed as in the construction of the building, beginning with the excavation and proceeding with the various divisions in the order that the work of the different lines starts at the job. A good specification follows this order, too, and when this is the case, it may be possible for the estimator to follow the exact order of the specification. However, as has been stated before, nearly all specifications show overlapping of items, and it is the responsibility of the estimator to see that every item is provided for and that none is duplicated. He must be experienced enough to feel confident that the prices he applies to his estimates will be correct for every important item and suitable for the conditions that will probably be required by the particular job under consideration.

An estimator likes a specification that states definitely just what is to take place on the job, exactly what materials are desired and what their quality should be, and exactly what will be done about inspecting the work in its various parts—in short, one that thoroughly covers the whole work. If the architect expects to see a thoroughly manned job, with ample job office and supervision facilities, instead of one that has only a superintendent (acting also as timekeeper, material clerk, layout engineer, etc.), he should so state in his specification, calling for what he wants. Otherwise, many contractors will be tempted to underman the job, in order to cut cost, at the expense of the quality of the work.

Plans and specifications must be checked carefully by the estimator. When a contract is signed, it is usually for all the work called for in the specifications or shown on the plans. This means that an architect does not have to include all the work in the specifications alone, but may show some of it on the plans without mentioning it in the specifications. For this reason, estimators double-check against the plans, and from their knowledge of construction work are able to add a number of items in their estimates for work that is not mentioned in the specifications. Architects are not closely enough in touch with builders' problems to enable them to arrange their specifications so that these may be relied on entirely, either in first figuring the job or in using them as a basis of direct reference in awarding subcontracts. There are many overlappings and omissions.

SITE INSPECTION

The examination of the site should be made before the estimate is far advanced. An experienced estimator will investigate the conditions relative to the handling of materials, the storage of these materials, the distance to the railroad (especially if carload shipments are expected), the means of unloading and transporting from the cars, etc. Some materials require temporary protection and substantial covers, sheds, or platforms. These temporary conveniences should be listed and measured and priced on a unit basis, the same as other carpentry work. The maintenance and dismantling of temporary work often is not given proper consideration in estimating. Temporary waterlines and temporary heating often entail extra expense to a large amount, because of the daily (and sometimes nightly) attention required for proper maintenance. Even the work of unloading and stacking materials may have to be a substantial item of cost in the estimate, especially if it involves the handling of heavy or fragile materials or if the material must be carried or wheeled a considerable distance from the point of unloading to the storage places. Such matters are tests of an estimator's practical knowledge of job problems; he has to visualize the working conditions in order to know what to expect and what to provide for. When unusual conditions arise with which the estimator has no experience, it is his duty to call upon the prospective job superintendent and others for their advice. In that way he can better provide for the expected costs.

Comparison often has to be made between the cost of materials delivered to the job by truck and the cost of the same kind of materials shipped by freight and then unloaded and hauled to the job. When they are shipped by freight, the uncertainty of delivery on time must be judged, as well as the availability of sufficient storage space for large lots of material. If carload shipments require that temporary storage sheds be built for protecting materials until they are needed, it may very well prove foolhardy to set down a low price and later have to face the cost of the sheds. If there is not ample room around a job and if materials must be stacked close together and close to the work, it will probably be necessary to move some of them more than once—and every handling adds to the expense. It sometimes happens that a job is so cramped that men cannot work efficiently. In such cases, the lower output of work must be carefully taken into account. In addition, overtime work may become necessary, entailing premium pay for men who work overtime, either to move materials or to do construction work that must be accomplished in order that the job may run smoothly the following day. This overtime work, moreover, may initially have been made necessary by poor judgment in ordering the materials.

Labor conditions at the site must be looked into if they are not already known. The availability of sufficient men of the needed skills is important to the smooth running and proper sequence of the work.

What is to be done with excavated material that is needed at the site for backfilling or for filling inside the building should be considered in the pricing of an estimate. In some extreme cases, it is better to haul away part of this material and then haul it back or buy other material for filling, rather than have piles of dirt in the way of the men for a considerable time, which may prove more expensive if this dirt has to be moved out of the way several times. It may even be more economical to concentrate on the foundations of one part of the job, letting the other parts wait, and then to backfill the first part with the material taken from the other parts. All these items, of course, are considered under the heading of Excavating. They are discussed here because of their importance in relation to the inspection of the site.

The expected date of delivery of the structural steel is often the deciding factor in considering the general handling of jobs involving steel. Even the handling of the excavating may be affected by it. If the steel is expected quickly, the plan should concentrate on those footings that are to receive the first steel deliveries and in this way enable the work to proceed continuously thereafter with the structural frame of that part of the building, even before the other portions of the building have been started. Thus the steelwork affects excavating, concrete work, backfilling, and perhaps other work.

A general study of the method of laying out the job and running it is made at the time the estimate is being prepared. An approximate progress schedule will be found helpful in this connection. It may prove better economy to spend more money speeding up some parts of the work in order to be better prepared to do other parts. It may also be found necessary to speed up portions in this way, to meet promised dates of completion that may be specified in the contract.

ALLOWANCES FOR WASTE

An element of cost is waste. Forms for concrete involve waste if they can be used only once or twice on a job rather than a great number of times. Concrete may be wasted if the forms are made larger than called for, or if some of it has to be thrown away because too much has been ordered for a particular pouring, or because the forms are not ready to receive it. Mortar for brickwork drops to the ground and is wasted, or too much is made and the surplus is thrown away. Improper mixing of concrete or mortar at the job may involve the use of more cement, the expensive ingredient in these items, and thus both money and time are wasted. Estimators often wonder where all the cement goes on a job. Perhaps if they saw the work being done they would note this waste. One careless, wasteful man can throw away hundreds of dollars on a good-sized job if he has a position in which he controls the supply of an item that can readily be wasted. The fault, of course, lies with the foreman or superintendent who does not check the figures every few days and so does not discover these leaks.

Face brick and glazed-tile blocks break in transit and while they are being moved about the job; lumber and scaffold planks break; doors and windows become marred so that they have to be rejected. All these and other items of waste must be considered by the estimator and provided for. On some jobs there will be very little such waste, but on others, especially where speed is essential or where carelessness and lack of system prevail, it will amount to a considerable loss.

Time wasted is money wasted. The estimator has no control over the amount of time wasted on a job. He must allow for a reasonable amount of lost time by realistically estimating output per man-hour. After that it is the responsibility of the job superintendent to see that the estimated output is attained.

JOB COST CONTINGENCIES

It is difficult for the estimator to provide for contingencies and yet have his estimate low enough to win the contract. Winter weather must be taken into account, if the work is to extend into that season, so that costs cover temporary enclosures and temporary heating and general loss of efficiency on the job during bad weather. Incidentally, if a job is expected under normal conditions to be closed in before bad weather comes, and if additional work is given by the owner or changes are made that hold up the work, the estimator, immediately upon finding this to be the case, should have compensation demanded from the owner for costs thus made necessary.

If a job is to last several months, it may very well be that the wage rate of one or more of the trades will be increased before the work is completed. Rarely is it possible for the contractor to get additional money from the owner for this increased cost. Therefore the estimator must be aware of the various labor agreement expiration dates and the demands for pay increases being made by the various trades so that he can make realistic allowances for these increased costs.

The time required for constructing a building is of great importance to a contractor, because his funds and also his working staff are tied up in the work. To become too involved in jobs may cause his financial ruin, especially if his funds are limited. For this reason, it is better for him to stop figuring new jobs for a while and to use estimating talent in connection with jobs on hand, to improve efficiency and advance the finishing date where possible. Too little work on hand is bad, but too much work on hand may be worse.

It is always advisable to make an analysis of the specifications and plans before starting an estimate. Enough detail should be incorporated in this analysis so that it will form a complete checklist. First the specification is analyzed and then items from the plans are added to the list, as well as other items gathered from the estimator's own knowledge of construction work and of the special requirements involved in the particular job being estimated. It is the estimator's duty to see that every item of expense is included in the estimate, either among his own items or among those of the subcontractors whose figures he incorporates in the estimate.

SUBCONTRACTORS

Subcontractors' estimates require careful study before the figures presented in them may be used. The work included by the subcontractor in each case must be ascertained. Even those estimates that read "according to the plans and specifications" may not, when studied, really cover all the work that at first glance may seem to be included. If a plumbing contractor, for example, says that he has included all the work in his line, this does not necessarily mean that he has accounted for all the items that the architect chose to specify under the heading of Plumbing. The architect may have mentioned in the plumbing section many items of equipment that are ordinarily hooked up by the plumbers, but the plumbing contractor may take the stand that these items, or some of them, are to be furnished by other parties and not by him, that he is merely to hook them up to the plumbing system. Thus the cost of furnishing all such items may be omitted from the estimate if care is not exercised. Similarly, if an electrical contractor says that he has included all the work called for in his portion of the specifications, he may not be counting in the lighting fixtures, if they have not been specified therein, even though they may be shown and perhaps listed in detail on the plans.

The lowest subcontract estimate in a given line is not always the best to choose. One that is far below the other estimates received should be checked carefully before being incorporated in the contractor's own estimate. For one reason or another the subcontractor may not take the job if it is offered to him. He may have found out in the meantime that he made a mistake in figuring or that he omitted some of the work. Even if he signs a contract at the low figure he submitted, trouble may start while he is working on the job; he may find that he is losing money and ask for more than he contracted for, or he may be financially unable to proceed. At any rate, he probably will not be very enthusiastic about the work or give it proper attention, as he would if he had the prospect of a good profit. The estimator must keep all these considerations in mind as he weighs the pricing of his estimate for the whole job, taking every reasonable precaution.

Subcontractors often wish to use a different material or one of a different grade from that specified. Sometimes they state this in their estimates, perhaps noting the substitute; and sometimes they take a chance and later state that they had anticipated using different material. If the substitution is perfectly fair, usually no trouble results, but in other cases a dispute may ensue. At the time of estimating there is no opportunity to anticipate what the subcontractor may have in mind to do afterward. If, however, a subcontractor in his estimate gives any intimation that he plans to make a substitution or if he verbally states any such intention, the cautious estimator, before using that subcontractor's estimate in preparing his own bid for the job, will make a thorough check as to the possibility of a misunderstanding.

Occasionally, a subcontractor, at the time he is figuring the job, will tell the estimator of a substitution that he plans to make, but will neglect to state this in his estimate. Later he may claim that he told the estimator and then try to force an adjustment. While no legal claim may be involved, an embarrassing situation is created that could have been avoided by the estimator's taking proper steps when he first learned of the planned substitution. He should at least have given warning that it would be the architect's responsibility to accept or reject any substitutions.

UNFAIR DEALINGS

Architects and owners may not always be fair in their dealings with contractors. Many estimates are made for building that is never done. Yet the cost to the contractors bidding on it is never considered by those who unhesitatingly ask for bids. Architects and owners should not submit plans for bidding unless they have made a commitment to follow through with their plans. This is not to say that plans can never be withdrawn for any number of reasons. The point is that plans should never be submitted just to learn how much a job will cost.

Architects sometimes specify that only approved subcontractors may be used. This gives rise to confusion in the selection of subcontractors by the contractor. It could be eliminated if architects would furnish full sets of plans and specifications to subcontractors who meet with their approval at the time bids are first asked for, at least in the main lines of work. These subcontractors could then send a copy of each bid to each of the contractors bidding on the job, and thus eliminate their doubts about being approved.

Another thing that annoys estimators is to find out, after a job is well under way, that an architect had in his possession surveys and other information regarding ground levels and conditions existing at the site and in its surroundings that he did not issue with the plans when bids were asked for. It is in the best interest of all parties concerned for the architect to include all pertinent information in his hands along with the plans and specifications when asking for bids. The estimator would do well to check with the architect when there appears to be a possibility of obtaining more information.

All work should be deemed to be union work, with no overtime work considered. The standard form of lump-sum contract of the American Institute of Architects, without alteration, should be understood to be used for all work. If any variations from these two requirements are desired by the architect or the owner, it should be clearly stated in the original bidding specifications, in order that contractors and their subcontractors may take them into account at the time of making their original calculations.

Rock excavating, pumping, and underpinning and foundation work not shown on the architect's plans, and other work or expense upon which it is impossible for the contractor to make a satisfactory estimate should be paid for separately, in addition to the work proper set forth in the contract.

A fair price should be chargeable for all drafting or engineering services that contractors or subcontractors are called upon to render, whether these are called for at the time of bidding or at any other time.

Neither the contractor nor any subcontractor should be held responsible for loss due to any delay in the execution of a contract when such delay is in no way the fault of the contractor or of one of his subcontractors; nor should any payment be held up on this account.

The contractor and each subcontractor should be paid in current funds at least 90 percent of the value of the work completed, every two weeks, or at least 95 percent every month for the work done and the materials delivered.

Every contract should provide for prompt payments and also should require final inspection and payment in full within thirty days after the completion of the work of each division of the specifications, regardless of the final settlement of the job as a whole.

Differences arising between the contractor and other parties to the contract or concerned with it should be subject to and settled by arbitration.

No changes should be made and no work should be held up pending any changes until an agreement is entered into for the adjustment of the contract price on account of the changes. This should apply to subcontracts also.

Unless specific provision is mentioned in the contract, an extra charge should be made for any variation from standard stock materials and methods of construction.

When liquidated damages are specified, a corresponding bonus also should be included.

All the foregoing suggested practices are aimed at making contracting more of a business or profession and less of a gamble. They also serve to point out some of the business troubles encountered by the estimator in his daily work.

EXERCISES

1   What are preliminary estimates? (60 to 100 words)

2   What should a complete builder's estimate contain, and what is the general arrangement of such an estimate? (100 to 150 words)

3   The unit costs given in this and other books on estimating cannot be used for all jobs. Why? (75 to 100 words)

4   What is the general procedure in making an estimate? (100 to 200 words)

5   State some contingencies that an estimator must consider providing for. (60 to 100 words)

6   How are subcontractors' estimates handled? (75 to 100 words)

7   Write at least 300 words of notes regarding estimating procedure, from several of the books listed in the Bibliography. Name the books used.

8   List some unfair dealings and give some suggestions for handling them.

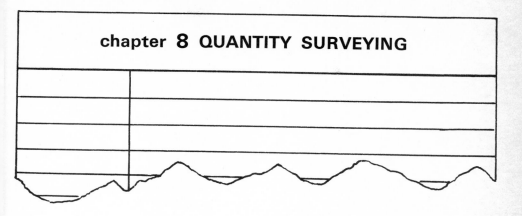

chapter 8 QUANTITY SURVEYING

INTRODUCTION

The quantity-survey portion of an estimate lists every item that will affect the cost of the proposed building. It is not a material list, however. Concrete, for example, will be listed in number of cubic yards needed, not the amount of cement and aggregate needed to make the concrete. Formwork will be given in number of square feet of formwork required, not the materials needed to build it.

After the quantity survey is made, the estimator may use it to price the job. From the survey he ascertains the amounts and costs of the various materials needed. He also uses the survey to estimate the amount and kinds of labor needed for the job.

In the case of some subcontract work, the survey may simply indicate that the item must be included in the job without actually listing the materials needed.

ORGANIZING A QUANTITY SURVEY

A quantity survey is generally organized in the order in which work progresses and costs occur. Land surveys, legal fees, permits, etc., may be among the first divisions listed on a survey. These are followed by divisions for site clearing (if necessary), excavation, backfilling, foundation work, concrete, masonry, carpentry, etc., just as the various types of work occur in the construction of a building.

It is usually necessary to list a number of different items under a division. Accuracy and neatness in listing dimensions and quantities cannot be overemphasized. The entries should be made with a view to facilitating reading and checking the survey some time after completion. A properly completed survey can even be understood by persons other than the surveyor without explanation.

To reduce the time required to prepare a quantity survey, some estimators make it a practice to list dimensions in such a way that they may be reused a number of times throughout the survey. When this is done, accuracy in listing becomes even more important, because an error would be compounded each time an entry was used. Using an entry a number of times can be a real advantage. Reference to the plan need be made only once for a particular dimension; once listed, the figures are easily copied; areas and volumes need to be figured fewer times, and as a result the plan is handled less. There is the one disadvantage that an error could be compounded a number of times.

Various types of forms are used in preparing a survey. These forms are made up in lines and columns and have spaces for descriptions, dimensions, areas, volumes, and other extensions (see Appendix B). Some surveyors have forms printed to suit their methods, while others will use a lined legal-sized pad for their listings.

Some estimators, immediately after reading the dimensions on the plans, turn the dimensions of feet and inches taken from the plans into feet and decimal parts of a foot, or feet and fractional parts of a foot. They then enter these figures on the quantity sheets, instead of entering feet and inches. The theory is that this makes it easier for an office assistant to extend the figures, because he would otherwise have to use his own judgment in handling the fraction of a foot. There are three objections to this procedure:

1 It forms another mental operation for the estimator's already busy mind, because the figures are either given in feet and inches on the plans for him to read there, or else are scaled in feet and inches for him to read from the scale. Not only is an extra mental burden imposed through the process of reading and entering the figures, but one more opportunity for error is added in the handling of every entry.

2 Simplifying the work for the office assistant may seem defensible, but it is a poor reflection on the assistant if he (or she) cannot handle the simple calculations in feet and inches. In such a case it is to be seriously doubted that he has the ability to be trusted with the estimating sheets at all.

3 Changing the dimensions to decimals could cause confusion later, whenever the sheets are used for reference. The figures should be written on them in a way consistent with the method commonly used on plans and as expressed verbally among construction men, that is, in feet and inches.

MAKING THE QUANTITY SURVEY

To a certain extent math is required in making the survey, amounting to little more than the simple arithmetic used in determining lineal footages, areas, volumes, and amounts of material needed for a given set of factors. In the following chapters the various formulas used in preparing the survey will be introduced and explained as they are required by the type of survey being done.

Plan reading is one of the most important aspects of preparing the survey. On the survey, the estimator should list dimensions from the plan rather than scale distances. Often, when a dimension is not given, it can be determined by addition or subtraction of dimensions on the plan. Scaling of a plan should be done only as a last resort or as a check if the dimensions do not add up properly. When errors are found, they can be referred to the architect for clarification.

Some method or sequence should be followed in listing dimensions to avoid overlooking a part of the plan. One method is to start at the top of the plan and list all dimensions from left to right as you work down the plan. Then, to get listings running from top to bottom of the sheet, all necessary dimensions are recorded by starting at the left and moving across to the right of the sheet. When working in this manner, the estimator is less likely to overlook a portion of a wall or other section of the building.

All entries should be clearly identified as to location in the building, type of material, and units used. Properly identified listings make it possible to check the survey, and later the estimate, with comparative ease. It is frustrating to try to check a survey that has few identifying notes and constantly changing units that are not labeled.

After the entries have been made, they can be extended. That is, the areas, volumes, board feet, number of pieces, etc., can be calculated. The work of extending surveys is often done by someone other than the estimator, especially in a large office. When the extensions are done by a clerk, it is important that the estimator check to see that the work has been done properly.

Various aids are available for making quantity surveys. Among these are checklists, tables of quantities, adding machines, and calculators.

SUMMARIZING THE SURVEY

When the survey has been completed, it will be noted that many areas will require the same type of materials.

In the process of making extensions, the estimator or clerk may also start to summarize the survey. Areas of wall surfaces of a given type may be totaled, and floor areas may be grouped and totaled in a similar manner. When items are grouped and summarized, the job of estimating costs becomes less time-consuming because there are fewer operations to accomplish.

As each section of the survey is summarized, it is either carried out to a separate column or marked in a bold manner to make it stand out on the page. Later these individual sections containing like materials can be summarized to further simplify the survey and the estimate.

EXERCISES

1 What is a quantity survey? (75 to 100 words)

2 Name several items that are customarily measured by each of the following units: lineal foot, square foot, square yard, cubic yard, pound, ton, thousand.

3 What divisions should be included in the summary of a quantity survey?

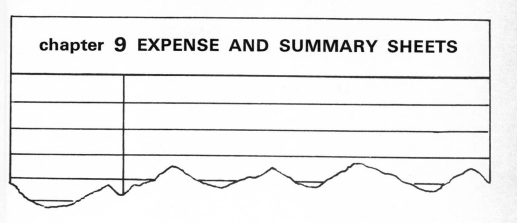

chapter 9 EXPENSE AND SUMMARY SHEETS

INTRODUCTION

In preparing an estimate of building cost, the two most obvious expense items are for materials and for labor. There are other expenses which must be included in the estimate that are directly connected to the cost of construction. Among these are charges for equipment, job offices, utilities (water and electricity), temporary construction such as temporary stairs and shelters, rubbish removal and cleanup, and superintendents' and engineers' wages. Other items of job expense which must be allowed for are drafting costs, cost of signs and progress photographs, and the cost of bonds and insurance.

Another type of expense which must be allowed for in preparing a cost estimate is overhead expense. *Overhead* takes in all the costs of running the construction company which cannot be charged directly to any one job. Salaries of management and office personnel and the general cost of maintaining and operating the company office are items which would be classed as Overhead.

To aid in preparing the estimate and in keeping a record of labor and material expenses, there are a number of expense and summary sheets available (see Appendix B). Specific forms are available for preparing the survey, a general estimate, a summary of the estimate, etc. Other sheets are available for job time keeping, labor distribution, daily construction reports, and equipment cost and depreciation records.

JOB EXPENSE

The various costs which are incurred as a result of doing a job may be referred to as *job expense*. As has already been stated, material and labor costs are the two most obvious job expenses.

Performance bonds are a job expense which must be allowed for in the cost estimate. On a small job the cost will be comparatively small. On larger jobs, where the amount of the bond is greater and the period of time for which the bond is required is longer, the cost may become a major item. Some contractors may elect to provide a certified check in place of a bond. The cost of putting the required amount of money aside for bonding purposes should not be overlooked. It is at least equal to the amount lost by not being able to invest it, perhaps 4, 5, or 6 percent, or more, of the principal.

Various types of insurance are required on a construction job. Workmen's compensation, unemployment compensation, and social security insurance are directly connected to wages or labor costs and may be figured as a part of the hourly rate which must be charged for labor. Regardless of how this cost is handled, it is important to make sure that it is included somewhere in the job cost.

Insurance carried by the contractor which adds to job costs is insurance for public liability, personal injury, fire and theft, storm damage, and property damage for property other than the new construction. The cost of such insurance can best be determined, after the major cost of the job is known, by obtaining the advice of the company's insurance carriers. Again it is important, here as elsewhere in the estimate, not to overlook this item.

Most communities have some sort of building code which requires building permits and approval of plans before construction can begin. The fee for these permits will vary, but may be $.30 or more per 100 cubic feet. Permits may also be required for removal of sidewalks and the use of roads. The cost of these and of all other required permits should not be overlooked.

Temporary job offices, toolhouses, storage sheds, and other such conveniences are part of the expense of carrying on a job. Temporary fences, barricades, runways, bridges, stairways, and platforms are also to be considered as items of cost. The law demands that proper safeguards be constructed and maintained in good order to prevent accidents at open shafts, wellholes, and other places that are likely to be the locations of accidents if not so guarded. The law also demands temporary toilets, drinking water, and other conveniences for the health and comfort of the workmen. Trade unions also demand these, and other things besides.

Water and light are common requirements for building work, yet many estimators neglect to make provision enough in their estimates for these items. Water involves not only the water charges, but also the installation, maintenance, and removal of the temporary lines and the changing about of these lines when necessary; and, similarly, for temporary light and power there is the charge for current, the cost of installing and maintaining the lines, and the cost of bulbs and fixtures.

To heat a construction job in winter is a costly undertaking. Some of the elements of this cost are the installation and first cost of the system or devices used for heating, the fuel cost, the additional temporary enclosure work required, the labor of attending to the heating, the repairing and rearranging of the equipment, the loss of time resulting from the men's working under these conditions, and the extra cost of supervising.

Special equipment of various kinds may be required to complete a job. The cost of this equipment must be added to the job cost. This cost may be in the form of rental charges for rented equipment or prorated ownership costs based on the length of time the equipment is used in relation to its normal useful life. Ownership costs on equipment are often overlooked, and after a period of time when replacement becomes necessary, the contractor may find himself without sufficient funds for equipment replacement.

Almost all construction jobs require the services of one or more persons who do not directly work on the production of the building. Among these persons are the job superintendent, structural engineers, surveyors, and watchmen. Because these men do not work on the actual construction, it is easy to overlook the cost of their services.

Nearly all jobs require a superintendent who will start the job and follow it through to completion. The superintendent will be on the job even on some days when no work is performed. The estimator must allow for the total number of days on which the job will require superintendence plus a contingent for delays which may be expected due to weather changes, material shortages, etc.

Where the services of an engineer are anticipated, the length and type of service should be indicated on the job expense form and the cost of that service entered. By entering the type, length, and cost of the service, it is easy for the contractor to check the estimate against the actual cost and charge the owner for extras if there are any.

Surveys are always required on a construction job. In addition to the initial survey, several surveys may be required during the course of construction. The estimator must check the specifications to see if any are required and make the proper allowances. In some cases additional surveys may not be required, but the contractor may do well to provide for them in the event he may have to prove that his building is constructed in the place called for by the plans and specifications.

Most large jobs and many smaller ones require night watchmen as well as day watchmen. The number of days and nights for which watchmen are required must be determined and the cost entered on the job cost sheet. By keeping this cost item separate on the job expense sheet it is easy to determine if the actual cost and estimated cost are in agreement.

During the course of construction it may be necessary for the contractor to prepare working drawings of various types. The estimator should anticipate the amount of this type of work required and list it along with its cost.

Pictures taken during the course of construction form

a permanent record of construction progress at specified intervals. The number of pictures to be taken and their cost should be estimated as one of the job expenses.

Signs on the construction site indicating the name of the building, the architect, engineers, general contractor, etc., are generally furnished by the general contractor. In preparing a job expense sheet the estimator must allow for the cost of the sign or signs, their installation, maintenance, and removal.

Because it is common practice to withhold a portion of money due the contractor for work completed, it is often necessary for the contractor to borrow money to meet his obligations. The cost of borrowing necessary revenue should be anticipated and entered as a job expense on the estimate. Even when the contractor does not have to borrow money, he does have money invested in the job, and he is entitled to a fair return on it. In this case the estimate should make an allowance for the cost of having this money invested for whatever period of time is involved.

Rubbish removal and general cleanup are items which are easily overlooked when preparing a job expense sheet. Periodically during the course of a job it will be necessary to pick up and remove rubbish. This removal will require labor as well as equipment, such as buggies and trucks. It may also require the payment of fees for use of a dump or a permit to burn rubbish. The estimator must take all these factors into consideration when calculating the cost of job cleanup.

Some contracts call for the job to be left broom-clean, while others require the finished building to be cleaned ready for use. This means that windows must be clean, sills dusted, floors cleaned and polished, etc. The cost of this type of cleaning can be considerable and must not be overlooked.

Keeping a careful record of all job expenses is important and necessary in order to have a comparison of actual job costs and estimated costs. Each contractor may have his own method of accomplishing this. The job estimate and cost record form shown in Figure 9-1 illustrates how job expense may be tabulated against estimated costs.

OWNER J.C. Roman	JOB LOCATION 1458 North 4th St.		JOB NO. 169			
JOB ESTIMATE AND COST RECORD						
	Classification	Contractor	Estimate Amount	Contract Amount	Changes Amount	Actual Cost
1.	Survey	W.C. Schmidt	50 00	50 00		50 00
2.	Plans & Specifications	J.J. Wells	300 00	300 00		300 00
3.	Permits	City	75 00			64 75
4.	Excavation & Grading	P.A. Jones, Excavator	625 00	610 00		610 00
5.	Foundations	A+J Const. Co.	2100 00	2090 00		2090 00
6.	Dampproofing	A+J Const. Co.	20 00	20 00		20 00
7.	Cement Floors & Walks	A+J Const. Co.	790 00	765 00		765 00
8.	Structural Steel	Northern Steel Wks.	275 00	275 00		275 00
9.	Misc. & Orn. Metal					
10.	Masonry	A+J Const. Co.	860 00	880 00		880 00
11.	Carpenter Labor-Rough	F+S Const Co.	4259 00			4210 00
12.	Lumber-Rough	North Side Lbr.	1950 00			1962 00
13.	Carpenter Labor-Finish	F+S Const. Co.	650 00			640 00
14.	Lumber-Finish	G+S Lbr. + Milwk.	586 00	580 00		580 00
15.	Door & Window Frames	G+S Lbr. + Milwk.	1345 00	1325 00		1325 00
16.	Doors & Sash	Incl. in #15				
17.	Door & Window Screens	Incl. in #15				
18.	Storm Doors & Sash	G+S Lbr. + Milwk.	225 00	198 00		198 00
19.	Garage Doors	American Door Co.	250 00	250 00		250 00
20.	Finish Wood Flooring					
21.	Wood Stairs	G+S Lbr. + Milwk.	800 00	780 00		780 00
22.	Cabinets	G+S Lbr. + Milwk.	1150 00	1300 00	150 00	1300 00
23.	Hardware-Rough	Builders Supply Co.	100 00			112 00
24.	Hardware-Finish	J.C. Smith, Hdw.	185 00	178 00		178 00
25.	Weatherstripping	Metal Weatherstrip Co.	50 00	50 00		50 00
26.	Caulking	F+S Const.	58 00			62 00
27.	Sheet Metal	Atlas Sheet Metal	250 00	250 00		250 00
28.	Roofing-Material	Roofing, Inc.	375 00			345 00
29.	Roofing-Labor	F+S Const.	275 00			268 00
30.	Glass & Glazing	L-P Glass Co.	750 00	750 00		750 00
31.	Insulation	B+B Insulation	260 00			248 00
32.	Lath & Plaster	O+D Plastering Co.	1385 00	1385 00		1385 00
33.	Painting & Decorating	Art-Craft Painting	1275 00	1225 00		1225 00
34.	Resilient Flooring	Atlas Floors, Inc.	298 00	298 00		298 00
35.	Ceramic Tile	J.L. Tile	850 00	850 00		850 00
36.	Bathroom Accessories	Incl. in #35				
37.	Medicine Cabinets	Sentry Hdw.	98 00	98 00		98 00
38.	Plumbing	G.B. Plumbing Co.	2280 00	2265 00		2265 00
39.	Sewer Work	K-M Co.	200 00	200 00		200 00
40.	Heating	J.D. Heating Co.	1285 00	1280 00		1280 00

FIGURE 9-1 Job estimate and cost record.

OVERHEAD AND PROFIT

Overhead expense is the name given to all those items that are necessary for the general maintenance of a business. This expense continues even when there is no contract work on hand. It does not belong exclusively to any particular part of the contract work and is therefore spread over all the work by prorating a percentage to each job, based on the cost of the job.

All expense that is not incorporated in other entries in the estimate must be considered as being included in the Overhead entry. The percentage allowance, therefore, must be large enough for this purpose. This is emphasized because many contractors do not fully realize the many items of expense involved in maintaining a business. The percentage is at best an approximation based on the contractor's own cost records and his judgment as to the requirements of each individual job. Some jobs may require a smaller allowance than others because the work to be done involves large subcontract items which require little more actual office effort than small items would require. Obviously, small jobs require more, in proportion, than do large jobs. All jobs must carry their share of the cost of maintaining the business while no work is on hand.

Tools, equipment, trucks, etc., used on the jobs should not be charged to overhead expense. The cost of permits, bonds, supervision, drafting, job gratuities, insurance and taxes in connection with these items, and other expense directly connected with the jobs should not be charged to overhead expense. All these items should be charged to the individual jobs. They should be included under the general Job Expense heading and other headings in the estimate to suit the requirements for each job.

Although not always so handled, Overhead should be reserved for the cost of running the main office. If we think of all the expenses necessary to maintain a contracting business which has no work on hand, then we will have a picture of the items concerned. Table 9-1 gives a list of such items as applied to the construction company shown in Figure 4-6. This does not include any engineering or drafting expenses, since these items would be directly charged to the jobs for which they were expended. A smaller business will cost less to maintain, but in any case, the expense must be spread among the jobs that are actually performed. By keeping track of the overhead expense, a contractor will know after a few years the exact relation it bears to the job cost of the work actually done.

Profit might be considered as the contractor's pay for doing the job. It is usually a percentage of the total of all job costs, including overhead. The percentage added

Table 9-1 Overhead Expense

Employees:			
Manager	$30,000	Rent	$16,800
Manager's secretary	8,420	Furnishings (depreciation)	1,800
Solicitor	15,000	Stationery and supplies	1,742
Chief estimator	20,000	Postage	951
Contract clerk	9,020	Electricity	1,422
Estimators	33,400	Telephones	1,805
Payroll office	25,600	Legal expense	2,000
Accountant	10,000	Advertising	2,684
General superintendent	20,000	Trade reports	206
Material clerk	9,280	Use of autos	5,817
Stenographers	9,280	Car and taxi fares	1,051
Receptionist	5,380	Travel expense	1,583
Plan clerk	5,380	Entertaining	975
Vacations (included above)		Gratuities and contributions	480
Sick leave (included above)		City business taxes	15,822
Christmas bonuses	14,200	Miscellaneous	4,746
Social security taxes	5,796	Total for year 1969	$297,328
Unemployment taxes	4,800	Job cost for year	$3,303,644
Insurance	11,888	Overhead expense	9%

to the job cost for profit will vary with the risk involved, the amount invested in the job, the availability of work, and the competition for work. Therefore the profit figure might range from 2 to 20 percent of all job costs.

By its nature, profit is the last item to be added on to job cost, and incredible as it may seem, may be overlooked in the rush to complete the estimate in time for bidding. It is therefore in order to caution the estimator to make sure that he has added the profit item to the cost estimate.

ESTIMATE SUMMARY

A summary enables the estimator and the contractor to see quickly the relation and the proportions of the various branches of the work. This is valuable as a general check on the amounts extended, and it also serves as a basis for determining the office overhead and the profit. One pitfall in summarizing an estimate, however, is that some of the totals may not have been carried over from the regular makeup sheets or last-minute changes may have been made in some of the items and the corresponding amounts may not have been changed in the summary. For this reason, a check should be made by adding up all the individual sheets of the estimate separately from the summary, to see that this total agrees with that on the summary.

The summary of the quantity survey is usually made on a form designed for that purpose and may be called a *recapitulation*. This form has columns for description, quantity, unit, unit price for materials, estimated material cost, unit price for labor, total labor cost, and total estimated cost. To use this type of sheet the estimator simply copies the total quantities from his quantity survey, labels them, and applies the company's unit prices. (See Figure 9-2.)

RECAPITULATION

PRACTICAL
Form 517 MFD IN U S A

PROJECT *P.S. 101*
LOCATION *S. 4th + W. WILLOW, CITY*
ARCHITECT ENGINEER *SOUTH + SMITH*
SUMMARY BY *S.J.B.*
PRICES BY *S.J.B*
ESTIMATE NO. *192*
SHEET NO. *1*
DATE *DEC 16, 1970*
CHECKED BY *A.C.B.*

DESCRIPTION	QUANTITY	UNIT	UNIT PRICE	TOTAL ESTIMATED MATERIAL COST	UNIT PRICE	TOTAL ESTIMATED LABOR COST
EXCAVATION – GENERAL	13,755	CY			.95	13067 25
SPECIAL	220	CY			1.60	352 —
						13419 25
CONCRETE FOUNDATIONS						
4000# CONCRETE – WALL FOOTINGS	130	CY	14—	1820 —	2.40	312 —
COLUMN FOOTINGS	95	CY	14—	1330 —	2.50	237 50
FOUNDATION WALLS	570	CY	14—	7980 —	2.90	1653 —
FORMS– FOUNDATION WALLS	30,150	SF	.12	3618 —	.40	1206 —
WALL OPENINGS	290	SF	.15	435 —	.50	145 —
				15183 —		3553 50
REINFORCED CONCRETE						
4000# CONCRETE – COLUMNS	165	CY	14—	2310 —	4.25	701 25
SLABS + BEAMS 1st FL.	586	CY	14—	8204 —	2.25	1318 50
" " 2nd FL.	580	CY	14—	8120 —	2.75	1595 —
" " ROOF	502	CY	14—	7028 —	2.75	1380 50
STAIRS + PLATFORMS	47	CY	14—	658 —	14—	658 —
FORMS – COLUMNS	13,600	SF	.11	1496 —	.50	6800 —
SOLID SLAB FORMS	3,362	SF	.12	403 44	.41	1613 74
DECK SLAB FORMS	72,328	SF	.10	7232 80	.48	34717 44
BEAMS – SPANDREL BOTTOMS	2,134	SF	.15	320 10	.65	1387 10
" SIDES	3,424	SF	.15	513 15	.65	2223 65
INTERIOR BOTTOMS	3,987	SF	.12	478 44	.60	2392 20
" SIDES	2,654	SF	.12	318 48	.60	1592 40

FIGURE 9-2 Recapitulation.

```
                    SUMMARY OF ESTIMATE
                    ─────────────────

STORE AND SHOWROOM BUILDING.              Submitted
Webster Ave. & 188th St.              April 1, 1971.
Owner: Mayfair Co.              Wells & Brown, Archts.

─────────────────────────────────────────────────────

General Job Expense                      $ 3,480

Excavating                                 5,478
Concrete Work                              7,120
Mason Work                                12,654
Granite                                      300
Cast Stone                                 1,050

Structural Steel                          12,200
Miscellaneous Iron                           675
Concrete Floor & Roof Arches              16,105
Cement Finish Work                         3,555
Roofing & Sheet Metal                      2,424

Dampproofing                                 265
Caulking                                     115
Plastering                                 4,937
Carpentry                                  2,681

Kalamein Work                                452
Rolling Steel Doors                          400
Peelle Shaft Doors                           600
Overhead Garage Door                         140

Tile Work                                    372
Rubber Flooring                            1,347
Metal Toilet Partitions                      110
Finish Hardware                              300
Glass & Glazing                              227
Painting                                   1,484

Plumbing                                   2,750
Heating                                    2,552
Oil Burner                                   800
Electric                                   1,670
Elevator                                   3,000
                                          ───────
                        Job Cost           89,243
                        Overhead 7%         6,247
                                          ───────
                        Total Cost         95,490
                        Profit 4%           3,820
                                          ───────
                              BID         $99,310
```

FIGURE 9-3 Summary of estimate.

The bulk of the estimate can be further reduced by taking the totals from the recapitulation for each different item and entering them on an estimate summary sheet. This summary of estimate may be a printed form which has the most common classifications already listed (see Appendix B) or it may be a simple listing on plain bond paper (see Figure 9-3). The advantage in using the form with printed classifications is that it saves time in preparing, and it also acts as a reminder of most of the common classifications.

There is always the possibility of overlooking an item or making an error when copying data from one form to another. For this reason extreme care must be taken when preparing the recapitulation and summary of the estimate. This cannot be overemphasized.

EXERCISES

1 Name ten items of expense that should be considered under the heading Job Expense.

2 What cleaning and rubbish-removal work are done on a building job and therefore require consideration as elements of cost?

3 What does an estimator need to know about insurance?

4 Name ten items of expense that should be considered as included in the main-office, or overhead, expense.

5 Make a general job expense sheet for the house estimate.

6 Make a summary sheet for the house estimate.

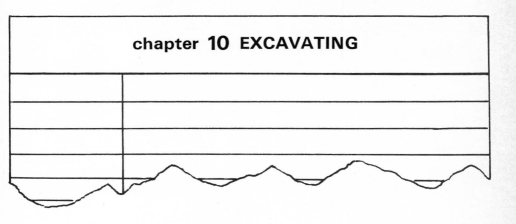

chapter **10** EXCAVATING

INTRODUCTION

Excavating for building work generally consists in digging a big hole, called the *main excavation,* or *general excavation,* and digging other parts, that is, *pit excavating,* or *trench excavating,* etc. The work is measured in cubic yards. The three dimensions of each part are taken in feet, multiplied together to get cubic feet. This result is divided by 27 to get cubic yards, since there are 27 cubic feet in one cubic yard. Since many estimators find it easier to multiply than divide, they will multiply cubic feet by .037 to get cubic yards, which is allowable because .037 is approximately equal to $\frac{1}{27}$.

Plans never show the outline of the excavation, nor do they generally indicate the ground level, or original grade, of the site. It is necessary for the estimator to visit the place and determine the conditions that will affect the size of the excavation required. The outline of the banks of the excavation should then be drawn on the cellar plan, and a profile of the excavation drawn on one of the cross sections. By this means the estimator is better able to visualize the actual excavating work. If a plot plan, or survey, is furnished with the plans, this should be referred to for any information it may contain relative to the ground, the location of the building, trees that may have to be protected or removed, and other data that will affect the estimate.

Ordinary excavating denotes the kind that can be done with shovels by hand. *Heavy earth* denotes clay or any other dense formation for which picks would be required before shoveling could be done. *Hardpan* denotes a tough formation of gravel that is held together with a natural cementing material and that cannot practicably be loosened with an ordinary pick. *Rock excavating* is excavation of either solid rock or a formation of large boulders which generally require blasting to break them up.

Not enough care is given to estimating excavation work, especially where conditions are complex. Frequently, it is necessary to install considerable temporary construction because the excavating work can be completed. Rock excavation, groundwater, adjoining buildings, and streets often make the work so complicated that the excavating becomes an engineering problem, requiring exhaustive research and planning. In the case of large buildings in New York City, there are many additional plan difficulties and operating handicaps, and only the most highly organized specialists in this field are capable of properly estimating the work and doing it. The excavation of rock under these conditions and the removal of dirt and mud incidental to caisson work and pile driving are not ordinary estimating items.

In estimating for ordinary work, proper study should be made of the nature of the material to be removed, the general method of removal, special handling that may be necessary for topsoil or plants, temporary storage of material for later backfilling, method of disposal of the excess material, distance to the dump, cost of dumping, equipment and trucking costs, permits, protection of sidewalks and pavements, temporary roads and runways, ramps, safeguards, lights, watchmen, foremen, labor, public liability insurance, general and overhead expense, risks, weather conditions, breakdowns, cave-ins, and rehandling.

In estimating for complex excavations, engineering skill is necessary and should be provided. Most excavations should be considered to be complex if they have rock or water to be cared for or if they are more than 10 feet deep or if there are adjoining buildings in which the foundations do not extend down as far as the bottom level of the new excavation.

Excavations are always made deep enough to enable the foundations to be extended at least 4 feet below the finish grade, in order to escape the action of frost. At lower levels, also, soils are more condensed and less moist and will bear a greater load. Footings must be made wide enough not to exceed the bearing capacity of the ground. Rock, of course, in its native condition, will carry any load put upon it. In preparing a rock bottom, it is necessary to trim the rock to a level surface under all footings.

In soft ground, piles are sometimes driven on which to rest the foundations. Wood piles are used only where they will always be below the groundwater level; otherwise they would soon rot away. Concrete piles are driven or are cast in place after a steel shell has first been driven.

METHODS OF EXCAVATING

The site should be visited by the estimator so that he may ascertain the type of ground, whether it is hard or soft, wet or dry, etc. The labor cost varies according to these conditions. The general method of doing the work must also be given consideration at the site—whether it shall be done by hand with picks and shovels, or by drag scrapers, bulldozer or power shovel, or some other means.

A bulldozer is used to clear the ground, remove trees and shrubs, and scrape off the topsoil. Shallow excavating, on jobs where the material is not to be hauled away but merely taken out and then spread over the balance of the plot, is also done with a bulldozer. In such cases an ordinary house excavation may require the use of a bulldozer for only one day.

A power shovel, usually operated by a diesel engine, is required when the excavated material is to be loaded into trucks. A loading machine is a variation of a power shovel, and the larger types are as effective as power shovels of ordinary size.

Back hoes and ditching machines are used for digging pier holes and trenches and for other excavating of this type.

Pits and other handwork must be kept separate in the estimate, so that they may be figured at different prices from those for the main excavation.

The cost of maintaining a shovel involves expense for fuel, repairs, depreciation, and the time required to move it to and from the job, as well as the payroll and incidental costs of the crew. A $\frac{3}{4}$-cubic-yard shovel can dig and load into trucks about 250 cubic yards of ordinary earth per day if there is free room for it to operate properly. In cramped quarters it will do much less.

Motor trucks carry from 4 to 12 cubic yards or more per load, depending upon the capacity of the individual truck. At one time the average capacity of trucks in general use was 5 cubic yard. However, in recent years this has changed, and trucks of 12 cubic yard capacity are more commonly used for general excavating work. On very large operations, other equipment is often used, such as enormous carryalls which cut into the ground and carry away 15 to 30 cubic yard at a time. Obviously, a job has to involve thousands of cubic yards for such large pieces of equipment to be operated economically.

DETERMINING THE SIZE OF THE EXCAVATION

Space must be allowed all around the outside of the structure for proper working room for installing the temporary forms for the footings and the walls. The projection of the footings beyond the outer face of the walls must be taken into account, as well as the natural sloping of the banks of the excavation.

The depth of the excavation is measured from the present, or original, grade, and not from the finished condition that may be indicated on the plans and sections. When the area to be excavated is fairly flat but slopes in one or more directions, the depth of the excavation, for estimating purposes, may be determined by finding the average existing grade and subtracting the grade at the bottom of the excavation from the average grade elevation. The average grade elevation is found by adding together the elevations at the four corners and dividing the sum by 4.

The deeper the excavation is to be made, the more thorough should be the study of the profile that the banks around the excavation will take—not only at the time the excavation is being dug, but afterward also. If a deep excavation is to be left open for several weeks or months, it will be necessary to provide bracing for the banks or else to make the excavation wide enough at the top so that earth washed down by rain or accumulated because of continual disturbance by working conditions will not hinder the proper construction of the foundations.

Text and reference books mention the "angle of repose" in connection with excavating. This is largely theoretical and has little practical value for builders. The angle is that which the bank of earth or other material makes with the horizontal without being held in place. Tables are drawn up for reference, but a glance at the wide range of the figures they give will convince anybody of their worthlessness in accurate estimating. The only safe procedure is to know the locality well enough to be fairly sure of the probable ground conditions.

Isolated buildings of regular type, where only plain dirt excavation is to be considered, present no particular problem in estimating the costs under the Excavating heading. By allowing 12 to 24 inches of clear space all around the exterior walls, the matter resolves itself into a case of care in measuring the plans and in determining the present ground levels. The work is computed in cubic yards, as it is—in the ground—before being removed. If the work is priced loose or by the truckload, the natural expansion of the material will have to be considered. This expansion amounts to an increase of about 15 percent for earth and up to 50 percent for gravel or rock.

FINDING THE VOLUME OF THE EXCAVATION

For residential work it is common practice to excavate 12 inches beyond the foundation line when the ground is reasonably stable. In some cases where additional work space is required, the excavation may extend 24 inches or more beyond the foundation line.

The depth of the excavation may be determined by checking the foundation section where grade elevations of the footing and adjacent finish grade are given. In some instances the height of the wall is given, along with the distance from the exterior grade to the top of the wall. When this is done, the depth of the excavation is determined by subtracting the distance above grade from the height of the wall.

Example   Calculate the volume of soil to be removed for a foundation 26 by 48 feet. The grade at the top of the footing (bottom of the excavation) is 82.8 feet. The existing grades at the four corners are 90.8, 89.8, 90.4, and 90.8 feet. Excavate 1 foot 0 inches beyond foundation walls.

Find: Average exterior grade   90.8
                                                    89.8
                                                    90.4
                                                    90.8
                                    ―――――――
                                    4 | 361.8
                                    ―――――――
Average exterior grade   90.45 feet

Find: Depth of excavation   90.45
                                                82.80
                                    ―――――――
Depth of excavation = 7.65 feet

Find: Volume in cubic feet

$$50 \times 28 \times 7.65 = 10{,}710 \text{ cubic feet}$$

Changing to cubic yards,

$$10{,}710 \times .037 = 397 \text{ cubic yards}$$

For a simple job such as this the calculations can be done right on the estimating form.

DETERMINING SPECIAL EXCAVATING

Excavating for column footings, trenching for wall footings, etc., would come under the heading of special excavating. This work might be done with some type of power equipment or by hand and should be grouped according to the method used for excavating.

In determining the amount of excavating for column

footings, the number and size of excavations are listed. Generally, a distance of 6 inches is allowed on each side for construction of footing forms. Therefore a footing 48 inches square would require an excavation 60 inches square, and the cubic content would be calculated on that basis.

When determining the amount of excavating for wall footings, the total lineal footage is determined and the width and depth listed. As with column footings, a distance of 6 inches is usually allowed on each side of the footing for the construction of footing forms if needed.

In determining the totals for wall-footing excavations, each length of footing is listed and identified according to location. The volume of each section may be calculated separately, or the total lineal footage for footing excavations having the same dimensions may be determined and then multiplied by width and depth to get the volume.

Listing the various wall- and column-footing excavations with their location is a good practice in that it makes checking the estimate easier and helps to avoid omissions due to oversight.

RELATED EXCAVATING COSTS

All items of expense directly due to the excavating work are provided for under this heading. Temporary guardrails, ramps, and other provisions for doing the work safely and economically are noted in the estimate and considered in the unit cost per cubic yard for completely removing the excavated material, or else they are listed and priced separately.

When soft banks are to be left standing, it is necessary to brace them or to drive sheeting for their support. This is called *skeleton sheeting* if only light bracing will suffice, or *sheet piling* if a continuous sheeting is required. Both need heavy wales and bracing to hold the sheeting in place. Ordinary wooden sheet piling consists of a continuous line of vertical planks held against the sides of the excavation by these horizontal timbers, called *wales,* or *breast timbers,* which are in turn supported by shores or by cross braces reaching to the opposite side of the excavation. Planks 2 inches thick are generally used for depths up to 12 feet, and 3-inch planks for depths up to 18 feet.

Steel sheet piling is used for deep excavations where great pressures must be supported or in ground that contains water.

When sheet piling is needed, cost items to consider include sheet piling, bracing, labor for installation and removal, equipment for installation and removal, and transportation costs. Because much of the piling can usually be salvaged, only the portion of the material actually used up or damaged on the job should be charged to the job. It is often possible to salvage 90 to 95 percent of sheet-piling material. Previous experience of the estimator or the contractor is necessary in order to make a judgment on the salvage value of the sheet piling.

BACKFILLING

The last material removed in an excavation is generally used for backfilling behind the foundation walls and elsewhere in those spaces that were excavated for working room in excess of the exact requirements for the structure itself. Sometimes this material may be taken directly from its original location and deposited where it is needed as backfill. This eliminates all extra handling, as well as the trucking costs and dump charges. Each job should be analyzed separately so that this line of reasoning may be developed as it applies to the particular case.

While figuring excavating it is natural also to calculate the amount of fill needed for backfilling. On simple jobs backfilling will be needed for the space between the side of the excavation and the foundation wall. To find the amount of fill needed, the volume of this space is calculated, and a percentage is added to allow for settling of the loose soil.

On larger jobs additional fill may be necessary if the original grade is below the planned grade elevation. When this is the case, the area to be filled and the average depth of fill must be determined. After the volume is determined, a percentage must be added to allow for settling of the loose fill.

EXAMPLES OF AN EXCAVATING ESTIMATE

Figure 10-1 shows a simple estimating sheet such as is used by some estimators. This is on a standard journal-ruled pad obtainable in practically all stationery stores.

In the hands of an experienced estimator, this form is quite satisfactory for simple jobs. Men with little experience, however, should use regular estimating forms like those in the chapters which follow. These provide more

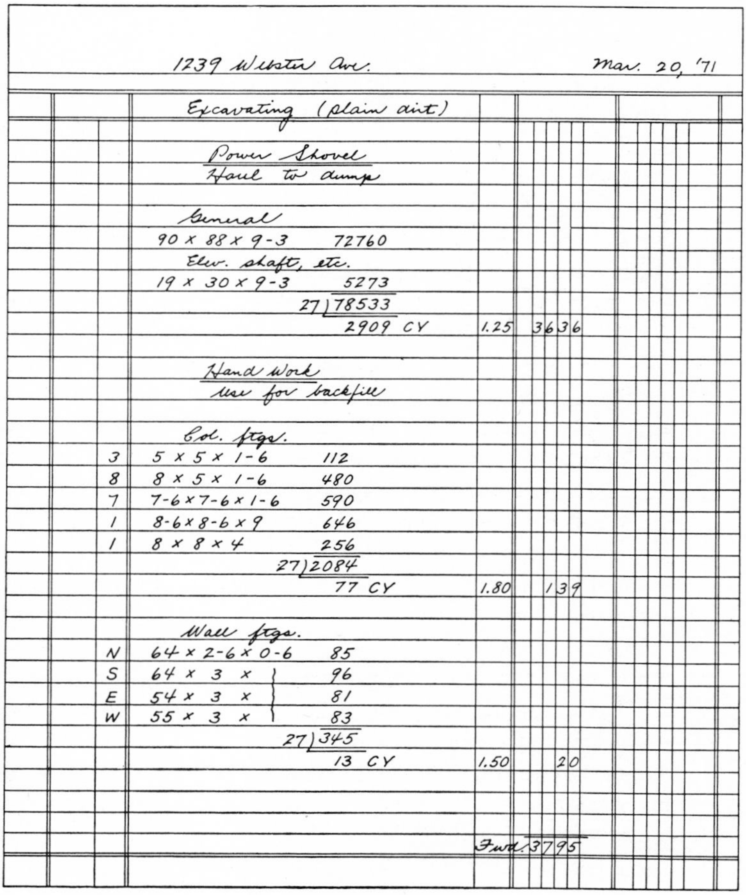

1239 Webster Ave.   Mar. 20, '71

Excavating (plain dirt)

Power Shovel
Haul to dump

General
90 x 88 x 9-3   72760
Elev. shaft, etc.
19 x 30 x 9-3   5273
27)78533
2909 CY   1.25   3636

Hand Work
use for backfill

Col. ftgs.
3   5 x 5 x 1-6   112
8   8 x 5 x 1-6   480
7   7-6 x 7-6 x 1-6   590
1   8-6 x 8-6 x 9   646
1   8 x 8 x 4   256
27)2084
77 CY   1.80   139

Wall ftgs.
N   64 x 2-6 x 0-6   85
S   64 x 3 x)   96
E   54 x 3 x)   81
W   55 x 3 x)   83
27)345
13 CY   1.50   20

Furn. 3795

FIGURE 10-1 An excavating estimate.

and better guidelines and thus help to eliminate errors. Furthermore, they do not require the numerous $\times$'s between figures, because guidelines take the place of these.

In Figure 10-1, the estimator has good headings and subheadings, the use of which is always to be recommended. The term "plain dirt" clarifies at the outset the kind of excavating that is involved. The estimate is then divided into two parts, power-shovel work and handwork. The estimator has noted the fact that the excavating done by the power shovel on this job will have to be hauled to the dump. Short notes like this should be inserted all through the estimate so that anyone reading it may quickly get a good mental picture of the work and conditions pertaining to it. Further down is another good note stating that certain material will be laid aside and used later for backfilling.

This is an illustration of an estimate sheet that is well arranged and on which the items are named and grouped so that various unit cost prices may be applied. These prices, of course, are for this particular job only and must not be thought of as standard reference prices suitable for other jobs.

The main excavation on this job consisted of the cellar excavation and an extension of this to provide space in which to construct a freight-elevator shaft and an adjoining book-storage vault. The excavating involved is all of the same character as to the depth and the manner of doing the work, and therefore the two items shown are grouped together so that one unit cost price may be applied.

There are twenty column footings on the job being considered, and they will require that pits, or pier holes, of the sizes noted, will have to be dug. These are below the bottom of the main excavation.

The wall footings are actually 12 inches deep. However, the bottom of the main excavation on this job is 6 inches below the top of these footings, and therefore it is necessary only that the footing trenches be excavated an additional 6 inches deep.

A simple excavation, as for a suburban house, costs the contractor between $1 and $1.75 per cubic yard. This is for simply loosening ordinary dirt and spreading it over the balance of the plot with the aid of a bulldozer. Sometimes the rich topsoil is taken off and piled up, to be spread carefully after the rough grading has been done.

An excavation for a building in the heart of the business section of a big city may cost the contractor between $4 and $6 per cubic yard. This is for digging, loading, hauling, and disposing of the excavated dirt, together with the incidental expense of dumping charges, lost time, temporary protection, watchman's services, etc.

If there is rock or if the banks require bracing, the extra cost of such items will have to be computed separately. If they are considered in the cubic-yard price, this may well amount to between $15 and $25 per cubic yard.

EXERCISES

1 Why is the depth of an excavation measured from the original grades instead of from the finish grade that can be seen on the architect's elevations?

2 About how much extra space is required around the outside of the walls below grade for the proper construction of them? Show by a sketch.

3 Compute the amount of excavating in the following portions of an excavation:

    a. 109′0″ × 86′0″ × 12′0″
    b.   22′6″ × 14′8″ × 10′9″
    c. 146′0″ ×   4′0″ ×   3′2″

4 Write at least 300 words of notes on excavating work, taken from one or two of the books listed in the Bibliography. Name the books used.

5 State the meaning and use of the following terms, and make sketches if possible: original grade, topsoil, hardpan, backfill, sheet piling.

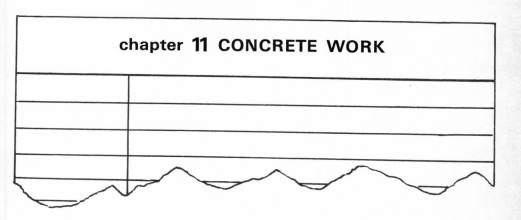

chapter 11 CONCRETE WORK

INTRODUCTION

Concrete work is usually divided into several parts for convenience in estimating. Sometimes all the work is placed under one heading, but more often portions are listed separately under such headings as concrete foundations, concrete walls, concrete floors, etc.

The general method of preparing a concrete estimate is to list the different items in each division in approximately the same sequence as the order in which they will be constructed. Therefore, under concrete foundations, the first item to be listed would be footings. All footing sizes would be entered under this heading, and all the forms, reinforcing steel, and concrete required would be entered.

The estimator should adopt a fairly uniform procedure when listing quantities for any kind of work and follow a regular system when putting down the dimensions: length first, width or thickness next, and then height. This is a custom, and to some extent it makes the figures easier to identify. Separating all the work into small items or groups makes checking and pricing easier.

Some estimators measure all the concrete shown on the plans, then all the formwork and all the reinforcing, separately. This method may seem concise and systematic because it keeps each of these three parts by itself. A better method, however, is to complete each item shown on the plan before going to the next. Start with the footings, as first stated, and list all the forms, reinforcing, and concrete for one kind of footing, such as the column footings; then take another kind of footing, such as the main-wall footings, and list all the forms, reinforcing, and concrete for these. Put a minor heading before each item of work thus handled and proceed in the same manner with the main walls, inside walls, area walls, etc., completing each one before considering the next.

This method is better because it has been found that fewer errors of omission and computation are made when it is used. It is better, too, because it enables the estimator to keep the work in groups that are complete in themselves. This is important in the later analysis of the construction details, in the analysis of the unit costs, and in making adjustments in the estimate.

All the work is estimated complete, in place, and the price thus includes all the material, labor, use of equipment, and incidental direct expense of every description. Each of the three parts of each item of work is listed and priced separately: the forms, the reinforcing steel, and the concrete. If no reinforcing steel is called for, this part is omitted or a note is inserted to the effect that none is required.

CONCRETE FORMWORK

Forms must be strong and rigid, and they must be well braced to prevent bulging. Wall forms have to resist a pressure of about 150 pounds per square foot for each foot of height, to hold wet concrete. At the same time, however, forms must be so arranged that they may be rapidly put in place and readily taken apart for reuse.

Temporary forms are used to hold the wet concrete until it has set sufficiently to allow removal of the forms safely. For ordinary walls forms may be removed in about two days, but for beams and floor slabs a week or more is required. The forms are used over again for other parts of the construction, where possible. Great care is taken in the construction of the forms so that the exact shape of the concrete will be formed and so that they will safely hold the weight of the wet concrete and the shocks of working conditions.

Forms should always be used for footings, except in rare cases where it can be plainly seen that they may profitably be omitted. Most specifications call for forms to be used for footings. When the excavating is very hard and the banks will stand without any caving in, even after a rainfall, then the excavation for the footings may be cut neat to the line of the concrete footings (if permitted by the specifications) and the trench thus formed filled to make a footing. If it is necessary to excavate within the building after the footings are thus formed, in order to place the floor or the base under the floor, it will probably not be worthwhile to consider omitting the footing forms. Footing forms are quite simple. If they are omitted, considerable extra time is consumed in trimming the trench sides very neat, and some of the concrete will undoubtedly be wasted. Furthermore, if space is needed outside the walls anyway, for easier installation of the wall forms or for waterproofing the walls or installing outside drains, etc., then surely the method of omitting the footing forms would seem uneconomical.

It is obvious that forms for walls and wall footings will not cost the same price per square foot of contact as forms for column footings and other isolated items. There is no direct relation between the quantity of forms and the quantity of concrete, either. Every difference in the size and shape of the concrete to be constructed will make a change in the quantity or type of forms required. This is another reason for adopting the method recommended for estimating concrete work, so that the various kinds of formwork may be kept properly separated and be priced differently where the character of the work calls for different prices.

Wall forms are removed within two or three days after the pouring of the concrete is completed, but thin walls in winter are allowed at least five days. Ordinary floor- and roof-slab forms are stripped in six or seven days in summer and two weeks in winter. Beams and girders require about two weeks in summer and four weeks in winter. Columns require two days in summer and four days in winter. Girders and slabs should be shored as the forms are being removed and left supported for several days longer.

Several factors enter into the cost of formwork, not the least of these being the possible reuse of the lumber or of made-up panels or, as in the case of column footings, of the entire form box. Besides, it may be that not all the wall forms on a job will take the same unit price, because one series of walls may require more bracing than others or the lumber in one may not be available for further use afterward.

The square feet of contact area of the forms against the concrete is found by measuring, on the plans, the concrete surfaces that will require this temporary support. The dimensions of each item are entered in some suitable order on the estimate sheets in feet and inches, and the total square feet extended for each part, or for each group, when a group can readily be made.

REINFORCING STEEL

Most concrete work will require some type of steel reinforcing. However, in residential work it is not uncommon to have footings, walls, and floors of plain concrete. When reinforcing steel is used, it may be in the form of welded *wire fabric* (often incorrectly called wire mesh) or in the form of reinforcing bars.

Wire fabric is available in square and rectangular patterns. Fabric having a square pattern is commonly used for reinforcing slabs on grade. It is also used for temperature reinforcement on supported slabs. The fabric may be one-way reinforcement, with heavy wires running in one direction closely spaced and lighter wires farther apart running at right angles to the heavy wires, or it may be two-way reinforcement, with equal-size wires equally spaced in both directions.

Welded wire fabric is available in rolls in the lighter gauges and in large sheets in the heavier gauges. It is manufactured in many different sizes, but generally only a few will be stocked by local suppliers, and then only in sizes which are commonly used in that area. Therefore the estimator must be alert to determine if the material is available locally or if it will have to be special-ordered.

Reinforcing bars are referred to according to their nominal diameter or by their size number. These numbers and the weights of the bars, per lineal foot, are given in Table 11-1.

Table 11-1

Bar No.	Pounds per Foot
2	.167
3	.376
4	.668
5	1.043
6	1.502
7	2.044
8	2.670
9	3.400
10	4.303
11	5.313

The No. 2 bars are plain round bars, and Nos. 3 to 11 are deformed round bars. The Nos. 9, 10, and 11 bars are equivalent, respectively, to square bars 1, $1\frac{1}{8}$, and $1\frac{1}{4}$ inches thick. The other bars are deformed round bars, and the numbers are based on the number of eighths of an inch in the diameter. A No. 5 bar is $\frac{5}{8}$ inch, a No. 4 is $\frac{1}{2}$ inch, etc. The grade of steel from which the bars are manufactured must also be noted.

CONCRETE

Concrete is made by mixing cement and sand with a coarser material, called the *coarse aggregate*. Sand is called the *fine aggregate*. The coarse aggregate is usually either coarse gravel or crushed stone, except in lightweight floor and roof arches, where cinders are used instead. Steel bars or welded wire fabric are embedded in the concrete when tensile strength is necessary, as in beams, girders, floor slabs, etc. When it has any form of reinforcing, concrete is called *reinforced concrete.* Without reinforcing, it is called *plain concrete.*

In the mixture of concrete, as the student should realize, the sand, cement, and water fill in the spaces between the pieces of broken stone or gravel or other material that forms the coarse aggregate. More than one cubic yard of materials, therefore, is required to produce a cubic yard of mixed concrete. For example, a cubic yard of six-bag mix (6 cubic feet of cement per cubic yard) might require 16.5 cubic feet of sand (fine aggregate) and 23 cubic feet of coarse aggregate, as well as 36 gallons of mixing water. Separately, these total approximately 48 cubic feet, but when mixed together they fill a space of only 27 cubic feet, or 1 cubic yard.

For ordinary work the concrete mix is generally specified by the number of bags of cement per cubic yard, the maximum size of coarse aggregate, and the amount of water per bag of cement. For work of any importance, it is now the practice to specify the strength of concrete desired, instead of the proportions of the mix: for example, 2,500-pound concrete, or 3,750-pound concrete. This means that the concrete must have the strength specified, per square inch, after 28 days—the period generally accepted as the complete curing period for concrete. Most concrete is bought ready-mixed, and the companies supplying it have accurate measuring devices at their plants to produce the concrete desired.

The mixtures of concrete that are generally used make concrete with a compressive strength of between 2,500 and 4,000 pounds per square inch. The strength depends upon the proportion of cement, the water-cement ratio, the quality of the workmanship, and other factors. Important work must be given constant supervision by the superintendent, the concrete foreman, the carpenter foreman (as to the formwork), the reinforcing foreman, and the job engineer. This adds to the general job expense as well as to the cost of the concrete ingredients if a richer mix is called for and of the lumber and labor required for forms that are better made than the ordinary. On a job of reinforced concrete with very rigid requirements, the complete structure may cost 50 percent more than on an ordinary type of job.

In concrete, between 5 and 7 gallons of water are required for each bag of cement used. Thus, if six bags of cement are used per cubic yard of concrete, between 30 and 42 gallons of water are needed for the cubic yard of concrete. This is a considerable amount of water, and if the concrete is mixed at the job, adequate provision must be made for obtaining the water and supplying it at the point of mixing. In some localities a meter must be installed and the water must be paid for. These are items of expense that the estimator must provide for in the estimate, wherever they are required. If long lines of temporary water piping have to be installed and maintained, especially in winter weather, the expense will be considerable.

The chemical action between the cement and water used in concrete is what causes the hardening, or setting, of concrete. This is a slow process, which continues for months. If the concrete is allowed to dry out too quickly, it does not gain its full strength; therefore specifications frequently ask that special attention be given to slowing up the drying process, or *curing* the concrete. This is done particularly in the case of concrete floors. Material to mix with the concrete or to apply on it after it is poured is sometimes called for. Whatever the case, it is the concern of the estimator to figure the cost involved and to provide for it in his estimate.

ESTIMATING CONCRETE

It is customary to estimate items of work in the order in which they are ordinarily done in the building. Therefore, after completing the excavation, concrete formwork would be next in the order of work done. However, because the amount of formwork required is based on the area of concrete in contact with the forms, many estimators will list the concrete first. This is the procedure we shall use in the following discussion.

In preparing the concrete estimate, each type of concrete needed for the building should be kept a separate heading. Sections or portions of the building requiring the

building construction estimating

different types of concrete can then be listed under these headings.

When preparing the takeoff form for a concrete estimate many estimators like to arrange the form with columns for description, number, width, thickness, length, cubic feet of concrete, square feet of forms, etc., so that a number

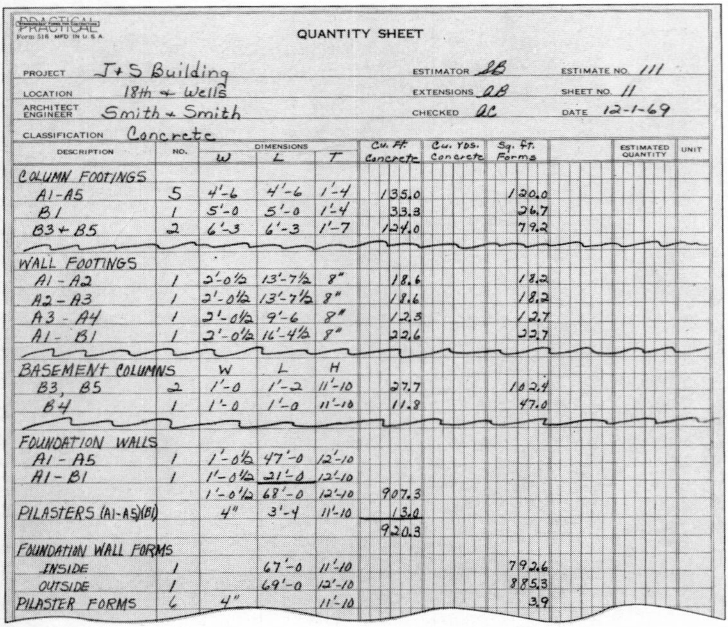

FIGURE 11-1 Concrete takeoff.

of items can be calculated from one entry (Figure 11-1). The only danger in this procedure is that of compounding an error if the original entry is wrong. However, if the estimate is carefully prepared and dimensions checked, this danger is minimal.

The first item entered in a concrete estimate would most likely be for footings. In residential work this would be for wall footings, column footings, and chimney or fireplace footings. These entries are easy to visualize. However, when dimensions for wall footings are listed, care must be taken to avoid overlapping at the corners. Figure 11-2 illustrates how dimensions for footings should be taken to avoid overlap at the corners which would occur if all overall dimensions were listed.

On larger jobs, where column footings are required at intervals along the foundation wall, these footings are listed first. It is important to identify the footing by its location, $A1$, $A2$, etc., and to enter its size and thickness on the quantity sheet in a clear manner.

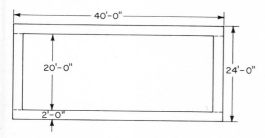

Outside perimeter - 128'-0"
Length of footing 24" wide - 40' + 20' + 40' + 20' = 120'-0"

FIGURE 11-2   Footing dimensions—overlapping.

After all exterior and interior column footings are entered, a separate heading is prepared for the wall footings. As with column footings, each section of wall footing is identified by location, and the length, width, and thickness entered.

Following the takeoff for the footings, the extensions are carried out to get the volume of concrete in cubic feet, totaled and changed to cubic yards.

For simple foundation walls the length, thickness, and height of each section are listed and identified. Determining the volume is then a simple matter.

If the wall sections contain any openings or decreases in thickness, these are listed separately and considered as *outs,* or deductions from the original volume. Where there are increases in the wall thickness, such as for pilasters, these are identified, listed separately, and considered as *additions*.

Concrete columns are identified by location on the takeoff sheet. When there are a number of columns the same size, they are grouped, with each identified and the total number given. The length, width, and height are listed in succeeding columns on the takeoff sheet. The height is generally listed as being from the top of the footing to the top of the floor slab for basement columns, and from the top of the floor slab to the top of the next floor slab for succeeding stories. Some estimators prefer to list column heights to the underside of the concrete beams. Whatever system is used, it is necessary to be consistent to avoid confusion.

The surface length of beams and girders is listed as being the distance between walls and columns. The location of the beams is listed along with the length, width, and height. A note is added to the listing whenever the estimator departs from his usual procedure.

Most concrete floors in a reinforced concrete frame building are made up with some type of joist system. On many jobs, because of varying requirements, a part of the floor may contain a joist system and a part may be a heavy solid slab. In preparing an estimate for this type of work, each type of floor should be listed separately and be clearly identified. Three possible types of concrete floor construction are the solid slab; the ribbed slab, or one-way joist slab; and the waffle slab, or two-way joist slab, as it is sometimes called.

Concrete for solid slabs is estimated by listing the length, width, and thickness of the slab on the quantity sheet. From this listing the cubic feet and cubic yards of concrete needed can be calculated.

For ribbed-slab floor construction the length and width of the slab are listed. The thickness of slab and size of joist are also indicated. From this information the area of the slab may be determined. The amount of concrete needed is found by multiplying the area by the amount of concrete needed per square foot for given conditions. The amount of concrete needed for some of the different joist sizes and slab thicknesses can be found in Table 11-2.

Table 11-2 Concrete Quantities for Ribbed Slabs Using Steel Flange Forms

20″ Widths

Depth of Steel Form	Width of Joist	Cubic Feet of Concrete per Square Foot for Various Slab Thicknesses				Additional Concrete for Tapered End Forms, Cu Ft per Lin Foot of Bearing Wall or Beam (One Side Only)
		2″	2½″	3″	3½″	
6″	4″	.262	.304	.346		.13
	5″	.279	.321	.363		.12
	6″	.293	.335	.377		.11
8″	4″	.298	.340	.382		.17
	5″	.320	.362	.404		.16
	6″	.339	.381	.423		.16
10″	4″	.336	.378	.420		.21
	5″	.363	.405	.447		.20
	6″	.387	.429	.471		.19
12″	4″	.377	.419	.461		.25
	5″	.408	.450	.492		.24
	6″	.437	.479	.521		.23
14″	5″	.456	.498	.540		.28
	6″	.490	.532	.574		.27
	7″	.522	.564	.606		.26
16″	5″	.507	.549	.590		.32
	6″	.545	.587	.629		.31
	7″	.581	.622	.664		.30

30″ Widths

		2″	2½″	3″	3½″	
6″	5″		.293	.334	.376	.11
	6″		.304	.346	.387	.11
	7″		.315	.357	.398	.11
8″	5″		.322	.364	.405	.15
	6″		.338	.380	.421	.15
	7″		.351	.392	.434	.14
10″	5″		.353	.395	.436	.19
	6″		.372	.414	.455	.18
	7″		.389	.430	.472	.18
12″	5″		.386	.427	.469	.22
	6″		.408	.450	.491	.22
	7″		.430	.471	.513	.21
14″	5″		.420	.461	.503	.26
	6″		.447	.488	.530	.24
	7″		.470	.511	.553	.24
16″	5″		.451	.493	.535	.29
	6″		.482	.523	.565	.28
	7″		.510	.552	.594	.27

The amount of concrete needed for waffle-slab construction is determined by calculating the volume of the slab as though it were solid. Then the volume of the voids created by the form pans is deducted from the total vol-

Table 11-3 Volume of Concrete Voids Created by Pan Forms in Waffle Slabs

19" × 19" Voids	
Depth of Steel Dome	*Regular, 19" × 19"*
4"	.77
6"	1.09
8"	1.41
10"	1.90
12"	2.14

30" × 30" Voids	
Depth of Steel Dome	*Regular, 30" × 30"*
8"	3.85
10"	4.78
12"	5.53
14"	6.54
16"	7.44
20"	9.16

ume. The volume of voids for different-size domed pans can be found in Table 11-3.

The amount of concrete required for slabs on grade is determined by listing the length, width, and thickness of the slab. The volume is then computed and listed in cubic feet. As with other types of work, the location of the slab is identified on the estimating form. Concrete for walks and driveways is determined in a similar manner.

Concrete stairways sometimes pose a problem in determining the volume of concrete needed to construct them, because of their irregular shape. To make figuring the concrete volume of a stair easy, the cross section of the stair may be considered as a rectangle. This rectangular area multiplied by the width of the stair gives the total volume, from which the voids of the steps can be subtracted. In cross section these voids are triangular in shape. Their total area multiplied by the width of the stair gives the total void.

A miscellaneous heading may be included under the concrete section to cover items which are not listed under any of the main headings. Construction joints and inserts for plumbing, heating, or electrical work might be entered under the miscellaneous heading.

After the amount of concrete needed under each division is determined in cubic feet, it is totaled and converted to cubic yards. The total yardage of each type of concrete is then determined and listed. The cost of the concrete is determined by multiplying the cost per cubic yard times the number of cubic yards required.

The cost of the concrete may be based on the price of ready-mix delivered to the job, or it may be based on the cost of concrete batched and mixed on the job. When job-mixed concrete is used, the estimator must consider the cost of aggregates, cement, water, equipment, labor to operate the equipment, and space for the mixing plant when determining the cost per cubic yard.

Labor required to place, consolidate, finish, and cure the concrete is estimated on the basis of the contractor's previous experience for a similar type of work. Often this cost is based on time required to place a cubic yard of concrete, or the time necessary to place a number of square feet of footing, wall, floor, etc.

By determining the work hours necessary to complete a job, it is easy to adjust the cost on the estimate because of changing wage rates.

When determining labor costs on concrete work, care should be taken to avoid omission of any part of the work involved. The cost of placing, consolidating, finishing, and finally curing the concrete must be considered. Overtime is often necessary on large concrete jobs. Because of the added cost, the amount of overtime must be determined and its cost allowed for.

Equipment needed on a reinforced concrete building will vary with the type and size of the building. The estimator working in cooperation with others in the contractor's office must determine the type, amount, and cost of all equipment required for the job.

Concrete work done in cold weather may require insulation on the formwork, temporary enclosures, and heaters to prevent freezing of the concrete before it sets. The cost of these items can be considerable. Therefore care must be taken to allow for it.

ESTIMATING FORMWORK

The amount of formwork required is based on the surface area of forms actually in contact with the concrete. Various kinds of lumber are used in the construction of forms. Nominal 2-inch planks are often used for footing forms. When boards are used for form sheathing, they are generally nominal 1-inch boards in widths varying from 6 to 10 inches. More often plywood is used for form sheathing. Usually, this plywood will be a plyform grade which was manufactured especially for concrete forming. The most commonly used thicknesses of plyform are $\frac{5}{8}$ and $\frac{3}{4}$ inch.

Bracing lumber for studs, walers, etc., may be 2 by 4 inches, 2 by 6 inches, 4 by 4 inches, etc., of a grade suitable for the type of forms being built. The amount of lumber and other materials required for the forms will vary with the type of form being constructed and is based on the area of forms in contact with the concrete (see Table 11-4).

Several sizes of nails are used in the building of the forms. Among the sizes used are 6d, 8d, 10d, and 16d common or box nails and double-headed nails. **Tie wire** used is No. 8, No. 10, and No. 12 black annealed wire. Various types of patented ties are also used in the construction of concrete forms. Patented forming systems of metal and plywood are available from various suppliers on a rental or purchase basis.

Each type of formwork is listed separately as the areas are determined. This is necessary because of the different amounts of materials and labor required for the different forms.

The area of wall-footing forms is found by multiplying the height of the footing by the length. The estimator must

Table 11-4 Approximate Quantities of Materials Needed for 100 Square Feet of Form Surface

Type of Form	Lumber, Bd Ft	Nails, Wire, Etc., Lb
Footings and piers	275	9
Walls and partitions	240	8
Floors	230	8
Roofs	250	8
Columns	260	9
Beams and girders	500	12
Stairs	450	11

remember that the footing has a form on each side, and include both in his estimate of surface area.

The area of column-footing forms is determined by multiplying the perimeter of the footing by the depth.

The outer and inner surface areas of concrete walls are determined without regard for normal-size openings because it is more economical to form over the openings and to prepare for the openings within the formwork.

The area of the formwork necessary to form the opening is listed separately. It is found by multiplying the perimeter of the opening by the thickness of the wall.

When offsets in the wall are necessary to form a ledge for brickwork, the area of the offset must be listed as part of the necessary formwork.

The area of column forms is based on the perimeter of the column multiplied by the height of the column, which may be taken to the underside of the floor slab or the underside of the beam, depending on construction details.

Round columns are usually formed with patented steel or fiberboard forms. When this is done, the estimator must list the diameter and the height of the column.

Concrete beams are often poured monolithically with the floor slab. This generally means that the height of the form will be less than the height of the beam. (See Figure

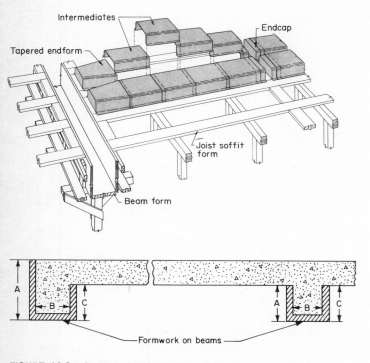

FIGURE 11-3 Concrete joist and beam forms.

11-3.) The estimator must be careful to list the area of formwork actually in contact with the concrete. The area can be found by adding the height and width of forms together (A, B, and C in Figure 11-3) and multiplying the sum by the length of the beam.

For reinforced concrete floor slabs the area of the slabs between the beams is determined and listed along with the usual identifying statement as to location.

Formwork for stairs is based on the area of the soffit, or slab form, which supports the concrete, the riser forms, and the side forms if needed.

When forms are needed for slabs on grade, they are figured in the same manner as wall-footing forms. Sidewalk and driveway forms are similar in nature, and the area of these forms may be determined in a manner similar to that for wall-footing forms. Each type of formwork should be listed separately.

Table 11-5 Labor Requirements for Various Types of Wooden Formwork

Type of Form	Approximate Time, Hr, per 100 Sq Ft of Formwork			
	Assemble	Erect	Strip and Clean	Repair
Footings	5	3	3	2
Walls	7	4	4	3
Floors and roofs	6	3	3	3
Columns	6	4	3	3
Beams and girders	8	4	4	4
Stairs	10	7	4	5

After the areas of the various types of forms have been determined, the amounts and cost of material needed can be calculated. Table 11-4 gives approximate amounts of material needed for common types of formwork. When patented forming systems are used, the supplier of the forms will quote the price of the forms per square foot and give information on other costs, such as for shoring, when needed.

The estimator must be careful to list all costs for form materials whether the materials are purchased or rented.

Labor costs on formwork will vary with the type of forms. The cost is usually based on the time required to place 100 square feet of formwork (see Table 11-5). The time required is based on the contractor's previous experience with the various types of formwork and may be adjusted to meet job conditions. By determining the time in man-hours required to do a job, it is easy to adjust the changing labor cost on the formwork due to wage increases.

Equipment costs for formwork can be quite small or fairly large, depending on the size of the job and the manner in which items are handled. The common equipment items would include power saws, extension cords, ladders, and sawhorses. Patented scaffolding may also be included under equipment costs, even when it is used as shoring for the forms. When this type of equipment is needed, whether it is listed under equipment or materials is not important, but it must not be overlooked.

ESTIMATING REINFORCING STEEL

The amount of reinforcing steel bars needed is obtained by listing the number of bars of each size and length required for each type of work, such as footings, columns, floors, etc. Reference to the specifications and to the notes on the plans may be necessary in order to find some of this information. The total length in lineal feet of each size is computed from the entries thus made in the estimate, and this figure is multiplied by the number of pounds that the bar weighs per lineal foot. This unit weight is sometimes given on the plans or in the specifications, but more often it is not, and must be looked up in a steel handbook or in one of the standard builders' reference books. The total weight of steel is extended for each item or for each group of similar items.

A specification may call for the reinforcing steel bars to be tied at every intersection. This is somewhat different from one requiring merely that enough intersections shall be tied to keep the bars in proper position. The tie wire has no value as reinforcing. If the bars are placed a few inches apart, two ways, there will be a great many intersections, and the time required for tying may be four or five times that for plain tying. An experienced estimator notices this in specifications and gauges his pricing accordingly. Although he may not take written notes of such deviations from the usual run of work, they all tend to set his mind for the pricing range he is going to use—a low range for jobs that have liberal specifications and higher ranges for those of more rigid requirements. A good estimator will not assume too much liberalization of vaguely written specifications, or he may be surprised later to learn that the inspector on the job for the architect is accustomed to rigid specifications, and it may be embarrassing to have to differ with him regarding the interpretation of the requirements.

Labor for placing reinforcing steel is based on the time required to place a given amount of steel (see Table 11-6). This time required is determined from the contrac-

Table 11-6 Approximate Labor Requirement for Handling 100 Pounds of Reinforcing Steel

Operation	Time, Hr
Unloading, stockpiling, and sorting	.15
Placing and tying foundation steel	.90
Placing and tying small bars (Nos. 2–5)	1.15
Placing and tying large bars	.7 to .9

tor's previous records, and it may be based on the number of rods of a given size and length, placed per hour, or on the time required to set 100 pounds of steel.

The amount of time allotted for a unit of work may be adjusted to job conditions and the cost of labor found by applying the proper wage rate.

Equipment needed might be as little as a bolt cutter or it may include a number of small hand tools, a welding unit, and a crane needed to deliver the steel to the work area. The estimator should exercise care in determining equipment needs and costs when preparing the estimate, to avoid omitting a cost item.

SUMMARIZING THE ESTIMATE

After the entire estimate takeoff is completed and the extensions carried out, the estimate is summarized to group like cost items together and to shorten the estimate.

In summarizing, care must be taken not to overlook any item. There is little consolation for having an item properly listed on the takeoff only to be left off the summary when the pricing is done—an omission which could be costly. The greatest care must be exercised at all times when preparing cost estimates.

EXERCISES

1   What is the general procedure of preparing a concrete estimate?

2   What parts of a building are generally estimated under the Concrete heading?

3   By what units of measure are formwork, reinforcing bars, and concrete priced?

4   Name the materials used in concrete work.

5   What is meant by six-bag-mix concrete, 4,000 pounds concrete?

6   Compute the amount of concrete in the following walls:
  a. 132'0" × 12'6" × 1'4"
  b.   47'8" × 13'9" × 2'2"
  c.   22'9" × 6'2" × 1'0"
  d.   34'3" × 10'4" × 1'3"

7   State the meaning and use of the following terms, and give sketches where possible: footings, wall forms, reinforcing bars, coarse aggregate.

8   How is the amount of formwork and concrete required for beams and columns determined?

9   How is the amount of formwork and concrete required for ribbed slabs determined? For waffle slabs?

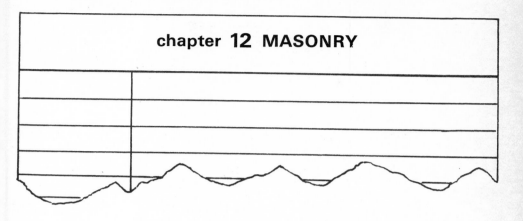

chapter 12 MASONRY

INTRODUCTION

The Masonry division of the estimate includes all the work done by bricklayers and bricklayers' helpers. It will include work done with a variety of materials. Among the most common materials installed by bricklayers and their helpers are concrete block, foundation drain tile, brick, terracotta, gypsum block, and various types of natural and manufactured stone. With the exception of drain tile, all the masonry materials mentioned above are installed with some type of mortar in the joints between the individual masonry units.

The first part of the chapter gives a description of the various common materials and their use. In the following sections estimating amounts of materials is discussed. Estimating labor and equipment need is discussed in the latter part of the chapter.

CONCRETE BLOCK

Concrete Blocks are described by nominal dimensions, especially their thickness. Thus, one measuring $7\frac{5}{8}$ inches thick, $7\frac{5}{8}$ inches high, and $15\frac{5}{8}$ inches long is called an 8-inch block, or an 8- by 8-inch block. When laid with $\frac{3}{8}$-inch joints, this block will occupy a space 8 inches high and 16 inches long. Today some blocks are 17⅝ inches long and occupy a square foot.

Solid concrete blocks are obtainable, but generally a solid block means one in which the open-core area is not more than 25 percent of the gross cross-section area of the block. A hollow concrete block means one with a core area greater than 25 percent.

Concrete blocks are also available in nominal 10- and 12-inch widths. As with the 8-inch block, the actual width of these blocks is ⅜ inch less than the nominal size. When 10- and 12-inch blocks are used, special L-shaped corner blocks are available for maintaining normal bond. Single- and double-corner blocks with smooth ends are available, as well as a number of auxiliary shapes to meet various needs. One of the best sources of additional information on concrete block is the *Sweet's Architectural File.*

Concrete blocks are made with either heavy or light-weight aggregates, a heavy 8-inch block weighing 40 to 50 pounds and a light block 25 to 35 pounds. Heavy blocks are made with sand, gravel, or crushed stone. Light blocks are made with cinders, slag, or other lightweight materials. The lightweight blocks provide insulation against heat and cold.

DRAIN TILE

When it is necessary to carry groundwater away from the foundation walls and footings, drain tiles are installed. These tiles are placed around the outside perimeter of the footing or foundation wall to collect groundwater and are connected to a sewer or sump well so the water can be removed from the soil to help maintain a dry basement.

The most commonly used drain tiles have an inside diameter of 3 inches and may be made of concrete or burned clay. The tiles are 12 inches long and are placed end to end with no seal over the joints. To prevent soil from filling in the tiles, an asphalted paper may cover the joints, and the tiles are covered with a layer of stone or crushed rock.

FACE BRICK AND COMMON BRICK

Each type of brick needed for a job is listed separately. Face brick is available in many colors and surface textures. Standard-size American face brick measures $2\frac{1}{4}$ by 8 inches on the face by $3\frac{3}{4}$ inches depth. The price of brick is given as cost per 1,000 bricks, and the price varies with the color and surface texture.

Other sizes of face brick commonly available are Roman brick, which measures $1\frac{5}{8}$ by 12 by $3\frac{3}{4}$ inches, and Norman brick, which measures $2\frac{1}{4}$ by 12 by $3\frac{3}{4}$.

Common brick may be clay brick of no special appearance quality or it may be concrete block. It is used for the backing up of the walls that have face brick, for rear-wall construction, and for brick chimneys and partitions.

TERRA-COTTA AND GYPSUM BLOCK

Terra-cotta blocks, as considered under the Masonry heading, are structural clay tile blocks, and not the type that has specially treated surfaces. The latter are referred to as architectural terra-cotta and often are put under a special heading. Non-load-bearing, or partition, structural clay tile blocks are made in thicknesses of 2, 3, 4, 6, 8, and 10 inches. They are all 12 by 12 inches in face size. Structural clay tile for use in load-bearing walls is available in thicknesses of 4 and 8 inches and face sizes of $5\frac{1}{3}$ by 12, 8 by 12 and $10\frac{2}{3}$ by 12 inches. When estimating needs for structural clay tile, each type must be listed under a separate subheading to assure proper pricing.

Chimney flue linings are a type of terra-cotta. They are manufactured in various square, rectangular, and round sizes. The flue sections are usually made in 24-inch lengths.

Gypsum block is made mainly from calcined gypsum to which water has been added to promote a setting action. These blocks are used for interior nonbearing partitions and as fire protection for structural steel members. Gypsum blocks, sometimes referred to as plaster blocks, are made in thickness of 2, 3, 4, 5, and 6 inches. The 3- and 4-inch thicknesses are the most commonly used. They are all 12 by 30 inches in size; therefore one block equals $2\frac{1}{2}$ square feet, whereas nonbearing structural clay block is 1 square foot. Being made of porous plaster composition, they are much ligher in weight and of less strength than structural clay blocks. Gypsum block provides an excellent base for gypsum plaster.

STONEWORK

Stonework is a general term for several divisions that may be required in the estimate. Some subcontractors handle several kinds of stone, others only one.

Plain cellar walls or other walls of rubblestone are measured in cubic feet. However, rubblestonework is more often included with the regular masonwork instead of being treated as a subcontract item.

Granite and limestone are the two kinds of stone most commonly used for facing purposes, but bluestone is also used, especially for sills, copings, lintels, and curbing.

Cast stone is an artificial stone which, by the right combination of the proper ingredients, can be made to imitate any of the natural stones.

Stonework used for buildings has changed considerably in type of usage with the changes in construction in recent years. Before the advent of steel-frame construction, cut stone formed the basis for the solid walls required. The exterior walls supported the entire structure, and cut granite or limestone provided the ideal material for these walls, which generally were several feet thick at the base of the structure and diminished in thickness in the upper stories. Present-day construction, with steel, reinforced concrete, or prestressed concrete frames, relieves the exterior walls of the necessity of supporting the weight of the structure. This makes it possible to use the stone as a veneer facing, supported and anchored on the frame at each floor level.

Stone used as a veneer, 2 inches and sometimes less in thickness, is priced per square foot, the price depending on the type of material and finish.

Cut stone in thicknesses greater than 2 inches is priced per cubic foot, the type of material, the color, and the finish being determining factors.

MORTAR

Mortar is a mixture of cement, sand, and water, usually about 1 part cement to 3 parts sand. To make the mixture more workable, lime is generally added, especially when the mortar is to be used by bricklayers and spread with a trowel. A good mortar for brickwork is also made of 1 part cement, 1 part lime, and 6 parts sand.

Most mortar used for masonry work is made from a mortar cement which is formulated for specific masonry work. This mortar cement contains the proper amount of cement, lime, and admixtures. When mixed with sand and water in the proper proportions, the resulting mortar is durable and easy to work with.

Mortar cement is preferred in the masonry field because it eliminates the need for proportioning lime and cement on the job. Proportioned at the plant under exacting conditions, it yields a more uniform mortar than can be obtained under job-proportioning conditions.

Sand used for mortar is classified as masonry sand, is washed free of mud and silt, which would contaminate it for use in mortar, and is graded as particle size.

The final ingredient of mortar is water. It should be clean and not contain any dissolved substances which would react with the cement and cause weak mortar. In addition to being used as mixing water, sufficient quantities must be available for cleaning tools and equipment.

ESTIMATING CONCRETE BLOCK

The size of concrete block required for a given job may be found on the plan view, the wall sections, and in some cases on the wall elevations. The number of blocks required is determined by finding the areas of the concrete-block walls and dividing that area by the area of one block.

Example Find the number of regular concrete blocks needed for a wall 32 feet long and 8 feet 8 inches high.

$$32 \times 8\tfrac{2}{3} = 277\tfrac{1}{3} \text{ sq ft}$$

Block area:

$$\frac{8''}{12''} \times \frac{16''}{12''} = \frac{128}{144} = .8888 \text{ sq ft}$$

$$277.33 \div .8888 = 312 \text{ blocks}$$

When first listing the dimensions of block walls, any openings in the walls are ignored. These openings are later listed as outs. When the extensions are done, the area of the outs is subtracted from the gross area before the number of blocks required is determined.

Generally, all walls requiring the same type of block will be grouped under the same heading. However, even in walls which require all 8-inch blocks, there may be a need to order different types of blocks. Smooth-end blocks

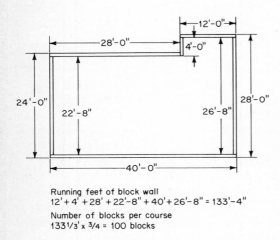

Running feet of block wall
12' + 4' + 28' + 22'-8" + 40' + 26'-8" = 133'-4"
Number of blocks per course
133 1/3' x 3/4 = 100 blocks

FIGURE 12-1   Foundation plan.

may be needed around door and window openings, control-joint blocks for control joints, pilaster blocks for pilasters, cap blocks for the top of walls, and various types of bullnose blocks for corners or door and window openings.

The number of each type of special block needed is listed under separate headings and identified as to their location in the structure. The total number of special whole blocks (two half blocks equal one whole block) is subtracted from the total number of regular blocks figured earlier. Each type of block is then priced separately.

On some jobs the estimator may find it easier to determine the total number of blocks required per course of masonry. This is done by finding the total length of the walls, being careful to allow for overlap at the corners (see Figure 12-1). The number of blocks required per course is found by dividing the length of the wall by the length of the block, 16 inches, or $1\frac{1}{3}$ feet, or simply by multiplying by $\frac{3}{4}$.

The building shown in Figure 12-1 has an outside

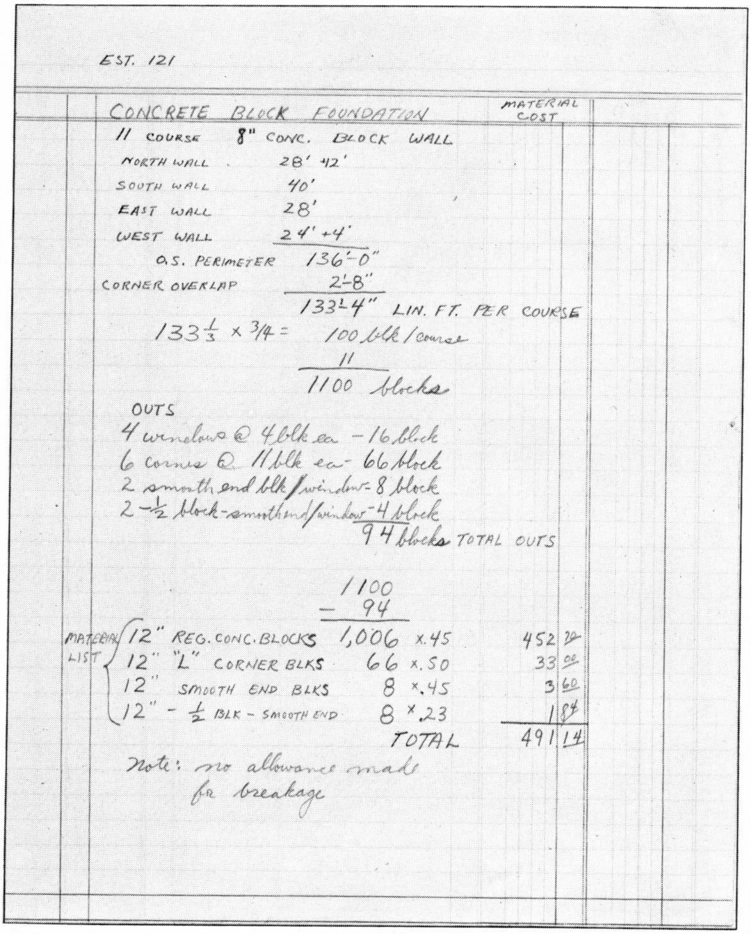

EST. 121

CONCRETE BLOCK FOUNDATION		MATERIAL COST	

11 COURSE   8" CONC. BLOCK WALL

NORTH WALL   28' 42'
SOUTH WALL   40'
EAST WALL   28'
WEST WALL   24'+4'
  O.S. PERIMETER   136'-0"
CORNER OVERLAP   2'-8"
       133'-4" LIN. FT. PER COURSE

$133\frac{1}{3} \times 3/4 =$ 100 blk/course

       11
   1100 blocks

OUTS
4 windows @ 4 blk ea — 16 block
6 corners @ 11 blk ea — 66 block
2 smooth end blk/window — 8 block
2 -½ block-smooth end/window — 4 block
     94 blocks TOTAL OUTS

    1100
    - 94

MATERIAL LIST				
12" REG. CONC. BLOCKS	1,006	x .45	452	70
12" "L" CORNER BLKS	66	x .50	33	00
12" SMOOTH END BLKS	8	x .45	3	60
12" - ½ BLK - SMOOTH END	8	x .23	1	84
		TOTAL	491	14

Note: no allowance made for breakage

FIGURE 12-2   Takeoff sheet for concrete block.

perimeter of 136 feet. However, because of overlapping at the corners, there is only 133 feet 4 inches of running block wall. The number of blocks required per course is 133⅓ × ¾, or 100 blocks. If the wall is eleven courses high, the total number of blocks required will be 1,100.

If the wall is other than 8 inches thick, L-corner blocks are needed for all corners. One L-corner block per corner per course of block is allowed. In Figure 12-1 there are 6 corners, each requiring 11 corner blocks, for a total of 66 L-corner blocks.

The number of smooth-end blocks needed for door and window openings is listed, and the total number of special blocks is deducted from the total number of blocks required to determine the number of regular blocks needed (see Figure 12-2).

ESTIMATING DRAIN TILE

The number of drain tiles required is found by determining the total lineal footage required and allowing one tile per foot. Generally, drain tiles will be required around the outside perimeter of the wall and the inside perimeter of the footing. Bleeder tiles are required at 8- to 10-foot intervals, and the lineal footage of these tiles must be included in the total lineal footage of drain tile. The length of interconnecting lines from the inner ring to the central collecting point must also be included. A small allowance of about 1 to 2 percent is made for breakage when the total number of tiles is listed.

ESTIMATING BRICK

The number of bricks required for veneered walls (brick walls 4 inches thick) is determined by finding the area to be veneered and multiplying that area by the number of bricks per square foot. There are seven standard-size bricks per square foot when laid with a ¼-inch mortar joint. Because face bricks are usually laid with a heavier mortar joint, allowing seven bricks per square foot automatically makes a small allowance for waste and breakage. When a large amount of bricks is used with thicker or thinner mortar joints, the number of bricks required per square foot should be investigated. If bricks of other sizes are used, the number required per square foot for a given mortar joint should also be investigated before determining the total number required.

The area of walls to be brick-veneered is initially determined without regard to openings in the wall. When determining this total area, care must be taken to make proper allowances at intersecting corners to avoid overlapping or shortage in the total calculated area.

Window and door openings are listed as outs. Their areas are determined and deducted from the total area to find the area actually covered by the brick. The number of bricks can then be found by multiplying the net area by the number of bricks per square foot.

Thick brick masonry walls require a slightly different approach for determining the number of bricks required. In thick walls the total volume of the wall is found in cubic feet. The volumes of door and window openings are listed separately as outs and are deducted from the gross volume. To find the number of bricks required for the job, the net volume is multiplied by the number of bricks per cubic foot. For standard-size brick it is generally assumed that there are 21 bricks per cubic foot (see Figure 12-3).

The number of bricks required for a fireplace is usually determined by the cubic-content method. The total volume of the fireplace is first determined as though it contained no openings. Then the volumes of the chimney flues, the heat passages, and the hearth are determined and listed, along with the dimensions used in the determination. These voids are listed as outs and deducted from the gross volume.

Next the volume of the firebrick, face brick, and/or stone veneer must be determined. These are listed for two purposes: first, as part of the outs for determining the amount of common brick needed for the fireplace, and second, as materials of the various types which must be figured in the cost estimate.

By deducting the total outs from the gross volume of the fireplace, the volume of common brick required is

EST. *502*			Mason Work							SHEET *7*	
					QUANTITY		LABOR		MATERIAL		
	Common Brick										
	Basement										
	Boiler room										
	69-0	11-10	1-0		8 1 7						
	Cuts										
	3-4	7-6	1-0	25							
	5-0	7-4	1-0	36	-6 1						
					7 5 6						
					x 2 1						
					1 5 8 7 6	Bk.	.06½	1 0 3 2	.07	1 1 1 2	
	First Floor										
	North wall										
	102-8	17-3	0-4		5 9 0						
					x 2 1						
					1 2 3 9 0	Bk.	.07½	9 3 0	.07½	9 3 0	
	North parapet										
	20-0	3-6	1-0		7 0						
	East wall										
	83-2	20-9	1-0		1 7 2 6						
					1 7 9 6						
					x 2 1						
					3 7 7 1 6	Bk.	.06	2 2 6 3	.07	2 6 4 1	
	Garage front & rear										
	20-0	20-6	0-8		2 7 3						
	19-0	17-0	1-0		3 2 3						
					5 9 6						
	Cuts										
	12-0	12-2	0-8	97							
	6-9	8-6	1-0	57	-1 5 4						
					4 4 2						
					x 2 1						
					9 2 8 2	Bk.	.07	6 5 0	.07	6 5 0	
								4 8 7 5		5 3 3 3	

FIGURE 12-3 A masonwork estimate.

determined. The net volume is multiplied by the number of bricks per cubic foot to determine the number of bricks required.

ESTIMATING TERRA-COTTA AND GYPSUM BLOCK

The amount of structural clay tile or gypsum block needed for a wall is based on the area of the wall. Walls requiring different materials and different material thicknesses are listed separately. Door and window openings are listed as outs, and the actual amount of material is determined for the net area.

The face of structural clay tile units is usually 12 inches square. Therefore the number of regular tiles needed will be equal to the net area of the wall. Any special tile which might be needed must be listed separately.

The face of gypsum block units usually measures 12 by 30 inches. Therefore each block covers an area of 2.5 square feet. The number of blocks of each thickness required is found by dividing the net wall area by 2.5.

When gypsum block is used as a fireproofing medium and plaster base on a steel column, the amount of gypsum block needed is based on the finished size of the column, and not the size of the steel column alone.

Architectural terra-cotta (glazed clay tile) is available in a number of colors, sizes, and shapes. The amount of this type of material needed for a job is based on the area of the wall. In addition to the regular rectangular blocks, most jobs also require cove base blocks, bullnose blocks of various types, and special corner blocks, where horizontal and vertical bullnose corners meet. Each type of architectural terra-cotta must be entered separately because of the varying cost per unit.

ESTIMATING STONE FOR STONEWORK

All the different kinds of stone are measured in approximately the same manner for estimating. The plain work of ashlar facing is measured in square feet. Curbs and copings are measured in lineal feet. Sills, lintels, keystones, and other small units are counted per piece. Special shapes are analyzed, and in the case of cut stone, the size of the block from which each piece will be cut is taken into account.

Random ashlar differs from rubblestone in that it is available in exact heights and, with a $\frac{1}{2}$-inch mortar joint, can be coordinated with brick. Random ashlar is shipped to the job in lengths that enable the mason to set it in a practical manner. Using a masonry saw, he can break the stones to the lengths required. Rubblestone, often referred to as native stone because it can be found in practically every state, does not have standard course heights. This type of stone permits a more random, or rustic, effect. Rubblestone is found in a variety of colors ranging from white to dark pink or red. For the most part, use of random ashlar and rubblestone is confined to residential construction. It is also adaptable, however, to commercial and religious buildings when used with a cut-stone trim, which provides a contrast in color and texture.

Stonework, other than plain ashlar surfaces, such as sills with raised lugs, carved work, molded trim, lintels, etc., must be analyzed, and the amount of handwork and machine work, type of finish, and size of the rough block must be taken into consideration in determining the cost.

Limestone, marble, bluestone, and cast stone run slightly less in price than granite because the fabricating costs are slightly less. The erection costs are the same for all types of exterior stone.

In most cities the cut stone is set by stonesetters. In other areas it may be set by the bricklayers. Local regulations should be investigated and taken into account when making up the estimate.

In some cases, prices on the stone will be furnished to the general contractor by firms that do only quarrying and fabricating. These prices are based on delivery of the fabricated stone to the job; the contractor will have to add the cost of setting in order to establish a complete price. Sometimes the small isolated pieces of stone are delivered by the stone contractor but are set in the brick walls by the bricklayers. In all cases the stone contractor will exclude the cost of mortar, anchors, scaffolding, and the protection of the stonework at the job.

Occasionally, as in the case of certain types of stone arches, timber braces, or supports, called *centers*, must be provided while the stone is being erected. These temporary supports are removed after the stonework is completed, or in the case of a stone arch, after the keystone has been set in place. The erection of these centers is handled by the carpenters on the job, and this cost must also be taken into consideration.

Table 12-1 Mortar Requirements for Concrete Masonry Walls Joints $\frac{3}{8}$ Inch Thick — 10 Percent Allowance for Waste

Actual Unit Size, Width × Height × Length, In.	Nominal Wall Thickness, In.	Mortar, Cu Ft for 100 Sq Ft of Wall	Mortar, Cu Ft for 100 Concrete Units
$3\frac{5}{8} \times 3\frac{5}{8} \times 15\frac{5}{8}$	4	13.5	6.0
$5\frac{5}{8} \times 3\frac{5}{8} \times 15\frac{5}{8}$	6	13.5	6.0
$7\frac{5}{8} \times 3\frac{5}{8} \times 15\frac{5}{8}$	8	13.5	6.0
$3\frac{3}{4} \times 5 \times 11\frac{3}{4}$	4	12.0	5.5
$5\frac{3}{4} \times 5 \times 11\frac{3}{4}$	6	12.0	5.5
$7\frac{3}{4} \times 5 \times 11\frac{3}{4}$	8	12.0	5.5
$3\frac{5}{8} \times 7\frac{5}{8} \times 15\frac{5}{8}$	4	8.5	7.5
$5\frac{5}{8} \times 7\frac{5}{8} \times 15\frac{5}{8}$	6	8.5	7.5
$7\frac{5}{8} \times 7\frac{5}{8} \times 15\frac{5}{8}$	8	8.5	7.5
$11\frac{5}{8} \times 7\frac{5}{8} \times 15\frac{5}{8}$	12	8.5	7.5

There may be many contingent parts that go together to make up the complete cost of the stonework, particularly if several types of stone are involved. The estimator must make a careful study of the plans and specifications in order to become familiar with the requirements in each case. He must also make sure that any subcontractor's

Table 12-2 Mortar Requirements for Structural Clay Tile, Cubic Feet of Mortar per 100 Square Foot of Wall Joints $\frac{1}{2}$ Inch Thick — No Allowance for Waste

Size of Tile, In.	Mortar, Cu Ft
2 × 12 × 12	1.30
3 × 12 × 12	1.60
4 × 12 × 12	2.00
6 × 12 × 12	2.60
8 × 12 × 12	3.25
10 × 12 × 12	4.00
12 × 12 × 12	5.00

Table 12-3 Mortar Requirements for Modular Clay Tile, Cubic Feet of Mortar per 100 Square Feet of Wall Joints $\frac{1}{2}$ Inch Thick — No Allowance for Waste

Size of Tile (Nominal, In.)	Wall Thickness, In.	Mortar, Cu Ft
4 × 4 × 12	4	4.7
8 × 4 × 12	8	9.3
4 × 5$\frac{1}{3}$ × 12	4	3.7
8 × 5$\frac{1}{3}$ × 12	8	7.2
4 × 8 × 12	4	2.8
8 × 8 × 12	8	5.1
4 × 8 × 16	4	2.6
8 × 8 × 16	8	4.9

prices he anticipates using are complete in all respects and are based on the use of materials acceptable to the architect.

ESTIMATING MORTAR FOR MASONWORK

Materials for mortar may be based on the number of masonry units of a given size to be installed, or on the

Table 12-4 Mortar Requirements per 100 Square Feet of Brick Wall, Brick Size 2$\frac{1}{4}$ by 8 by 3$\frac{3}{4}$ Inches, 10 Percent Allowance for Waste

Joint Thickness	Cubic Feet of Mortar Required, Wall Thickness of:			
	4″	8″	12″	16″
$\frac{3}{8}$″	6.1	8.3	9.0	9.4
$\frac{1}{2}$″	8.2	10.5	11.3	11.8
$\frac{5}{8}$″	10.4	12.8	13.7	14.1
$\frac{3}{4}$″	12.5	15.2	16.1	16.5

Table 12-5 Mortar Requirements per 1,000 Bricks

Joint Thickness	Cubic Feet or Mortar Required, Wall Thickness of:			
	4″	8″	12″	16″
$\frac{3}{8}$″	8.7	11.8	12.9	13.4
$\frac{1}{2}$″	11.7	15.0	16.2	16.8
$\frac{5}{8}$″	14.8	18.3	19.5	20.1
$\frac{3}{4}$″	17.9	21.7	23.0	23.6

amount of mortar needed for 100 square feet of wall for a given-size masonry unit.

The amounts of mortar needed for some of the commonly used masonry units are given in Tables 12-1 to 12-6.

While the major cost ingredients of mortar are Portland cement, lime, masonry cement, gypsum mortar for gypsum block, and masonry sand, it should be noted that water is also needed. The cost of water needed to produce mortar and to clean tools and equipment must be considered in the estimate. It may run from little or nothing to a sizable sum, depending on availability on the job.

Cement mortar is used as a waterproofing medium on concrete masonry walls. The amounts of sand and cement needed for various thicknesses of backplaster are given in Table 12-7.

Table 12-6 Amount of Mortar Needed per 100 Square Feet of Wall for Materials Listed

	Cubic Feet
Architectural terra-cotta	8
Ashlar veneer, 4 inches	10
Gypsum block:	
3 inches	$1\frac{3}{4}$
4 inches	$2\frac{1}{4}$
6 inches	$3\frac{1}{2}$

Table 12-7 Materials Required for 100 Square Feet of Wall Surface for Varying Thicknesses of Backplastering

Thick- ness, In.	1 Cement, Sack	1½ Sand, Cu Ft	1 Cement, Sack	2 Sand, Cu Ft	1 Cement, Sack	2½ Sand, Cu Ft	1 Cement, Sack	3 Sand, Cu Ft
¼	1.4	2.1	1.1	2.2	.8	2.0	.7	2.1
⅜	1.9	2.9	1.4	2.8	1.1	2.8	.9	2.7
½	2.8	4.2	2.1	4.2	1.7	4.3	1.4	4.2
¾	3.7	5.6	2.8	5.6	2.2	5.5	1.9	5.7
1	5.6	8.4	4.2	8.4	3.3	8.3	2.8	8.4

ESTIMATING LABOR

Labor needed for masonwork may be divided into skilled and semiskilled or unskilled categories. The skilled labor will include the bricklayer and stone masons, who will do the necessary layout work and the actual work of installing the masonry units.

The semiskilled or unskilled help are often referred to as helpers. The helpers build scaffolds, mix mortar, supply materials, and assist the masons as directed.

Labor requirements are based on the amount of masonry to be installed. The unit of measurement may be the square foot, cubic foot, or the number of pieces, such as 1,000 bricks or 1,000 concrete blocks. Labor requirements for each type of work are determined separately, because of the different rates at which the various types of work may be performed.

The time required to place 1,000 bricks in a low wall where a minimum of scaffolding is needed will be quite different from the time required to place 1,000 bricks in a high wall requiring a considerable amount of scaffolding and climbing. The estimator must carefully analyze each part of the work and apply the proper expected output when extending the estimate.

A well-run masonry job will have a proper ratio of bricklayers or masons and helpers doing their work. On a simple job where materials are easily accessible, one helper may be able to keep two or more masons properly supplied. On a specialty job a ratio of one mason to one helper may be needed. The estimator must make a careful judgment as to the ratio of helpers and masons when preparing the cost estimate. The approximate time required to install various types of masonry is given in Table 12-8.

Table 12-8   Masonry Labor Requirements per 100 Square Feet of Wall Surface

Material	Helper-hours	Mason-hours
Concrete block	5	5
Common brick	3	6
Face brick veneer	6	12
Structural clay tile	5	5
Gypsum block	$3\frac{1}{2}$	3
Architectural terra-cotta	14	7
Stone veneer	22	12

It should be noted that these times are approximate, and no allowance is made for varying job conditions or the size of crew performing the work.

ESTIMATING EQUIPMENT

Equipment needs for a masonry job will vary with the size and type of job. Items which must be included in the equipment cost for the job are mortar mixer, scaffolding (planks and horses), water hose, power hoist, small tools (shovels, trowels, etc.), mortarboards, wheelbarrows, and trucks necessary for the transportation of mixer and equipment.

The cost of the various equipment needed is usually based on a company's cost records for previous similar jobs. This cost is usually broken down into easy-to-use units, such as 100 square feet or 1,000 masonry units.

When estimating equipment costs, the estimator must be careful to list or allow for every item that will be needed on the job. Omission of an item of equipment cost can be just as detrimental to the final estimate as any other cost omission.

EXERCISES

1   What items are included under the Masonry heading of an estimate?

2   List ten materials used in masonwork.

3   State the general method of estimating concrete block.

4   Compute the number of concrete blocks in the following walls:

    a. 119′0″ × 11′6″ × 1′0″
    b.   63′0″ × 8′9″ × 1′4″
    c.   82′9″ × 10′10″ × 0′8″
    d. 121′0″ × 11′6″ × 1′0″
    e.   68′0″ × 14′3″ × 1′8″

5   Compute the number of bricks required in the following walls:

    a. 119′0″ × 11′6″ × 1′0″
    b.   63′0″ × 8′9″ × 1′4″
    c.   82′9″ × 10′10″ × 0′8″
    d. 121′0″ × 11′6″ × 1′0″
    e.   68′0″ × 14′3″ × 1′8″

6   Estimate the amounts of mortar materials needed in Exercises 4 and 5 above.

7   Estimate the amounts of labor required in Exercises 4 and 5 above.

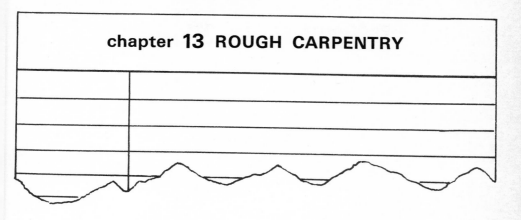

chapter 13 ROUGH CARPENTRY

INTRODUCTION

Most estimators prefer to have at least two headings for carpentry work, one for rough carpentry and one for finish carpentry. On large jobs, special headings may be set up for millwork, wood stairs, wood flooring, and other divisions of carpentry, to provide separate total prices for these items or to make comparison with subcontract estimates that may be received for them. Even on small jobs, it is good practice to split up the work in this way.

Rough carpentry takes in all the framing and sheathing. *Finish carpentry* includes the trim, moldings, baseboard, windows, doors, cabinets, shelves, etc. Wood flooring and wood stairs are included in finish carpentry unless special headings are set up for them. Finish hardware also is placed under finish carpentry, but on larger buildings this is generally given a separate heading. Frequently, a lump-sum allowance of money is specified for the purchase of the hardware. Of course, any item that is provided for elsewhere in the estimate does not require handling under any of the carpentry headings.

LUMBER GRADING

Softwood lumber grading is carried on under the rules of the California Redwood Association, Southern Pine Association, Western Wood Products Association, and others. The rules of these associations were incorporated into what is known as the American Lumber Standard through the efforts of the U.S. Department of Commerce. In recent years efforts have been made to revise the American Lumber Standard to take into account the moisture content of the lumber in determining size and to incorporate new information on stress-graded lumber.

Because of the delay in revising the lumber standard, lumber is being graded under the rules of separate organizations and marked accordingly. Board lumber used in frame construction may be graded No. 1, No. 2, No. 3, No. 4, or No. 5 common. However, No. 5 boards are seldom used in frame construction due to the large number of defects in this low grade. Boards are also graded Construction, Standard, Utility, and Economy, Construction grade being the best in this category.

Framing lumber may be graded Structural, No. 1, No. 2, No. 3, and No. 4. In some cases the number grades are replaced by Construction grade for No. 1, Standard for No. 2, Utility for No. 3, and Economy for No. 4.

Softwood Plywood is graded under Product Standard PS 1-66, developed by the American Plywood Association and the U.S. Department of Commerce. This standard classifies the various species of lumber according to strength and stiffness into four groups. Plywood bearing the stamp of any group may contain any species in that group. Plywood commonly used in framing may be graded Standard, Structural I, Structural II, or C-C Exterior.

FRAMING LUMBER

Yard lumber is lumber less than 5 inches thick intended for general building purposes. Most lumber used for floor framing, wall framing, ceiling construction, and roof structural members are 2 inches thick. However, some designs will call for 3- and 4-inch-thick joists, studs, etc.

Of the common framing lumber sizes, 2 by 4's, 2 by 6's, 2 by 8's, 2 by 10's, and 2 by 12's may be used for joists or rafters, depending on the span, while 2 by 4's are used almost exclusively for plates and studs in wall construction. This framing lumber is usually made from Douglas fir or southern pine. However, a considerable amount of 2 by 4's, 2 by 6's, and some larger sizes are available in white fir, hemlock, spruce, and other species.

One-inch boards may be used for subflooring, wall sheathing, and roof sheathing. These boards may be square edge, shiplap, or tongued and grooved in 6- or 8-inch widths. Wider boards, sometimes used, are to be avoided because of excessive shrinkage. Square edge 1 by 4 and 1 by 6 boards are often used for corner braces and ribbons in light-frame construction.

One-inch boards used in frame construction may be made from southern yellow pine, hemlock, spruce, and a number of other species.

A considerable amount of plywood is now being used for subflooring, wall sheathing, and roof sheathing. It is available in 4- and 8-foot sheets and $\frac{5}{16}$-, $\frac{3}{8}$-, $\frac{1}{2}$-, $\frac{5}{8}$-, $\frac{3}{4}$-, $\frac{7}{8}$-, $1\frac{1}{8}$-, and $1\frac{1}{4}$-inch thicknesses. The thickness used is governed by the grade of plywood, the spacing of supports, and local building codes.

CALCULATING BOARD FEET

The price of lumber is given as dollars per 1,000 board feet. A board foot is a price of lumber 1 inch thick, 12 inches wide, and 1 foot long. Any piece of lumber which has the same cubic content as the piece above is said to contain 1 board foot. Pieces 2 inches by 6 inches by 1 foot, 1 inch by 8 inches by 1 foot 6 inches, 2 inches by 4 inches by 1 foot 6 inches contain 1 board foot of lumber each. Therefore, to calculate the number of board feet contained in a quantity of lumber, it is necessary to multiply the number of pieces by the thickness in inches, by the width in inches over 12, by the length in feet.

Example 1 Find the board feet contained in eight pieces, $-1'' \times 6''$ thick, $- 16'$ long

$$8 \times 1 \times \frac{6}{12} \times 16 = 64 \text{ bd ft}$$

Example 2 Find the board feet contained in ten pieces

$$- 2'' \times 4'' \text{ thick, } 12' \text{ long}$$

$$10 \times 2 \times \frac{4}{12} \times 12 = 80 \text{ bd ft}$$

To find the amount of lumber contained in a lineal foot of material, the same rule applies.

Example 3 Find the amount of lumber contained in each lineal foot of 1 by 6, 2 by 4, 2 by 8, and 2 by 10.

$$1'' \times \frac{6''}{12} \times 1' = \tfrac{1}{2} \text{ bd ft per lin ft } 1 \times 6$$

$$2'' \times \frac{4''}{12} \times 1' = \tfrac{2}{3} \text{ bd ft per lin ft } 2 \times 4$$

$$2'' \times \frac{8''}{12} \times 1' = 1\tfrac{1}{3} \text{ bd ft per lin ft } 2 \times 8$$

$$2'' \times \frac{10''}{12} \times 1' = 1\tfrac{2}{3} \text{ bd ft per lin ft } 2 \times 10$$

HOUSE FRAMING

Among the three common types of house framing are balloon framing, braced framing, and platform, or western, framing.

In *balloon framing* the wall studs extend in one piece from the foundation sill to the top plate which supports the rafters. One of the advantages in using balloon framing over other methods is that it minimizes the amount of settling due to shrinkage in the framing lumber, making it suitable for two-story brick-veneered buildings. The main disadvantage in using balloon framing is unequal settling due to shrinkage in the bearing partition.

With *braced framing,* heavy timbers are used to support the floor and ceiling loads, thereby making the exterior walls a type of curtain wall. Braced framing has been modified considerably, and when it is used, the heavy timbers are replaced by standard 2-inch framing lumber, the exterior walls becoming bearing walls.

Western, or *platform, framing,* along with some modifications, is probably the most popular type of framing. In this type of framing a floor platform is built on top of the foundation walls, and walls of one story are built on the platform. A second platform is built on top of the first-floor walls, and the second-story walls are built on the second platform. If a third story is required, the process is repeated. One of the main advantages in using platform framing is the equal settling due to lumber shrinkage throughout the building. However, because of settling due to shrinkage, platform framing is not suitable for two-story brick-veneer buildings.

HEAVY-TIMBER CONSTRUCTION

Also referred to as mill construction, heavy-timber construction utilizes exterior walls of noncombustible materials having a fire-resistance rating of not less than two hours and interior structural members, beams, and columns of heavy solid or laminated timber. Roof and floor decking often consists of 2 by 4 material laid on edge and securely spiked together. Other types of heavy plank or laminated decks are also used in heavy-timber construction.

TEMPORARY CONSTRUCTION

Temporary enclosures and protection, temporary arch centers, and other temporary construction items are sometimes specified under Carpentry. Sometimes they are not specified at all, but they will be found necessary nevertheless. The estimator must have these in mind on every job, and for this reason some offices use a printed general job expense estimating sheet on which these and other usual expense items are printed, so that they will not be overlooked. In any event, the estimator should figure these items just as he would any items of permanent carpentry, and apply unit prices per board foot or per square foot or in any other suitable manner.

SPECIAL FRAMING

Special framing or work that is out of the ordinary is to be watched carefully and analyzed closely in estimating. Roof trusses, tower framing, and odd-shaped structures belong in this class. New methods of timber framing developed in recent years call for special fastenings that require special tools. Every piece of lumber in special or heavy framing must be listed, and all the iron bolts, shear plates, connectors, etc., must be counted and listed separately.

Split-ring timber connectors are made of hot-rolled carbon steel and must fit snugly in prebored holes. Toothed-ring connectors are stamped from 16-gauge rolled sheet steel to form a circular, corrugated, sharp-toothed band, welded into a solid ring. Claw-plate connectors are malleable iron castings, each plate consisting of a perforated, circular, flanged member, with three-sided teeth on one side. Shear plates are of pressed steel or malleable iron, with a flange around the edge on one face.

ESTIMATING MATERIALS

A wide variety of materials may be included under the heading of rough carpentry. Therefore it is logical to start by listing the materials as they are required for installation and to keep each type separate to make summarizing and pricing easier.

Framing lumber varies in price with the species and grade required. It may cost the contractor $110 to $200 or more per thousand board feet. Timbers will run from $150 to $200 per thousand board feet. Common boards will run from $100 to $150 per thousand board feet, depending on the grade of lumber.

The price of plywood varies with the grade, thickness, and species and will cost from $80 to $150 or more per 1,000 square feet.

Various composition sheathings will cost from $50 to $100 per 1,000 square feet, depending on type and thickness.

WOOD GIRDERS AND COLUMNS

The size of wood girders (8 by 8, 8 by 12, etc.) is given on the plans. The length of these girders may be given as the distance from center of column to center of column or overall from wall to wall. In determining the length of material to order, it may be necessary to add on for the amount of bearing required on concrete walls.

Timbers are generally available in even foot lengths. Therefore, in listing timbers needed for girders, the next even foot of length should be entered on the quantity sheet.

The size of wood columns (6 by 6, 8 by 8, etc.) can also be found on the plans. However, the estimator will usually have to determine the length required. the distance from floor to floor is generally given, and to find the length of the column, the height of the beam is subtracted from the story height. The length listed is rounded off to the next even foot. However, if two columns 7 feet long are required, it would be economical to order one 14-foot timber in place of two 8-foot pieces.

FLOOR JOISTS AND CEILING JOISTS

The size of joists and joist spacing may be found on a typical wall section, or they may be indicated on the basement plan for the first floor in the following manner:

$$\frac{2 \times 10 - 16'' \text{ o. c.}}{\text{over}}$$

To determine the length of joists needed, dimensions may be taken from the plan and then rounded off to the next even foot. Because there is, generally, a need for several different lengths of material in a floor frame, it is advantageous for the beginner to make a rough sketch of the floor frame showing the outline of the building, girders, and floor openings (see Figure 13-1).

Sections A, B, and D in Figure 13-1 would require joist material 14 feet long. Section C would require joist material 10 feet long. In addition to regular joists, header joists 10 feet long would be needed for the stairs, and 16-foot-long material would be needed for the skirts.

The number of joists 16 inches on centers for each joist span may be determined by multiplying the length of the building by $\frac{3}{4}$ and adding 1. If the joists are 24 inches on centers, the number of joists required is found by multiplying the length of the building by $\frac{1}{2}$ and adding 1.

Additional joists in the proper length must be added for partitions running parallel to the joists, for headers and trimmers required to frame floor openings, and for the header, or skirt, across the outside ends of the joists.

The length of ceiling joists is determined by finding the distance from the outside walls to the bearing partition and rounding off to the next lumber length. Because the bearing partition does not always run continuously from one end of the building to the other, care must be taken

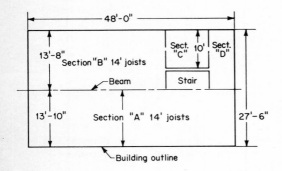

FIGURE 13-1 Outline of floor frame—aids in determining number of joists required.

to allow for differing lengths of ceiling joists. The number of ceiling joists required is determined in the same manner as for floor joists.

BRIDGING

Wood bridging of rough 1 by 3 stock is commonly used in frame construction. Most codes require one row of bridging in spans over 8 feet 0 inches and less than 16 feet 0 inches. Two rows of bridging are usually required in spans over 16 feet 0 inches.

To find the amount of bridging material needed, the length of each row of bridging is determined and tabulated. The sum of all the row lengths in lineal feet is then multiplied by a factor from Table 13-1 to get the total lineal feet of bridging material needed for the job.

When metal bridging is used, the total lineal footage of bridging rows is multiplied by $\frac{3}{4}$ to find the number

Table 13-1 Wood Bridging Material

Joist Size	Spacing, In. O.C.	Lineal Feet of Material per Foot of Bridging Row
2 × 6 to 2 × 10	16	2
2 × 12	16	$2\frac{1}{4}$
2 × 14	16	$2\frac{1}{2}$

of spaces between joists 16 inches on centers. This number of spaces is then multiplied by 2 to determine the number of pieces of bridging required.

If the joists are 24 inches on centers, the total lineal footage of bridging rows is equal to the number of pieces of metal bridging needed.

SUBFLOORING

Material used for subflooring may be of 1 by 6 or 1 by 8 boards installed either diagonally or at right angles to the joists, or it may be of plywood of various thicknesses.

To determine the amount of subflooring needed, the area to be covered must be calculated. When figuring the area to be covered, small openings are generally ignored and the area figured to include the area of the openings.

Table 13-2 Subflooring—Waste Allowance

Material	Allowance When Laid at Right Angles to Joists, %	Allowance When Laid Diagonally, %
1 × 6 tongued and grooved	20	25
1 × 8 tongued and grooved	15	20
1 × 6 shiplap	20	25
1 × 8 shiplap	15	20
1 × 6 square edge	12	17
1 × 8 square edge	10	15
48″ × 96″ plywood	3	

However, when figuring flooring for large buildings with many floor openings, deductions should be made for these openings.

After the area is determined, a percentage is added to allow for waste, and in the case of boards, to allow for material lost in dressing the lumber. The percentage used will vary for different types of material. Therefore care must be taken to make sure that the right percentage is used (see Table 13-2).

WALL FRAMING

A material list for wall framing includes wall plates, studs, headers, braces, and ribbons as required by the type of framing used. Because exterior walls may be framed differently from interior walls, it is good practice to divide the initial materials takeoff in two parts: exterior walls and interior walls.

Wall plates may be ordered in any convenient length readily available. However, because of the many different lengths of plates needed, it is common practice to order wall plates in 16-foot lengths. Starting with the outside walls, the procedure to follow is to check the plan for the number of plates required. With this information in mind, the total lineal footage of exterior wall is determined and listed. If the plan called for a single-bottom and a double-top plate, the lineal footage of wall is multiplied by 3 to get the total lineal footage of 2 by 4 plates needed. The result is divided by 16 and rounded off to the next full number to get the number of 16-foot 2 by 4's needed.

To determine the number of 2 by 4 plates for the interior partitions, the total lineal footage of interior walls must be determined. Because of the number of short partitions running in different directions, it is good practice to list all wall lengths from left to right first, and then all walls running from top to bottom of the plan. The total lineal footage of interior walls is handled in the same manner as that for exterior walls to get the number of 16-foot 2 by 4's needed for plates.

The length of 2 by 4 studding will vary with the finished ceiling height and the number of plates in the wall construction. In balloon framing, 18-foot-long 2 by 4's are often needed for studs. In platform framing 8-foot 2 by 4's are often needed, and in many areas it is possible to get precut studs 92⅝ inches long.

The number of 2 by 4's required for regular studs 16 inches on centers may be determined by multiplying the total lineal footage of walls by ¾. To allow for additional studs required for corner posts, two studs are added for each outside corner. Two additional studs must be added for backing at each intersecting partition, and to allow for door and window framing, two additional studs are added for each door and window opening. Figuring 2 by 4 studding in this manner will allow for all 2 by 4 door and window headers and all 2 by 4 blocking needed.

Shoulder studs needed to support headers usually measure just under 7 feet in length. Therefore one 14-foot 2 by 4 is added for each door and window opening to allow for shoulder studs.

Some estimators prefer a simplified method for determining the number of studs spaced 16 inches on centers. The procedure is to allow one stud for each lineal foot of wall and to deduct two studs for each door and window opening. One 14-foot 2 by 4 is allowed for the two shoulder studs at each opening, as previously stated. In this method a sufficient number of 2 by 4's for backing, corner posts, and blocking is automatically included, because no further deductions are made for openings in the wall. Figure 13-2 shows the typical construction around door and window openings.

On buildings with gable roofs it is necessary to order material for gable end studs. Because these gable ends are triangular in shape, one-half the plate length is used as a basis for determining the number of studs required for each gable end. This plate length is multiplied by ¾ if the studs are 16 inches on centers, and 1 is added to the result. The length of the studs may be determined by scaling the plan from the top of the wall to the top of the roof and rounding off to the next even foot. One piece of stud material will make a long and a short gable stud. This helps to account for the fact that only one-half the plate length is used.

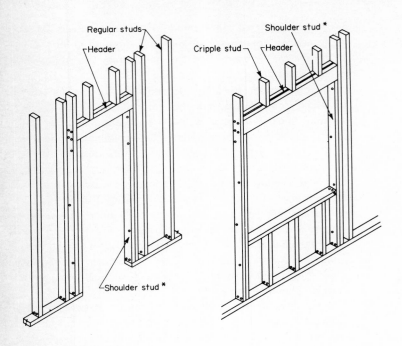

Regular studs

Header

Shoulder stud *

Cripple stud

Header

Shoulder stud *

Shoulder stud *

*Also know as trimmer

FIGURE 13-2   Door and window framing.

Openings over 4 feet wide in walls and partitions usually require headers larger than a double 2 by 4. The requirements will vary with different building codes. However, the sizes listed in Table 13-3 are generally acceptable.

The length of material for window headers is deter-

Table 13-3   Wall-header Sizes

Header Size	Maximum Span
Two — 2 × 4	4'—0''
Two — 2 × 6	5'—6''
Two — 2 × 8	7'—6''
Two — 2 × 10	9'—0''
Two — 2 × 12	11'—0''

mined by adding 12 inches to the glass size. The size and length of the material are listed separately for each opening, and in some cases, later combined into convenient lumber lengths.

In balloon framing it is necessary to order material for the ribbon which will support the second-floor joists. This ribbon is required on the two sides of the building which will support the joists. Therefore the lineal footage of the sides of the building requiring ribbons is totaled and divided by a convenient lumber length to get the number of pieces required. The result is rounded off to the next full length.

Diagonal braces of 1 by 4 material are often required at each end of all exterior walls. These braces run from top to bottom plate at an angle of approximately 45 degrees. Walls 8 feet 0 inches high would require material 12 feet long. The number of pieces needed for bracing is listed along with size and length.

WALL SHEATHING

To determine the amount of material required for wall sheathing, it is necessary to measure the area to be covered. This may be done by first determining the total lineal footage of wall and then multiplying by the height to get the gross area of the wall. Depending on the type of material to be used for sheathing, the area of openings may or may not be deducted from the gross area and there may or may not be an allowance for waste.

When wood boards are used for sheathing, deductions for door and window openings may be made. The deduction for window openings is based on glass area of the window; for door openings, it is based on the area of the door. Because the actual opening is slightly greater than glass or door size, a small allowance is automatically made for waste. However, because a board foot of wood sheathing does not cover a square foot of wall area, an additional allowance must be made. The percentage to be added to the wall area to determine the number of board feet of wood sheathing needed varies with the width of the boards and the method of application.

Table 13-4 Sheathing Material

Percentage to Add to Wall Area to Obtain Board Feet

Material	Applied Horizontally, %	Applied Diagonally, %
1 × 6 tongued and grooved	20	25
1 × 6 shiplap	20	25
1 × 8 tongued and grooved	15	20
1 × 8 shiplap	15	20

When plywood or composition sheathing is used, the number of sheets of material required is found by dividing the gross area of the wall by the area of one sheet of material (either 16 or 32 square feet). The result is rounded off to the next full sheet.

RAFTERS, RIDGE BOARDS, AND COLLAR BEAMS

The size of rafter stock and spacing can usually be found on the wall section. The number of rafters required for a shed roof may be determined by multiplying the wall length by $\frac{3}{4}$ and adding 1 if the rafters are 16 inches on centers. If they are 24 inches on centers, the length of the wall is multiplied by $\frac{1}{2}$ and 1 is added to the result. The lumber length required for these rafters may be determined by scaling a plan elevation and rounding off to the next even foot.

A similar procedure may be followed for a gable roof. The number of rafters required on one side of the building is determined and multiplied by 2 to allow for the rafters needed for the other half of the gable roof. The length of stock may be determined by scaling the plan and rounding off to the next even foot, or the length of the rafters may be calculated by finding the diagonal of the total rise and total run, including cornice projection. Because the lumber length needed is rounded off to the next even foot, it is usually satisfactory to scale the plan.

Hip roofs require hip rafters in addition to common

rafters and jack rafters. The length of rafter stock required may be found by using a table similar to that found on the carpenter's square, or may be found mathematically by finding the diagonal of the total rise and total run, or may be found by scaling the diagonal distance of total rise and total run. As usual, the length of material needed is rounded off to the next even foot.

Hip rafters run into the building at an angle of 45 degrees in plan view. Therefore the run of the hip rafter is the diagonal distance of the common rafter run. This must be remembered when scaling the total rise and total run, or when calculating the diagonal of total rise and total run to get the rafter length. If there is a cornice projection, its rise and run must be included in the calculations.

The number of hip rafters required for a square or rectangular building is four. However, if the building has a number of wings or offsets, the number of hip rafters required can best be determined by counting the number of hip rafters shown on the roof plan.

In addition, valley rafters may be required. The number and location may also be taken from the roof plan. The length of valley rafters is found in the same manner as the length of hip rafters.

Jack rafters for hip roofs and interesting roofs are nothing more than common rafters which have been cut to fit against a hip or valley rafter. For a plain hip roof the amount of material for jack rafters is found by assuming that the building has a gable roof and that all the rafters are common rafters. If the rafters are 16 inches on centers, the length of the building is multiplied by $\frac{3}{4}$ and 1 is added. When calculating the amount of material needed for common rafters and jack rafters, the length of the building must include the width of the cornice projection on each end of the building. This is necessary because the length of the tail on the rafter usually makes it impossible to get a long and a short jack rafter out of each piece of stock, but by adding the cornice projection to the length of the building, sufficient material will be allowed for all the jack rafters and common rafters.

On complicated hip and intersecting roofs the estimator may want to sketch the roof plan and determine the amount of material required for each triangular section. However, it will be easier and just as accurate to assume that the entire structure has common rafters and to figure materials for all jacks as outlined above.

The amount of material required for ridge boards is determined by finding the total lineal footage of ridge and then listing the material in convenient lumber lengths.

Many roofs require collar ties or collar beams. These may be made up of 2 by 4 or 1 by 6 material. The length of these members may be given on the plan, or in some cases it may be scaled from the plan. The number required is determined and ordered in convenient lumber lengths; e.g., 48 collar ties 6 feet 0 inches long of 2 by 4 material would probably be listed

$$24 — 2 \times 4 — 12'$$

ROOF SHEATHING

Material for roof sheathing will generally be of plywood or boards, but regardless of the material used, the initial step in determining the amount of material required is to calculate the area of the roof. This area may be found easily by adding a percentage from Table 13-5 to the level area covered by the roof.

Adding a percentage to the horizontal area covered by the roof is an accurate method of finding the roof area

Table 13-5 Converting Level Areas to Sloping-roof Areas for Given Unit Rise

Unit Rise, In.	Percentage to Add
2	1.25
3	3
4	6
5	8
6	12
7	16
8	20
9	25
10	30
11	36
12	41

and is especially useful when the roof has many different small sections which would require separate figuring. Care must be taken to include the area covered by the cornice projection, and not just the floor area of the building, when using this method.

To change square feet to board feet and also allow for waste, a small percentage must be added to the roof area. The amount to add will vary with the type of material used (see Table 13-6).

When plywood is used for roof sheathing, an allowance of 1 to 5 percent is made for waste. The allowance used

Table 13-6 Roof-sheathing Allowances

Changing Area to Board Measure

Material	Allowance, %
1 × 6 square edge	10
1 × 6 tongued and grooved	20
1 × 6 shiplap	20
1 × 8 square edge	12

depends on how "cut up" the roof is. Generally, the greater the number of offsets in the roof, the greater will be the allowance for waste. The amount allowed for waste is added to the roof area, and the total is divided by 32 (the area of a 4- by 8-foot sheet) to get the number of sheets of plywood needed.

ROOFING

Roofing is generally done by a roofer or roofing specialist. However, the carpenter may be called upon to install asphalt shingles and cedar wood shingles. As with roof sheathing, the first step is to determine the area to be covered. To allow for waste, a small percentage is added to the roof area, and the shingles are ordered to the next full bundle.

Asphalt shingles generally come in three bundles to a square (100 square feet); wood shingles usually have four bundles per square. Therefore asphalt shingles are

Table 13-7 Allowance for Waste

Asphalt and Wood Shingles

Type of Roof	Wood Shingle, %	Asphalt Shingle, %
Shed or gable	8	3
Hip	12	8
Intersecting	12	8

figured to the next $\frac{1}{3}$ square, while wood shingles are figured to the next $\frac{1}{4}$ square.

The number of wood shingles required to cover a square of roof will vary with the exposure to the weather. Various references make different statements as to how many bundles are required per square of roof. However, the number of bundles per square shown in Table 13-8 will serve to illustrate the number of bundles required for different exposures.

Table 13-8 Wood-shingle Coverage

Exposure to Weather	Bundles per Square of Roof
4''	3.6
$4\frac{1}{2}''$	3.2
5''	2.88
$5\frac{1}{2}''$	2.62
6''	2.4
$6\frac{1}{2}''$	2.216
7''	2.06

Example A hip roof has an area of 2,680 square feet. Find the number of bundles of wood shingles required if they are laid $4\frac{1}{2}$ inches to the weather.

2,680 + 12% waste = 3,002 sq ft, or 30.02 squares. At $4\frac{1}{2}''$ to the weather 3.2 bundles per square are required.
30.02 × 3.2 = 96.064, or 97 bundles

NAILS

Different sizes of nails and varying amounts are needed for the various types of rough carpentry. As a general rule the amounts of nails required are based on the quantity of lumber to be fastened. Table 13-9 lists many of the job categories and the amount of nails required.

Table 13-9 Nails Required for Rough Carpentry

Application	Nail Size	Amount
Joists	16d common	10 lb per 1,000 bd ft
Bridging	7d common	1 lb per 100 lin ft
Wall framing	8d common	5 lb per 1,000 bd ft
	16d common	18 lb per 1,000 bd ft
Roof framework	8d common	2 lb per 1,000 bd ft
	16d common	8 lb per 1,000 bd ft
Subflooring:		
Boards	8d common	32 lb per 1,000 bd ft
$\frac{1}{2}''$ plywood	6d common	10 lb per 1,000 sq ft
Wall sheathing:		
Wood boards	8d common	32 lb per 1,000 bd ft
Fiberboard $\frac{25}{32}''$	8d common	30 lb per 1,000 sq ft
Fiberboard $\frac{1}{2}''$	2'' barbed roofing	15 lb per 1,000 sq ft
Gypsum $\frac{1}{2}''$	$1\frac{1}{2}''$ barbed roofing	12 lb per 1,000 sq ft
Roof sheathing:		
Boards	8d common	32 lb per 1,000 bd ft
$\frac{1}{2}''$ plywood	6d common	10 lb per 1,000 sq ft
Roofing:		
Asphalt shingles	$\frac{3}{4}''$ roofing	3 lb per square of shingles
Wood shingles	$1\frac{1}{4}''$ shingle nail	$4\frac{1}{2}$ lb per square of shingles

The amounts and size of nails will vary from job to job, some jobs requiring more nails of a given size and others requiring fewer nails.

LABOR

In preparing a construction cost estimate, labor is the most difficult item to calculate. This difficulty stems from the different rates at which different tradesmen work; job conditions, which are difficult to predict; delays due to weather, etc.; and changing wage scales.

Labor costs are generally based on a contractor's previous experience with a similar type of job. The amount of labor needed may be based on the area of floor, wall, or roof, or it may be based on the amount of lumber to be installed. A beginner in construction estimating may use the information given in Table 13-10, which is based on material to be installed, to complete a carpentry labor estimate.

Table 13-10   Rough-carpentry Labor

Job	Labor Output
Joists and bridging	90 bd ft per hr
Wall framing (studs, plates, and headers)	45 bd ft per hr
Roof framing	40 bd ft per hr
Subflooring:	
Boards	70 bd ft per hr
Plywood	95 sq ft per hr
Wall sheathing:	
Boards	50 bd ft per hr
48″ × 96″ panels	100 sq ft per hr
Roof sheathing:	
Boards	50 bd ft per hr
48″ × 96″ plywood	75 sq ft per hr
Roofing:	
Asphalt shingles	$\frac{1}{2}$ square per hr
Wood shingles	$\frac{1}{3}$ square per hr

EQUIPMENT

The amount of equipment required for rough-carpentry work is comparatively small. Equipment needs will include ladders, scaffolding, power saws, power nailers, extension cords, and sawhorses. The cost of this and other equipment needed must be considered and added to the job cost on a prorated basis.

EXERCISES

1   List several special headings for carpentry work.

2   What items are included under the rough-carpentry heading?

3   What is yard lumber?

4   What is a board foot?

5   Calculate the amount of lumber (board feet) in the following list:

    16—2 × 4 —16′
    36—2 × 8 —14′
    40—2 × 10—16′
    28—2 × 6 —14′
    50—3 × 8 —16′

6   What are the general types of house framing?

7   List several types of temporary construction requiring carpentry work.

8   Outline the procedure for estimating floor joists.

9   Outline the procedure for estimating subflooring.

10   Outline the procedure for estimating wall-framing materials.

11   Outline the procedure for estimating wall sheathing.

12   Outline the procedure for estimating roof-framing materials.

13   Outline the procedure for estimating roof sheathing.

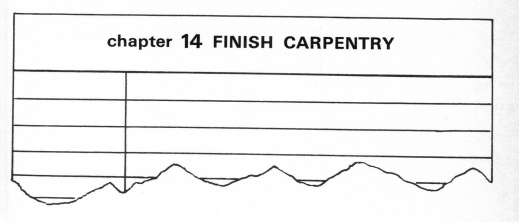

chapter **14** FINISH CARPENTRY

INTRODUCTION

Finish carpentry may be classified as exterior finish and interior finish. Each classification may be subdivided into a number of smaller categories.

Exterior finish carpentry would include cornice work and exterior trim, installation of door and window frames, wood porches and railings, and siding. Each of these categories could be broken down into smaller parts for the purpose of listing each item required.

Interior finish carpentry would include finish flooring, wood paneling, cabinets, trim on doors, windows, etc., stairs, and doors. The various categories can be broken down into smaller parts to better describe the job.

EXTERIOR TRIM—CORNICE WORK

The unit of measurement for exterior trim is the lineal foot. Each member of exterior trim and cornice is listed on the estimate along with the size, type of material, and lineal footage needed in each location. After the quantity takeoff is completed, it is summarized. The summary is used for pricing the material and also for determining the amount of labor required for the job.

Some of the common items included under exterior

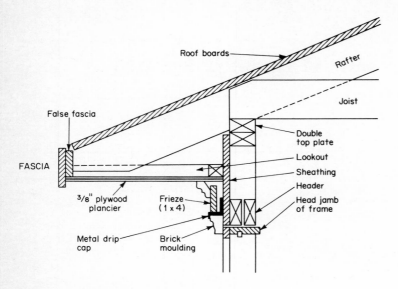

FIGURE 14-1 Typical cornice cross section.

trim are corner boards, water tables, rake boards, rake
moldings, fascia boards, plancier boards, frieze boards, and
crown and bed moldings. Figure 14-1 shows a cross section
of a typical cornice. A material takeoff for this type of
cornice is illustrated in Figure 14-2.

QUANTITY SHEET											
PROJECT _Smith Residence_			ESTIMATOR _SB_			ESTIMATE NO. _142_					
LOCATION _1414 FIFTH ST._			EXTENSIONS			SHEET NO. _17_					
ARCHITECT ENGINEER			CHECKED			DATE _12-30-69_					
CLASSIFICATION _CARPENTRY — EXTERIOR TRIM_											
DESCRIPTION	NO.	T	W	L	lin. ft	sq. ft				ESTIMATED QUANTITY	UNIT
false fascia	6	1"	4"	16'	96					32	BD. FT
Redwood Fascia	6	1"	6"	16'	96					48	BD. FT
3/8" Plywood Plancier	12	3/8"	24"	8'	96	192				192	SQ. FT
Redwood Frieze	6	1"	4"	16'	96					32	BD. FT
Bed Molding			2¼"		96					96	LIN. FT
Lookouts	50	2"	4"	2'	100					67	BD. FT
Lookouts ribbon	6	2"	2"	16'	96					32	BD. FT

FIGURE 14-2 Cornice-material takeoff.

DOOR FRAMES AND WINDOW FRAMES

The size, type, and number of each door and window frame needed is listed on the takeoff sheet. The necessary information may be taken from a door and window schedule on the plan; it may be taken directly from the plan view, or it may be taken from the exterior elevations.

In listing door and window frames, care should be taken to be sure that each frame is listed and that each is properly identified as to size, type, and manufacturer, if the manufacturer is specified.

SIDING

The exterior siding on a building may be made from a number of different kinds of wood, aluminum, plastic, etc. They are manufactured in a number of different types, sizes, and thicknesses and may be referred to as tongued and grooved, shiplap, beveled, rabbeted beveled, and drop siding. In addition, various types of plywood are available for use as siding. Most of the plywood used for siding comes in 4- by 8-foot sheets.

The unit of measurement for siding is the square foot. The first step in determining the amount of siding needed is to find the area to be covered. Wall areas are usually listed without regard for door and window openings. The areas of door and window openings are listed separately as outs and deducted from the gross area. In some cases, where there are few openings or where plywood sheets cut out for openings result in waste, the areas of openings are not considered.

After the area to be covered has been determined, a percentage is added to the area to allow for waste and overlap. The amount added depends on the type of material being used. Typical allowances for some of the commonly used materials are given in Table 14-1.

To illustrate the use of Table 14-1, assume that a building had a net area of 1,200 square feet to be covered with 8-inch bevel siding. From Table 14-1 we find that 25 percent must be added to the area to determine the amount of siding needed. Therefore, to cover an area of 1,200 square feet, 1,500 square feet of siding is needed.

FINISH FLOORING

In this section the three most commonly used types of flooring installed by carpenters and wood floorlayers will be discussed. They are underlayment (used under carpeting and resilient floor coverings), strip flooring (both hardwood and softwood), and parquet wood block flooring. With each type of flooring the unit of measurement is the square foot.

Underlayment is commonly available in 4- by 8-foot sheets. To determine the amount of underlayment needed,

Table 14-1 Allowances for Overlap and Waste on Siding

Siding	Nominal width, In.	Percentage Added to Wall Area
Bevel	6	40
	8	25
	10	20
	12	15
Tongued and grooved	6	20
	8	15
	10	10

the size of each room requiring underlayment is listed, and the total area determined. This total area is divided by 32 (the area of one sheet) and rounded off to the next full number, which is the number of sheets required to cover the floor. No allowance is made for waste because there is very little waste under most conditions. Only when the underlayment is laid in rooms of irregular shape must some allowance be made for waste. This allowance will vary and is left to the estimator's discretion.

Strip flooring is available in random lengths and is usually end-matched as well as tongued-and-grooved. Strip flooring is available in face widths of $1\frac{1}{2}$, 2, $2\frac{1}{4}$, and $3\frac{1}{4}$ inches. The most commonly used width in residential work is $2\frac{1}{4}$ inches.

To determine the amount of strip flooring needed, the area to be covered is first determined. Next a percentage is added to this area to allow for the amount of material which has been wasted in the manufacturing process. The percentage to add for the various widths is given in Table 14-2. The total of the actual area and the added percentage is the number of feet of flooring needed to cover the floor area. An additional 1 percent may be added for waste on the job.

In residential work the area of the floor is determined without regard for the width of partitions. The area covered by the partitions automatically allows for the small amount

Table 14-2 Strip Flooring—
Changing Square Feet to Board Feet

Face Width, In.	Percentage Added to Area
$1\frac{1}{2}$	50
2	$37\frac{1}{2}$
$2\frac{1}{4}$	$33\frac{1}{3}$
$3\frac{1}{4}$	25

of waste encountered when installing strip flooring, and no other allowance for waste on the job is necessary.

Parquet wood block flooring is made up in a number of different ways and a number of different sizes. The method of determining the amount of material is the same for all types of parquet flooring. First the area to be covered must be determined. A small percentage (2 to 5 percent) is added to allow for waste. The total is the amount of parquet flooring needed in square feet.

Parquet flooring must be laid on a smooth base. It is set in mastic over dry concrete floors or over underlayment. It cannot be laid successfully over wood-board subflooring. If the building has a wood-board subfloor, it must be covered with an underlayment before parquet flooring can be installed. The estimator must realize this when preparing an estimate for parquet flooring in an area which has a board subfloor.

Mastic for parquet flooring is available in 1- and 5-gallon cans. When determining the amount of mastic needed, the manufacturer's coverage recommendations for the expected conditions should be observed.

WOOD PANELING

Paneling may be solid wood in the form of patterned tongued and grooved boards, or it may be prefinished in the form of $\frac{1}{4}$-inch plywood or $\frac{1}{4}$-inch hardboard. To estimate the amount of paneling material needed, the area to be covered must first be determined. The unit of measurement is the square foot.

For wood board paneling a percentage is added to the net wall area to allow for waste. The percentage to be added is the same as for tongued and grooved siding, and can be found in Table 14-1.

When plywood or hardboard is used for paneling, the wall area is determined without regard to door or window openings. However, if the wall contains some large doors, arches, or windows, the area of these may be subtracted from the gross area to avoid overfiguring on material. The wall area is then divided by the area of one sheet (usually 32 square feet) and rounded off to the next full sheet.

In some cases the estimator may choose to determine the perimeter of the room in feet and divide by 4 to get the number of 4-foot-wide sheets necessary to panel the room. With this method also it is necessary to make deductions for large door or window openings to avoid overfiguring on materials.

INTERIOR TRIM

The heading of interior trim includes all the millwork in the form of jambs, casings, stops, baseboard, base moldings, shoe moldings, hook strips, shelving, etc., necessary to give the interior a finished appearance.

A number of different approaches may be taken when preparing an estimate for interior trim. Some estimators will list each room in the heading and then proceed to list all the trim materials needed in that room. Others will list a trim item and proceed to indicate the amount needed in each area. Still others will use a combination of the two methods. Whichever method is used, it is equally important that there be no omissions or oversights.

Because of the large number of different trim members, it is very easy to overlook an item. The estimator should therefore develop a method of surveying the plan and listing items in an organized manner (see Figure 14-3).

```
EST. 143                                    SHEET 10

INTERIOR    TRIM
WEST    BEDROOM - ALL  OAK  TRIM
  2 - WINDOW  STOOL   3/4" x 2½" x 3'-6"
  2 -   "     APRON   5/8" x 2¼" x 3'-6"
  2 -   "     CASINGS 4/16" x 2¼" x 3'-6"
  4 -   "       "     4/16" x 2¼" x 4'-0"
  1   DOOR  JAMB    5¼" x 2'-6" x 6'-8"
  1    "     "      5¼" x 5'-0" x 6'-8"
  2    "    CASINGS 4/16" x 2¼" x 2'-6"
  2    "      "     4/16" x 2¼" x 5'-6"
  8    "      "     4/16" x 2¼" x 7'-0"
  BASE BOARD   ½" x 3½" x 62 LIN. FT.
  BASE SHOE    ½" x 3/4" x 62 LIN. FT.
  HOOK STRIP (PINE) ½" x 3½" x 12 LIN. FT.
  CLOSET  POLE        1¼" x 6'-0"
  CLOSET  SHELF (PINE) 3/4" x 12" x 6'-0"
SOUTH  BEDROOM - ALL OAK TRIM
  2 - WINDOW STOOL   3/4" x 2¼" x 3'-6"
  2   "     APRON    5/8" x 2¼" x 3'-6"

DOORS — EXTERIOR - SOLID CORE (FLUSH OAK)
  1 - 1¾" x 3'-0" x 6'-8"
  1 - 1¾" x 2'-8" x 6'-8"
DOORS — INTERIOR - HOLLOW CORE (FLUSH OAK)
  8 - 1⅜" x 2'-6" x 6'-8"
  2 - 1⅜" x 2'-4" x 6'-8"
  3 - 1⅜" x 2'-0" x 6'-8"
  4 - 1⅜" x 1'-8" x 6'-8"
```

FIGURE 14-3 Millwork takeoff.

Door jambs are listed by the type of material, the width of the jamb (usually equal to the wall thickness), the width of the opening, and the height of the opening, along with the number of each size needed.

Door casings and doorstops can be listed at the same time that the jambs are listed. This is usually done by itemizing the kind of material, the number of pieces, the size or pattern, and the lengths of the various pieces of casing and stop needed for each door opening.

Windows may need several different types of trim. Each window is listed separately, and the lengths and sizes of the various trim members indicated, along with the kind of material. Individual items which must be listed in lineal feet with sufficient allowance for waste are subjambs (if needed), window stool, apron, casing, stops, and mullion casings.

Base trim is listed in lineal feet. Items which are included in base trim include baseboards, base moldings, and base shoe. When listing base trim, the perimeter of the room is taken, without regard for door openings, as the lineal footage of base needed. The pattern, kind of material, and size of the various base-trim pieces must be listed, along with the total lineal footage needed.

Hook strip is listed in lineal feet, along with the size and kind of material.

Closet poles are listed by the length and size of each individual piece needed.

Shelving is listed by the thickness, width, length, and kind of material of each piece needed.

Thresholds are listed by the thickness, width, length, kind of material, and number of pieces needed.

Other items of interior trim may be listed by the unit (each piece), as for turned columns and plints, or by the lineal foot, as for various types of moldings and overlap.

CABINETS

Cabinets are often included under the heading of finish carpentry or millwork. However, because they can be a large part of a job they may be listed under a separate heading.

Cabinets are usually described on the estimate form

by their location, type (such as base cabinet, wall cabinet, etc.), and length and material they are made of. The pricing of cabinets is usually done by the manufacturer, and the manufacturer's price is simply listed on the estimate.

Care must be taken, when listing cabinet prices in this manner, to make sure that all items, such as counter tops, drawer and door hardware, glass, shelves, etc., are included.

STAIRS AND HANDRAILS

Stairs consist of treads, risers, and stringers, along with the necessary handrailing. The individual parts of the stair may be listed on the estimate sheet along with their thickness, width, length, type of material, and the number of pieces.

Stairs, like cabinets, may also be listed on the estimate as a unit. When this is done, the location, the number of risers, and the type of material are stated on the estimate form, and the price entered is for the complete unit as supplied by the mill.

Handrails are listed in lineal feet for straight railing. Curved members, such as easements, curves, goosenecks, etc., are listed and priced by the piece. The kind of material and rail pattern must also be listed.

Newel posts and balusters are listed by the piece, length, style, and type of material.

DOORS

A number of different types of doors can be found on a typical job. Exterior doors are usually $1\frac{3}{4}$ inches thick. They may be paneled doors made of white pine or other material which is weather-resistant, or they may be flush doors of either solid-core or hollow-core construction. Interior doors are usually $1\frac{3}{8}$ inches thick, of either panel construction or flush hollow-core construction.

The size and type of doors required can be found on the door schedule included with the floor plan. Sometimes, in the absence of a door schedule, the size and type of door are given on the plan at each door location. Information on doors is also found in the specifications.

Doors are listed on the estimate form under a division heading of doors. The location of the doors by floor, identification number, or room is listed on the form, followed by the thickness, width, height, and type of door. Often similar doors are grouped under the heading. Then the number of identical doors is also listed (see Figure 14-3).

Table 14-3 Amounts of Nails Required
for Various Types of Finish Carpentry

Cornice work	1 lb per 100 lin ft of cornice material
Siding:	
6d	6 lb per 1,000 sq ft
7d	$6\frac{1}{2}$ lb per 1,000 sq ft
8d	9 lb per 1,000 sq ft
10d	11 lb per 1,000 sq ft
Frames, 16d casing	$\frac{1}{5}$ lb per frame
Door trim	$\frac{1}{2}$ lb per opening
Window trim	$\frac{1}{4}$ lb per side
Baseboard	1 lb per 100 lin ft
Base cap	2 lb per 1,000 lin ft
Base shoe	2 lb per 1,000 lin ft

NAILS

Finish carpentry will require a number of different sizes of nails in varying amounts for different types of work. Exterior finish work will require nails resistant to the weather and will be made of aluminum, stainless steel, or steel with hot-dipped galvanizing. Interior finish work requires a number of different-size finish nails, casing nails, and even wood screws for some work. The amounts of nails required for various types of finish work can be found in Table 14-3.

LABOR

Labor costs are generally based on a contractor's previous experience with a similar type of work. The amount of work needed will vary with the type of material being installed and the job conditions.

A beginner in finish-carpentry labor estimating may use the information in Table 14-4 to determine the amount of time needed for the installation of various trim members. In estimating labor costs a sufficient allowance should be made for delays due to material shortage, improper equipment, or job conditions.

Table 14-4   Labor Requirements for
Finish Carpentry

Interior

Plain window casings	$1\frac{1}{4}$ hr per side
Backband window casings	$1\frac{1}{2}$ hr per side
Molded window casings	2 hr per side
Plain door casings	1 hr per side
Backband door casings	$1\frac{1}{4}$ hr per side
Molded door casings	$1\frac{1}{2}$ hr per side
Jambs and stops	$1\frac{1}{2}$ hr per set
Oak doors and hardware	$2\frac{1}{2}$ hr each
Pine doors and hardware	$1\frac{1}{2}$ hr each
Hardwood base	12 hr per 100 lin ft
Pine base	9 hr per 100 lin ft
Base floor mold	4 hr per 100 lin ft
Picture molding	$4\frac{1}{2}$ hr per 100 lin ft
Cove cornice	13 hr per 100 lin ft
Two-member cornice	26 hr per 100 lin ft
Chair rail	10 hr per 100 lin ft

Exterior

Plain outlookers	$\frac{1}{4}$ hr each
Facia	8 hr per 100 lin ft
Plancier	8 hr per 100 lin ft
Verge boards	13 hr per 100 lin ft
Crown or bed mold	5 hr per 100 lin ft
Cove or quarter round	3 hr per 100 lin ft
Single window frame	$\frac{1}{2}$ hr each
Mullion window frame	1 hr each
Triple window frame	$1\frac{1}{4}$ hr each
Door frame	1 hr each
Entry door	2 hr each
Screen or storm door	$1\frac{1}{2}$ hr each

EQUIPMENT

Equipment needs for finish-carpentry work may include saw-horses, work benches, small power tools, extension cords, router templates, lock-installation jigs, and scaffolding. The cost of this and other equipment must be considered and charged to the job on a prorated basis.

EXERCISES

1 Into what classifications may finish carpentry be divided?

2 Outline the procedure for estimating exterior trim.

3 How are door and window frames listed on the estimate?

4 How is wood siding estimated?

5 Outline the procedure for estimating finish flooring (strip, parquet, underlayment).

6 Outline the procedure for estimating the various items of interior trim.

7 How are cabinets listed and priced on the estimate?

8 Outline the procedure for estimating stairs and handrails.

9 Outline the procedure for estimating doors.

10 Outline the procedure for estimating labor requirements for interior carpentry work.

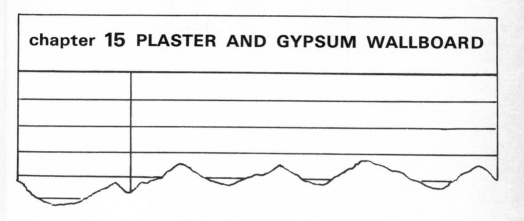

chapter 15 PLASTER AND GYPSUM WALLBOARD

INTRODUCTION

The heading for the plastering division is sometimes Lathing and Plastering. It usually includes all the work done by the lathers and plasterers.

Plaster is applied directly to brickwork, terra-cotta blocks, gypsum blocks, and other masonry and on wood or metal lath and plasterboards. Stucco, which is just exterior plastering, is included under this heading. Metal corner beads and the iron hangers installed by metal lathers in suspended ceiling construction also come under this heading.

Grounds are wooden strips made to a uniform thickness, which are applied by the carpenters and belong under the heading Carpentry. They are installed to act as guides for the surface of the plaster. They serve as stops against which the plaster is finished and also provide a means of fastening the trim to the walls. Grounds of $\frac{3}{4}$-inch thickness are required when two coats of plaster are applied on gypsum lath or masonry. Grounds $\frac{3}{4}$ inch thick are also required for three-coat work on metal lath.

There are many kinds of plaster and stucco materials and finishes. Prepared plasters, already mixed or partly mixed, are now in general use.

Gypsum wallboard, or drywall as it is often called,

is used extensively on walls and partitions in residential and commercial construction. Most applications of gypsum wallboard are ½-inch-thick material applied directly to the studs. The joints between sheets are reinforced with perforated tape and finished with joint cement. All nails or screws are also finished with joint cement. Gypsum wallboard is often given a sand coat finish, which has the appearance of plaster.

Various thin-coat-plaster systems are in use for walls and ceilings. These systems use a special gypsum board base. The sheets are fastened to the building framework with screws or nails in a similar manner as for gypsum wallboard. The joints between sheets are reinforced with glass fiber mesh. One or two coats of specially formulated plaster are applied over the entire area for a thickness of about ⅛ inch.

PLASTER BASES AND ACCESSORIES

Lath plaster bases may be divided into two categories, gypsum lath and expanded metal lath.

Gypsum lath is available in a number of types and sizes. The most commonly used gypsum lath comes in sheets ⅜ inch thick by 16 inches wide by 48 inches long. It is also manufactured on ½-inch thickness for use on walls with studs 24 inches on centers.

Perforated gypsum lath is identical with regular ⅜-inch gypsum lath, except that it contains ¾-inch holes on 4-inch centers over the entire surface. It is used to key the plaster to the lath in walls where increased fire resistance is needed.

Insulating gypsum lath is plain lath with an aluminum foil laminated to the back. The foil serves as a vapor barrier and insulation.

Long-length gypsum lath is 24 inches wide and manufactured in special lengths up to 12 feet. It is made in ½- and 1-inch thicknesses for use in solid gypsum plaster partitions and can also be used as furring over exterior masonry walls.

Metal lath is available in two types, diamond-mesh and ribbed-metal lath. The diamond mesh is available in weights of 2.5 pounds and 3.4 pounds per square yard. Ribbed metal lath is more rigid than diamond-mesh lath and is used on ceilings or in partitions where rigidity is required. The various types of ribbed lath are available in weights of 2.75, 3.4, and 4 pounds per square yard.

Trim accessories used with lath and plaster include outside corner beads of various types, inside corner reinforcement, screeds, and casing beads.

Cold-rolled-steel channel furring for use in fireproof construction is available in $\frac{3}{4}$-, $1\frac{1}{2}$-, and 2-inch heights and in 16- and 20-foot lengths. Tie wire for tying metal lath to channels is available in 50-pound coils and 25-pound hanks of 28-inch straight lengths. Hanger wire for suspending the channels is available in 50-pound coils.

PLASTERING MATERIALS

The three main categories of plaster materials are base-coat plasters, aggregates, and finish plasters. Base-coat plasters are used for the purpose of building up wall thickness and to provide a base for the finish plaster. Several types of base-coat plasters are available. These include gypsum neat plaster (often called gypsum cement plaster) to which aggregate and water must be added, gypsum ready-mixed plaster which includes mill-proportioned aggregates and requires only the addition of mixing water, gypsum wood-fibered plaster which requires only the addition of mixing water, and gypsum bond plaster which is formulated for application on interior monolithic concrete surfaces. Gypsum bond plaster is factory-prepared and requires only the addition of mixing water on the job site.

Aggregates for gypsum plaster include sand, perlite, vermiculite, and wood fibers. The most commonly used aggregate is sand. Sand used as plaster aggregate must be clean and contain a proper gradation of sand particles. Perlite is a volcanic glass which is mined and processed to produce a light plaster aggregate. Plaster with perlite aggregate weighs about one-half of plaster using sand aggregate. Vermiculite is another aggregate. It produces plaster which is more fire-resistant than plaster using sand aggregate. However, it also produces plaster

of lower strength than either sand or perlite aggregate an
must be carefully proportioned in the plaster mix.

Finishing plasters include hydrated lime, gauging plas
ter, Keen's cement, and acoustical plaster. Hydrated lim
is quicklime which has been partially hydrated during th
manufacturing process. It requires soaking in water or slak
ing for as much as twenty-four hours on the job befor
it can be used. Gauging plasters are specially groun
gypsum plasters which are added to the lime after slakin
to promote setting of the lime plaster. Keen's cement i
a gypsum plaster which is slower setting than gauging plas
ter. It is used when a hard plaster surface is requirec

Acoustical plasters are designed to absorb sound. The
are usually ready-mixed plasters requiring only the additio
of mixing water on the job. Most acoustical plaster is ma
chine-applied. Because acoustical plaster is softer than cor
ventional plaster finishes, it is limited to ceiling application
or parts of walls where abrasion will not be encountered.

ESTIMATING MATERIALS FOR LATHING AND PLASTERING

The work included under this heading is measured by th
square yard for flat surfaces and by the linear foot fo
moldings, cornices, corner beads, etc. Some estimator
make no deductions for the openings. Some take half o
these outs. Still others take no outs of less than 21 squar
feet and therefore would measure an average wall or parti
tion as though it had no windows or doors. Although th
last of these methods seems to be the one most commonl
used, it is best to state at the very beginning of the plaster
ing estimate which method is being used. In this way any
body reading the estimate will note the method adopted
and disputes will be avoided. Similarly, in bids and cor
respondence in which the method of measuring is con
cerned, it is a wise precaution to state which method i
assumed.

Care must be taken in listing the work to see tha
all the items are included. Not only are room walls an
ceilings plastered, but also walls and ceilings in passage
ways, halls, and storage rooms and bulkheads. Soffits o
stairs, landings, mezzanine platforms, and showrooms ofte

have work under this heading. In addition to the lathing and plastering, there are items of corner beads, arches, and outside plastering, or stucco, to be considered.

The student should not become too much bound by definite rules of procedure in estimating any trade. All the work should be written up, however, so that the estimate of the proposed building represents a complete story. The test of a good estimate is the ease with which another estimator can understand every item. With plastering work, care should be taken to separate the listing of the quantities into many parts, depending on the location in the building, the kind of plastering, the number of coats involved, the kind of lathing, etc. In this way the estimate may readily be checked or adjusted, and what is more important, it may be priced at proper cost prices to suit each individual item or group of items.

It is recommended that the work for each floor be kept separate from that of other floors. In this way, one large error, such as omitting an entire floor, is less likely to occur. Concentrating on one floor, the estimator of little experience will find it easier to visualize the work shown on the plans.

An illustration of part of an estimate in plastering is given in Figure 15-1. Note the general form of layout and the systematic arrangement of minor headings and the figures. The totals are extended for the quantities, and suitable prices are applied.

Gypsum lath may be priced by the piece (16 by 48 inches), by the bundle (six $\frac{3}{8}$- or four $\frac{1}{2}$-inch-thick pieces per bundle) or per 1,000 square feet. Most often the amount of gypsum lath needed is stated by the number of bundles or the total area, with the thickness and type noted.

Metal lath is priced by the square yard for each weight and type or by the pound for each type. To determine the amount of metal lath needed, a percentage for waste is added to the total area and the amount of lath stated, listing the type, weight, and total area in square yards (see Table 15-1).

Channels and metal furring required for metal lathing in suspended ceilings, etc., are usually priced by the pound. The amount of material needed is determined by allowing

	EST. 522													SHEET II				

PLASTERING

(FULL OUTS TAKEN)

BASEMENT

Stair walls, on T.C. blks.
  2 × 25'-0" × 12'-0"   6 0 0
  OUTS   2 × 3-0 × 7-0   — 4 2
                            9) 5 5 8
                              6 2 yds 1.70   1 0 5

FIRST FLOOR

Corridor walls, on T.C. & Gyp. blks.
  N.   100' — 0"
  E.   155 — 4
  S.   101 — 4
  W.   122 — 0
      478 — 8 × 14-0   6 7 0 1
  OUTS
      6 × 6-0 × 8-0   288
      24 × 3-0 × 7-0   504   — 7 9 2
                       792 9) 5 9 0 9
                            6 5 5 yds 1.60   1 0 4 8

Show room walls, on Gyp. blks.
      84 — 0
      55 — 0
      117 — 6
      97 — 6
      354 — 0 × 14-0   4 9 5 6
  OUTS
      3 × 6-0 × 8-0   144
      22 × 3-0 × 7-0   462
      1 × 12-0 × 8-0   96   — 7 0 2
                       702 9) 4 2 5 4
                            4 7 3 yds 1.60   7 5 7

                              FWD. 1 9 1 0

FIGURE 15-1 Plastering estimate.

a certain number of pounds per square yard for each type required (see Table 15-2).

Corner beading, etc., is priced by the lineal foot or per stock length piece. Each type and size of corner beading, screeding, casing beads, etc., is listed separately. The total lineal footage of each type is determined, and an allowance of about 5 percent is added for waste before pricing.

Plaster materials for base coats and the finish coat are priced by the ton or by the sack of 100 pounds. The amounts of the various materials needed per 100 square yards are given in Table 15-3. When figuring the cost of plastering materials, the estimator should make an allowance for the cost of water.

Table 15-1 Metal Lath Allowances for Waste and Lapping

Type of Work	Allowance, %
Plain surfaces	5–10
Beams, columns, etc.	10–15
Cornices	20–25
Doomed and irregular surfaces	25–30

Table 15-2 Channels and Metal Furring Required per Square Yard of Wall or Ceiling Surface

Size, In.	Amount per Square Yard, Lb
$\frac{3}{4}$	5–15
$1\frac{1}{2}$	$\frac{1}{2}$–5
2	1–5

Table 15-3 Approximate Amounts of Materials Required per 100 Square Yards of Plastered Walls and Ceilings

Plaster Base	Application	Material	Quantity
Gypsum lath	Brown coat	Gypsum plaster	1,100 lb
		Sand	$1\frac{1}{2}$ cu yd
Metal lath	Scratch and brown coats	Gypsum plaster	1800 lb
		Sand	2 cu yd
Unit masonry	Brown coat	Gypsum plaster	1,110 lb
		Sand	$1\frac{1}{2}$ cu yd
	Finish coat	Hydrated lime	300 lb
		Gauging plaster	50 lb
		Sand	$\frac{1}{3}$ cu yd

ESTIMATING LABOR FOR LATHING AND PLASTERING

The labor cost estimate for lathing and plastering will be based on the contractor's previous experience for the type of work being estimate. Generally, three types of workmen must be considered: lathers who will install the lath, plasterers who will actually apply and finish the plaster, and laborers who will build scaffolds, mix plaster, supply materials, and do the general cleanup work.

The time required to complete the various kinds of lathing and plastering jobs will vary with the skill of the workmen and the type of job. Jobs requiring large amounts of scaffolding and long material-hauling distances will obviously cost more per square yard than jobs requiring little or no scaffolding or shorter material-hauling distances. The estimator must take into consideration all the various job factors before deciding on a unit cost for labor. A beginner in estimating may use the labor output in Table 15-4 to get an idea of the amount of time required for various phases of lath and plaster work.

ESTIMATING EQUIPMENT FOR LATHING AND PLASTERING

Equipment needs will vary with the size of the job. The most commonly needed equipment includes ladders, scaffolding, planking, plasterboards and horses, hods, mixers, shovels, and small hand tools. The estimator should make a careful analysis of the equipment needed for each job and include its cost in the estimate.

GYPSUM DRYWALL MATERIALS

Gypsum drywall is available in sheets $\frac{1}{4}$, $\frac{3}{8}$, $\frac{1}{2}$, and $\frac{5}{8}$ inch thick. The sheets are 48 inches wide and available in lengths from 6 to 16 feet.

Various metal accessories are available for use with gypsum drywall. These include various types of corner beads and of channels for edge trim around door and window openings or elsewhere where a finished edge is required. These accessories are available in 6 feet 8 inches and in 7-, 8-, and 10-foot lengths, depending on the type.

Gypsum drywall may be fastened to the building framework with nails, screws, or an adhesive. A number of different types of nails and screws are manufactured specifically for drywall applications. Special adhesives are sometimes used in addition to nails to attach the drywall to the framework.

Table 15-4 Approximate Labor Output— Lathing and Plastering

Lathing	Hr per 100 sq ft
Gypsum lath	.5–1.0
Metal lath on wood furring	.5–2.0
Metal lath on metal furring	.7–2.0

Plastering (per coat)	Hr per 100 sq yd
Scratch or brown coat	6
Finish coat	6–12

Joint compound and perforated paper tape are used to conceal all joints. The compound is available dry in 5- and 25-pound bags or ready-mixed in 1- and 5-gallon cans. The perforated tape is available in 60-, 250-, and 500-foot rolls.

Gypsum drywall is often finished with some type of texturing material which gives it the appearance of sand float or textured plaster. Depending on the type, these texturing materials may be applied by brush, by paint roller, or by spraying.

ESTIMATING DRYWALL MATERIALS

The unit of measurement for gypsum drywall is the square foot. To estimate the amount of gypsum wallboard required, the areas of the walls and ceilings are determined in the same manner as for plaster. The areas are figured without regard for door and window openings. Only large openings are listed as outs. After the net total area of drywall required is determined, the number of sheets needed is found by dividing the net area by the area of one sheet and rounding off to the next full sheet.

The amount of nails, screws, tape, joint compound, and texturing materials needed is based on the area of drywall installed. Table 15-5 gives the amounts of various materials needed for 1,000 square feet of drywall.

Corner beads, edge beads, etc., are figured by the lineal foot. Each type is listed separately and identified as to location. The total lineal footage of each type is divided by the length of one piece to determine the number of pieces needed.

Table 15-5 Fastening and Finishing Materials Required for 1,000-square feet Gypsum Drywall

Material	Amount
$1\frac{1}{4}''$ annular ring nail	$6\frac{1}{4}$ lb
$1\frac{3}{8}''$ annular ring nail	$6\frac{3}{4}$ lb
1″ drywall screw	3 lb
$1\frac{1}{4}''$ drywall screw	$4\frac{1}{4}$ lb
$1\frac{5}{8}''$ drywall screw	$5\frac{1}{2}$ lb
Joint compound	50 lb
Perforated tape	360 to 400 ft
Texture paint	10 to 50 lb

Different drywall adhesives have different coverage capabilities. It is therefore recommended that the estimator check the coverage for the type of material to be used.

ESTIMATING DRYWALL LABOR

Cost of labor for drywall installation is based on the contractor's previous experience with a similar type of work. In some parts of the country, drywall is installed by carpenters and taped and finished by painters. In other parts of the country, other trades may do the installation and finishing. The estimator must be careful to take the various trades into consideration when preparing the estimate for drywalling costs. Table 15-6 gives some probable labor outputs for drywall installations.

ESTIMATING EQUIPMENT FOR DRYWALL INSTALLATIONS

Equipment needed for drywall installation will include ladders, scaffolding, sawhorses, electric screwdrivers, extension cords, taping machines, and small hand tools. The cost of equipment needed for the job must be considered and allowed for in the estimate of drywall installation, just as it is in all other types of work. Equipment costs are often determined from the contractor's cost records from previous jobs of similar nature.

Table 15-6 Approximate Labor Output
for Drywall Application

Type of Work	Hr per 1,000 Sq Ft
Gypsum wallboard application:	
Walls	18
Ceilings	24
Joint finishing	8–10
Texture painting (spray-on)	$\frac{1}{2}$–3

EXERCISES

1 In an estimate, what work is included under the heading of Lathing and Plastering?

2 What is the unit of measurement for lathing and plastering work?

3 Make a sketch plan of a plastered bedroom and closet, showing dimensions, and prepare a quantity survey of all the lathing and plastering work involved.

4 What is the unit of measurement for gypsum drywall?

5 Using the sketch in Exercise 3, prepare a quantity survey for the gypsum drywall.

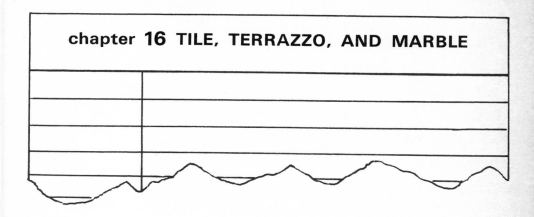

chapter 16 TILE, TERRAZZO, AND MARBLE

INTRODUCTION

Tile, terrazzo, and marble are three separate lines of work. Some subcontractors handle two or all three of them, others only one. Slate also is handled by marble subcontractors.

Plain floors and walls are measured by the square foot. Stair treads, door saddles, sills, and other such members are counted and priced per piece. Special items and special features require careful analysis of the shopwork and field labor required.

Bathroom-wall accessories are generally included under the Tile heading. For estimating their cost the type, size, and number of each are listed.

Plain bathroom-type tile flooring costs the general contractor about $1.50 per square foot, and tile wainscoting about $2 per square foot. Accessories cost $5 to $10 each. Medicine cabinets and other large fittings cost $30 to $70 each for the usual sizes and types, but these are often included under separate headings or may be listed under the Carpentry heading.

Marble floor and wall covering runs about $6 to $7 per square foot. Matched or molded marble may run to $9 per square foot.

Terrazzo flooring costs about $1.75 per square foot, but if only a small area is involved, a minimum of about

$250 is charged because of the expense of transporting the equipment and organizing the work of installation.

TILE

Tile is made in many different materials, colors, and sizes. Ceramic tile is a clay composition with glazed or unglazed surfaces. Metal tile is made of stainless steel, copper, aluminum, or porcelain-surfaced metal. Plastic tile is also available. All are made in individual tiles and in sheets of tiles or in sheets scored to look like tiles. Special tile shapes are made for corners, bases, caps, etc., and these are made of metal or plastic for use with either plastic or metal tile.

The unit of measurement for flat tile work is the square foot. Tile base, capping, and corners are figured by the lineal foot. Tile work for the various rooms is listed separately. Tile of different colors for each room is also separated, and each type of tile is also listed separately to make pricing easier.

The installation of tile work is done by tilesetters, who work for firms that specialize in tile work. In preparing an estimate, the estimator generally uses the tile bid submitted by the subcontractor. As a check, however, he may apply known unit costs to the tile areas to see if the subcontractor's bid is in line.

TERRAZZO

Terrazzo is a marblelike composition used for flooring, base, and stair treads, and occasionally for wainscoting and other uses. It is a plastic mixture of cement, sand, and marble chips, about 1 inch thick, mixed almost dry, and poured over a layer of concrete or cement mortar. It is then rolled with a heavy roller, and the surface is finally honed and polished with machines. The quality and color of the surface are determined by the selection of marble chips used.

Terrazzo floors are generally divided into panels, bands, or design patterns by the use of brass, zinc, or other strips, which are set in place before the first layer is poured. The strips extend up to the finish-floor level.

Wire mesh is often incorporated in the first course or laid under it. Precast terrazzo tiles, treads, base, and other members are also available.

The unit of measurement for flat terrazzo work is the square foot. Terrazzo work for each floor is listed separately. Special work for inlays of maps, figures, etc., is also kept under a separate heading because of the extra cost involved.

Terrazzo base is often listed separately, with the height, thickness, and lineal footage.

Stair treads and risers are also listed separately. The width of the stair is noted, along with the height of the riser and tread width. The number of steps is also indicated.

Terrazzo work is done by companies that specialize in that type of work. The estimator usually enters the bid of a terrazzo contractor when preparing his general estimate. As a check on the subcontractor's bid, the estimator should make his own takeoff and apply unit costs from previous jobs to see if the bid is in line. He should also check to make sure that each item of terrazzo work is included in the bid.

MARBLE

Marble and slate are made in thin slabs and special shapes and serve for flooring, base, door saddles, hearths, counter tops, shelves, toilet-stall partitions, and many other uses. Thick marble is handled by stonesetters and is therefore estimated under the Stonework heading. Thin marble used for facings and other purposes is put in place by marblesetters.

The unit of measurement for marble work on floors and walls is the square foot. As with other types of work, each different type of marble work is listed separately and properly identified, with the thickness, width, and height noted.

Bases, caps, and shelves are usually figured by the lineal foot, the thickness and width being noted.

As with terrazzo and tile, marble is installed by contractors who specialize in that type of work. Before the estimator includes a bid from a marble contractor in his estimate, he should complete his own takeoff and check the marble bid against his own work to make sure that there are no omissions and that the price is in line.

EXERCISES

1   What is terrazzo work?
2   How are prices for terrazzo work obtained?
3   What is tile work?
4   What type of work is entered under the Marble heading?

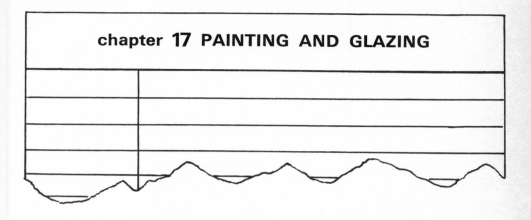

chapter **17 PAINTING AND GLAZING**

INTRODUCTION

The painting subcontract generally takes in all painting, papering, and wood finishing to be done at the job site. It is usually divided into separate categories for outside and inside work. The outside work may be divided into categories for wall painting and outside trim, which would include painting doors and windows. Inside work may be divided into separate categories for finishing wood or metal trim, finishing windows, finishing doors, painting walls and ceilings, and wallpapering.

PAINTING INTERIOR WALLS AND CEILINGS

The unit of measurement for painting walls and ceilings is the square (100 square feet). In preparing an estimate for painting walls and ceilings, each area requiring a different type of finish is listed under a separate heading. That is, all rooms requiring flat paint will be listed together, and those requiring enamel or some other finish will be listed in appropriate groups.

When figuring wall areas for painting, most estimators do not consider door and window openings, because the saving in paint is more than offset by the cost of trimming around these openings. The size of each wall and ceiling is listed on the estimate form on a separate line (see Figure 17-1). The area of each wall and ceiling is extended and used as a basis for determining the amount of paint needed and the labor cost involved.

The area of coverage for a gallon of paint will vary with the type of paint and the type of surface being painted. The coverage will also vary with each coat applied, the

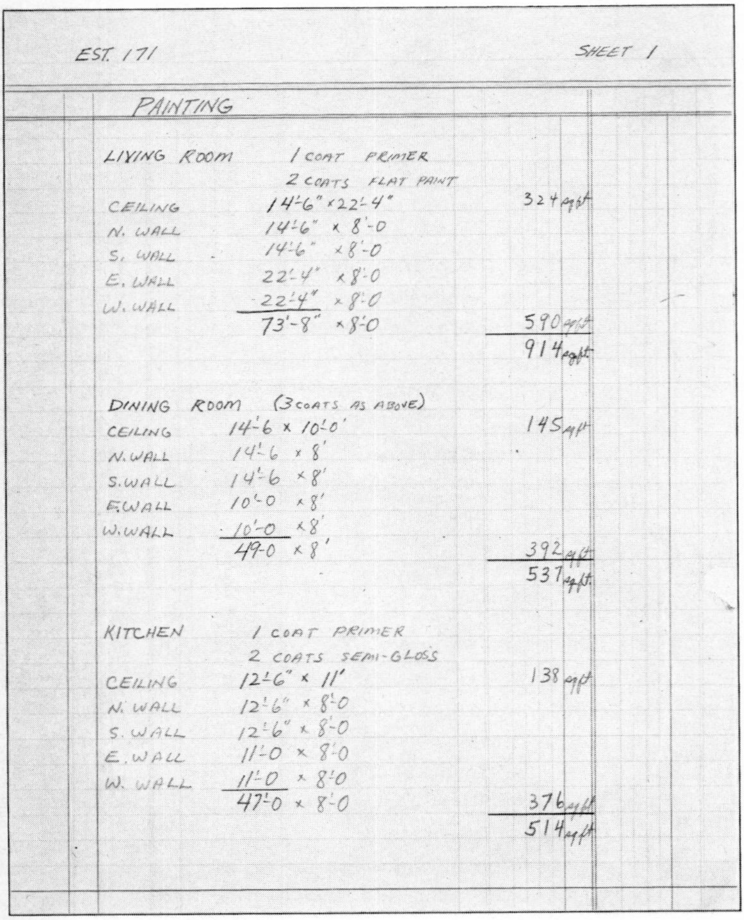

EST. 171   SHEET 1

PAINTING

LIVING ROOM   1 COAT PRIMER
                   2 COATS FLAT PAINT
CEILING   14'-6" x 22'-4"   324 sq ft
N. WALL   14'-6" x 8'-0
S. WALL   14'-6" x 8'-0
E. WALL   22'-4" x 8'-0
W. WALL   22'-4" x 8'-0
                   73'-8" x 8'-0   590 sq ft
                                               914 sq ft

DINING ROOM   (3 COATS AS ABOVE)
CEILING   14'-6 x 10'-0'   145 sq ft
N. WALL   14'-6 x 8'
S. WALL   14'-6 x 8'
E. WALL   10'-0 x 8'
W. WALL   10'-0 x 8'
                   49-0 x 8'   392 sq ft
                                               537 sq ft

KITCHEN   1 COAT PRIMER
                   2 COATS SEMI-GLOSS
CEILING   12'-6" x 11'   138 sq ft
N. WALL   12'-6" x 8'-0
S. WALL   12'-6" x 8'-0
E. WALL   11'-0 x 8'-0
W. WALL   11'-0 x 8'-0
                   47'-0 x 8'-0   376 sq ft
                                               514 sq ft

FIGURE 17-1   Painting takeoff.

first coat requiring more paint than the second or third coat. When determining paint requirements, the estimator should check with paint coverage charts supplied by the manufacturer of the product for calculating the amount of paint needed. Care should be taken to figure each coat needed and to note where different primer and finish coats are required. When coverage charts are not available, the estimator may assume an approximate coverage rate of 400 square feet per gallon.

Labor costs are based on the amount of time it takes to paint a given area with a specified kind of paint. The time requirements are determined from the contractor's cost records for a previous job of similar nature. The time requirements are usually stated as hours per square for each type of work.

When calculating the time required to do a certain amount of work, the estimator should keep in mind that varying job conditions will change the amount of time necessary to do a job. The skill and inclination of workmen also vary and must be considered as changing cost factors. By considering all these items, the estimator can avoid many of the pitfalls in labor cost estimating. Table 17-1 gives

Table 17-1 Approximate Labor Required
for Various Types of Painting

	Hr per *100 Sq Ft per Coat*
Exterior work	
Wood siding	.6
Doors and windows	.7
Cornice and trim work	.75
Interior work	
Trim (one lineal foot = one square foot):	
Staining	.6
Varnishing	1.0
Painting	1.0
Painting walls and ceilings	.75
Floors:	
Varnishing or sealing	.6
Waxing	.6

some approximate labor requirements for different types of painting.

Equipment needed for painting interior walls and ceilings may vary from a few drop cloths, stepladders, and extension planks to many drop cloths, ladders, and scaffolding. Brushes, rollers, and spray equipment must also be considered when estimating equipment costs. Each job must be carefully analyzed to determine equipment needs before that cost can accurately be charged to the job.

PAINTING EXTERIOR WALLS

The unit of measurement for painting exterior walls is the square. The surface areas of exterior walls are determined without regard for door and window openings in the same manner as interior wall surfaces. It is good practice to list each wall surface on a separate line of the estimate sheet by identifying it as to location and indicating its width and height. The areas can then be extended and totaled.

As with interior work, exterior walls requiring different finishes are listed separately so that they may be priced in accordance with the finish requirements. The coverage capabilities of different exterior finishes vary, and the estimator should check with the manufacturer's coverage charts to determine how much paint or other finish is required for a given area. When coverage charts are unavailable, the estimator may make a rough estimate by allowing 1 gallon of paint per 400 square feet of wood siding. Other surfaces may require more or less paint for a given area.

In addition to paint, the estimator should allow for paint thinners needed for cleanup, as well as thinning paints. He should also allow about 1 pound of putty for every 1,000 square feet for patching nail holes in the exterior work.

Labor requirements for painting exterior walls are based on the contractor's cost records for previous jobs of a similar nature. A beginner in estimating may use the information in Table 17-1 to approximate the labor requirements for exterior painting.

Equipment for painting outside walls may include extension ladders, stepladders, scaffolding, and planking, in addition to the usual brushes, rollers, etc.

FINISHING INTERIOR TRIM, DOORS, AND WINDOWS

Interior trim, doors, and windows finished with different types of materials are listed under separate headings for each type of finish required.

Trim members such as casings, base, and jambs are listed in lineal feet. In figuring the area of these members it is assumed that a lineal foot of trim less than 1 foot wide is equal to a square foot. This is done because the time required to finish these narrow members is nearly equal to that for finishing a square foot of surface and offsets the saving in finishing material. Generally, the trim for each room is listed as a group under the room heading. Listing it in this manner makes it easy to check that the trim in any room has not been omitted.

Doors are listed as to location, number, and size. When extending the area of doors, the estimator should include the area of the edges. He should keep in mind that the door has two sides, and include the area of both sides in the estimator. An easy way to measure the area of a door is to add the thickness to the width, multiply by the height, and multiply by 2 to get the area of both sides. The total area extended for all doors having a given type of finish is used to determine the amount of finishing materials needed and for estimating labor costs.

Windows are listed as to location, number, and size. The size is usually listed as the overall size, including the trim around the window. The overall area, including the glass area, is used as a basis for determining the amount of paint and labor needed for the windows.

Labor output is generally determined from the contractor's previous experience with a similar type of work. To get an idea of the approximate amount of labor needed for finishing interior trim, the information in Table 17-1 may be used.

Equipment costs are determined in a similar manner as for interior and exterior walls.

PAINTING EXTERIOR TRIM, DOORS, AND WINDOWS

Exterior trim is listed as to location, type, and size. In trim less than 12 inches wide, a lineal foot is assumed to be a square foot. When trim members are wider than

12 inches, the area is usually calculated for purposes of determining paint and labor requirements.

Exterior doors are listed as to location, type, number, and size. Glass areas in the doors are considered as part of the area requiring painting; so no deductions are necessary. As with interior doors, the thickness of the door is added to the width when determining the area. Doors requiring different finishes on each side are listed under appropriate headings. That is, an entrance door may require an interior-type finish on one side and exterior paint on the other. One side of the door would be listed under interior work, and the other side would be listed with doors under exterior work.

Exterior windows are listed as to location, type, number, and size. The size is generally taken as the overall width and height of the frame. The entire area, including glass, is used as a basis for determining the amount of paint and labor required for painting the windows.

Screen and storm-window painting costs are based on the overall size of the units, including screen and glass areas. When estimating painting costs for screens and storms, the estimator must remember that both sides require paint, and include them in the estimate.

The amount of paint needed for exterior trim work is based on the area to be covered. Coverage will vary with the type of material and surface being painted. Paint coverage may be determined from paint manufacturers' charts or from the contractor's past experience with a similar type of work. Lacking any other information, an estimator may assume a coverage of 500 to 600 square feet per gallon of paint.

Labor requirements for this type of work are based on the contractor's previous experience with similar work.

Equipment requirements for exterior trim, doors, and windows are the same as for painting exterior walls.

FINISHING FLOORS

The unit of measurement for estimating floor finishing costs may be either the square or the square foot. When determining the area of the floor to be finished, the inside room dimensions are used. These dimensions are listed under appropriate room headings. Areas requiring different types of finishes are put in separate groupings. The areas to be finished are totaled for each group, and the totals are used as a basis for determining material and labor requirements.

Floors may be given one or more coats of finish material. After the area to be finished is determined, the amount of material for each coat must be found and listed. The cost of the material is then found and entered in the proper column.

Labor costs will vary with the type of finish being used because it takes less time to apply some finishes than others. The labor required is based on the type of finish and the output per hour. The labor output is determined from the contractor's cost records for similar work on previous jobs.

Equipment costs are usually small and may require only brushes and rollers for applying the finish, along with brooms and rags for cleaning. In some cases a power buffer may be needed. It is the estimator's job to determine what will be required and to allow for its cost in the estimate.

WALL PAPERING

Wallpaper is available in many different patterns and types of material. Standard-size rolls of wallpaper are 18 inches wide, 24 feet long, and cover 36 square feet. These are referred to as *single rolls. Double rolls* are twice as long and cover 72 square feet. Double rolls are used to reduce the amount of waste caused by matching patterns.

Wallpaper is usually applied over plastered walls. These walls are prepared for papering by patching all cracks and holes, smoothing rough spots, and applying a coat of sizing. The sizing is a glue which helps the paper adhere to the wall, and also permits sliding the paper on the wall, making final positioning easier.

To determine the amount of sizing and paste required for a wallpaper job, the estimator must first find the area of the wall to be covered. Small openings in the wall for doors and windows are ignored at this point. One pound of sizing mixed with sufficient water will cover about 500 square feet. Coverage of wallpaper paste will vary with the type of paper being applied. On an average, 1 pound of wallpaper paste is sufficient for approximately 400 to 500 square feet of wallpaper.

The amount of wallpaper needed may be based on the area of the walls, or it may be based on the number of strips needed for the job. When the area of the wall is used as a basis for determining the amount of paper needed, it is best to use the actual wall area. This area is found by multiplying the perimeter of the room by the height from the top of the baseboard to the ceiling and subtracting the area of door and window openings. The area of returns is added to the above net area. An allowance of 10 to 20 percent is made for waste caused by matching patterns. The size of the allowance depends on the pattern, large patterns making for more waste.

After the allowance for waste has been made, the total area is divided by 36 to get the number of single rolls needed, or by 72 to get the number of double rolls needed. The result is rounded off to the next full roll.

When the strip method is used to determine the amount of paper needed, the perimeter of the room is divided by the width of one strip (1.5 feet). The result is rounded off to the next full number, which is the number of strips needed if there are no openings. One strip is subtracted for each door and window opening. Additions are made for returns around windows if necessary.

To find the number of rolls needed, the number of full-length strips per roll must first be determined. This is done by dividing the length of a roll (24 feet for single rolls or 48 feet for double rolls) by the length of a strip and dropping the remainder. The number of strips per roll is divided into the number of strips needed, and the result rounded off to the next full roll.

Labor for paperhanging is based on the area of the work. Flat work with no openings can be done more quickly than the same area requiring many cutouts. Therefore labor output varies greatly. It is estimated based on the contractor's previous experience for similar work.

Equipment costs for paperhanging are low. The hanger

generally needs only a cutting table, pails, brushes, and small hand tools. An allowance must be made for these and for transporting them to the job.

GLAZING

A very small amount of glazing is done at the job site on residential work because most doors and window sash are glazed at the factory or mill. The only glass set into frames or sash on residential jobs is usually in large picture windows which require plate glass or insulating window units. Because of the small amount of glazing done on residential job sites, the estimator will generally use the glazing contractor's bid in his estimate for glass costs.

On commercial jobs all glass is set into place after the frames are installed. Generally, the glass installation is put off as long as possible to avoid breakage, which will surely occur during construction.

Large plate glass is usually not installed until the very last, and even then it is immediately protected against being scratched or broken. This protection should be provided for under the heading of General Job Expense.

Ordinary glass is subject to considerable breakage, which the contractor will generally accept rather than stand the expense of protecting the glass. Allowance for this in the estimate is left to the judgment of the estimator. The amount to allow will depend upon the type of building, the type of neighborhood, the time of the year, and the amount of glass involved.

Depending on the location and type of building, a glazing estimate may include the installation of metal frames, plate glass windows, insulating window units, reflective window units, patterned glass, wired glass, tempered safety glass, mirrors, tempered glass doors, etc.

On commercial jobs, as on residential job estimates, the estimator will use the glazing contractor's price for whatever glass is needed. The glazing contractor, however, has to make a detailed estimate to determine what materials he must supply, how much labor is required, and how much equipment will be needed for the job. The normal procedure is to list one floor at a time on the estimate and to list each type of glass work separately, noting the size of glass and type of setting. The price of the glass is based on cost per square foot for the various brackets (glass sizes).

If the glass is set in glazing gaskets, the type and amount of gasketing needed are also listed. Gaskets which are made to fit a light of glass are priced per unit, and those which are cut to length on the job are priced by the lineal foot. When the glass is set in glazing compound, enough compound of the proper type must be allowed for in the cost estimate. The amount of compound needed is based on the perimeter of the glass and determined in accordance with the glazing contractor's experience with similar work. Glazing compound is priced by the pound, gallon, or 5-gallon pail.

Labor costs for glazing will vary with the type of work and are based on the glazing contractor's previous experience with similar work.

Equipment needed on the job will vary from a few stepladders to extension ladders, scaffolding, and planking and special equipment to handle large lights as well as the usual small hand tools. Each job is carefully analyzed to determine equipment needs and to allow for the cost of this equipment in the final estimate.

EXERCISES

1   How are painting estimates divided?
2   What is the unit of measurement for wall painting?
3   What equipment costs are figured on painting jobs?
4   How is the area of narrow-trim members calculated?
5   How are doors and windows figured on the painting estimate?
6   Outline the procedure for estimating wallpaper.
7   Outline the procedure for preparing a quantity survey for glazing.

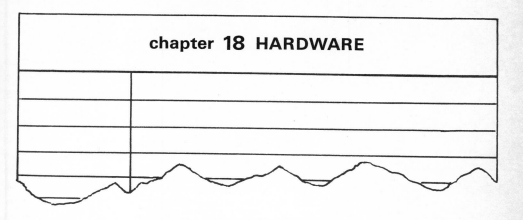

chapter 18 HARDWARE

INTRODUCTION

Preparing a hardware specification or schedule is an involved matter. Writing a complete list of the hardware required for a job calls for close attention to many details and considerable experience, if it is to be done properly. Architects sometimes call in the representative of a hardware manufacturer or dealer for this service on larger jobs and to help in selecting the hardware. This usually means that the order for the hardware is given to the person who prepares the list. On small jobs the contractor is expected to submit a list and catalog cuts to the architect for his approval.

Architects frequently specify that a certain amount of money for the hardware shall be included by the contractor in his bid. This is generally understood to be his cost price for the hardware, delivered to the job. He would later have to show his hardware bills and adjust the total contract amount to suit any savings or any additional cost. This method is not followed in public work, however; for such jobs the hardware is usually specified in detail.

EXPENSES CONNECTED WITH HARDWARE

In addition to the cost of the hardware and its installation, there are other expenses connected with hardware that the estimator must allow for. He may have to prepare the detail lists and schedules or have them prepared by others. Samples must be procured and submitted to the architect. Revised lists, and more samples, may be required before the hardware can be ordered. Shop drawings must be checked and coordinated, and templates for some items may be required. The types of screws and bolts for the hardware must be indicated.

Finally, when it is received at the job, great care must be taken to store the hardware and keys safely, preliminary to sorting out the items and sending them to the locations throughout the building where they are to be installed. In some cases it is necessary to send certain items of hardware to material manufacturers, subcontractors, and others, in order that proper provisions for the hardware may be made in doors, frames, and other parts for which the hardware is needed. The additional cost of all this varies with each job but must be included in the estimate under Hardware or General Job Expense or other appropriate headings. A good estimator will not hesitate to put in $100 to $500 to cover this expense on a fair-sized job.

Key racks or cabinets are sometimes specified. In addition to the cost of these, the labor of installing them, and probably also the labor of preparing key tags and schedules to accompany them, must be provided for in the estimate. Master keys and extra keys, especially for hotels, offices, and institutional buildings, also involve extra expense which must be considered.

The estimator must take all the foregoing details into consideration when working on a hardware estimate.

HARDWARE OMISSIONS

The hardware division of an estimate does not provide for all the hardware required on a job. It applies only to the finish hardware, and seldom includes even all the items of this nature. It is necessary for the estimator to read all the specifications and to examine all the drawings carefully, to determine what to put under this heading. Other divisions of the specifications will undoubtedly demand provision for some hardware expense.

Many types of doors, such as fire doors, all-glass doors, overhead doors, some sliding doors and folding doors, and some metal doors, come equipped with hardware, and this would therefore be included under the appropriate headings. Most steel windows and some wood windows also come equipped with all or some of the hardware for them.

Cabinets, wardrobes, and lockers sometimes come with the hardware on them and sometimes they do not.

Hardware allowances and hardware lists may or may not include such items as coat hooks, clothes-hanger rods, shoe racks, hat racks, shelf supports, bathroom-wall fittings, shower-curtain rods, drapery fittings, mirrors, medicine cabinets, door chimes, coal chutes, package receivers, grilles, dampers, cleanout doors, display racks, handrail brackets, thresholds, weather strips, etc. Items that are not placed under this heading must, or course, be shown elsewhere in the estimate.

Rough hardware should not be put under the Hardware heading. Items such as nails, spikes, bolts, bridle irons, etc., belong under the carpentry headings. Iron railings and other large iron items should be put under the Iron heading.

As always, the estimator must be careful to see that all items required by the plans and specifications are included in the estimate.

FINISHES

High-grade hardware, especially for exterior use, is generally of solid bronze, brass, stainless steel, or other noncorroding metal. Other hardware may be of these metals or of plain steel, plated steel, or plastic. Obviously, the grade of material specified will greatly affect the cost of the hardware. On fine work, matching hardware and matching finishes are required. To obtain this, the specifications may sometimes state that all the hardware is to be of one manufacture. This, of course, limits the contractor by prohibiting his splitting up the hardware order if he should wish to do so.

Some hardware items are available locally while others must be ordered from the manufacturer. When special hardware items are specified, the estimator should check on the availability of the item. Delays in obtaining some hardware items can hold up a job and add to the job expense.

DOORS AND DOOR HARDWARE

The *hand* of a door is established from the outside of exterior doors and from the hall side of interior doors. If the butts are on the right, the door is a right-hand door. If the butts are on the left, it is a left-hand door. See Figure 18-1 for a diagram illustrating the hand designation of doors.

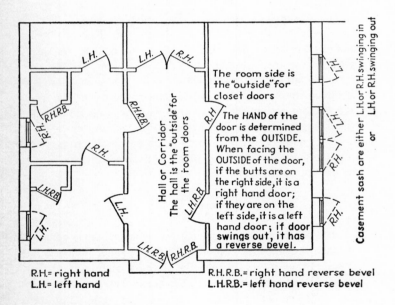

The room side is the "outside" for closet doors

The HAND of the door is determined from the OUTSIDE. When facing the OUTSIDE of the door, if the butts are on the right side, it is a right hand door; if they are on the left side, it is a left hand door; if door swings out, it has a reverse bevel.

Hall or Corridor
The hall is the "outside" for the room doors

Casement sash are either L.H. or R.H. swinging in or L.H. or R.H. swinging out

R.H. = right hand
L.H. = left hand

R.H.R.B. = right hand reverse bevel
L.H.R.B. = left hand reverse bevel

FIGURE 18-1   Designation of doors.

If you are standing outside a door and the door opens away from you, the door is a regular-bevel door. If it opens toward you, it is a reverse-bevel door. Some locks are reversible and therefore may be used without regard to the hand or bevel of door. However, it is better to specify the hand of the door to avoid the need for reversing the locks on the job or the possible need to exchange locks because they cannot be reversed.

The common types of door hinges are called *butts*, or *butt hinges*. Some have fixed pins and some loose pins. Some are ball-bearing.

The lock sets most commonly used are mortise locks, tubular locks, and unit locks. They fit into mortises or into holes cut in the edge of the door. The bolts of these locks extend into strike plates screwed to the jamb of the opening.

The hardware on doors is applied before any weather stripping is started. Hinges and lock sets or latches are used for front and rear doors, interior doors of many uses, and screen and storm doors. The front-door hardware may be quite elaborate and expensive and may also include a letter box and door knocker. Some doors require door checks, holders, bumpers, panic bolts, pull handles, push plates or bars, kick plates, and even saddles, grilles, numerals, and other fittings. Sliding doors require tracks, hangers, guides, and pulls, and may also have locks. Pairs of doors require top and bottom bolts.

Skilled carpenters are needed for properly installing hardware, especially lock sets and other items requiring careful alignment and close adjusting. Architects examine this work, and some even insist that all screw slots be uniformly set vertically.

Floor-type hinges and door holders fastened to the floor require that recesses be provided or cut into the floor to receive them. These and similar extra labor items are often overlooked by estimators.

Hollow metal doors require reinforcing at all the hardware locations. This is usually provided for in the door order, but if not, it must be listed with the hardware intended for such doors.

WINDOW HARDWARE

Double-hung wood windows may require sash chains or cords, sash weights and pulleys, or sash balances. However, these are usually estimated in the carpentry divisions of the estimator or are part of the window unit and need not be estimated separately.

Sash lifts and sash locks are put under the Hardware heading.

Wood casement windows require hinges and latches and may also have sash adjusters or sash operators. Pairs of casements may require cremone bolts, or one leaf may have top and bottom bolts. However, most casement units come complete with frame, sash, and all operating hardware. Additional hardware for casement windows may not be required.

Wood window screens and storm sash require hangers and hooks, and sometimes adjusters are also specified. Shutters and louvers may require hinges, handles, latches, and hooks.

Metal windows generally come fitted complete with hardware, and sometimes with screens.

CABINET AND MISCELLANEOUS HARDWARE

Harware for cabinetwork includes hinges and catches for hinged doors, tracks and pulls for sliding doors, slides and pulls for drawers, and possibly locks for some of the doors and drawers. Fittings for cabinets are often included under the Hardware heading and may consist of shelf supports, shelves, trays, racks, bins, display devices, and many other things. In fine cabinetwork, the hardware may be very expensive and may include concealed hinges and other items requiring more than the usual amount of labor.

Transoms which open over doors and windows require hinges or pivots and catches, and usually also have transom chains and lifts or adjuster rods.

Closets require coat-and-hat hooks and clothes-hanger rods. They may also have shoe racks, hat racks, and other special fittings.

LABOR AND EQUIPMENT

Labor and equipment costs for hardware are normally included under the Carpentry heading, hinges and locks being part of door installation. Whether labor and equipment costs are included under Carpentry or under Hardware is not important, so long as allowance is made for them. This is particularly important when there is much hardware requiring special equipment and extra care during installation.

EXERCISES

1 Outline the procedure you would follow in preparing a hardware list for a small office building.

2 What expenses are connected with hardware installation?

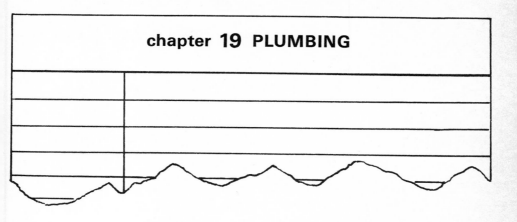

chapter 19 PLUMBING

INTRODUCTION

The term *mechanical trades* is generally applied to the piping, wiring, and machinery lines of work. On regular building work these lines include plumbing, heating, electrical work, and elevator work. On most jobs they are done under separate subcontracts. Some subcontractors, however, handle both plumbing and heating.

The mechanical trades, especially plumbing and heating, are often given out by the owner or the architect separately from the general contract for the construction work. In such cases, the general contractor may theoretically have nothing to do with these lines of work, but because the work is done in the building at the same time that the construction work is being done, conflict of interest may occur. To avoid this, sometimes the general contractor is given jurisdiction over these separate contracts even when they are separately awarded. Regardless of the specifications covering these lines, the general contractor is governed only by his own contract and the specifications that accompany his contract.

Excavating for the mechanical trades is an item that must always be checked by the general contractor's estimator. Sometimes these trades do all their own excavating and backfilling; at other times they will do only excavating, backfilling, and street cutting and patching outside the building. The estimator must check for any omissions in this type of excavating work and make whatever adjustments may be necessary.

The plumbing subcontractor's job takes in the bathtubs, lavatories, and water closets in the bathrooms and toilet rooms, and the sinks and washtubs in the kitchens and cellars. Showers and shower curtains are part of the plumbing work also, and sometimes the glass shower doors are included. Sheet lead, placed under the tile floors of standing showers and in special watertight floor construction, is installed by plumbers and listed under Plumbing. Hot-water storage tanks and heaters come under Plumbing, except when they are an integral part of the main heating plant installed by the steamfitters. In any event, all the water supply and water connections are handled by the plumbers. All the water-supply and drainage lines, both inside the building and out to the mains in the street, are in this division. A plumbing contractor is required to have a city license.

Temporary water and toilet facilities for the job may involve the plumbing contractor. If, for example, a large amount of water is required for the construction work, it may prove advantageous to have the plumbers install galvanized steel pipes, rather than depend upon the more customary hose lines. This is especially true if the run to the supply source is long or if other conditions make the use of galvanized steel pipe worthwhile. If it is possible to make use of a sewer connection or other sewage-disposal connection, it is worthwhile on a large job to install regular toilets for the workmen, from the beginning of the job. After the water closet roughing is in, the building contractors generally do install such water closets, even having the plumbing contractor furnish second-hand water closets for the purpose. The plumbing contractor is generally called upon to provide a temporary water connection for the job use. The cost of all these items must be considered by the estimator and provided for in the plumbing division or in the General Job Expense division of the estimate.

Sewers, catch basins, septic tanks, and manholes, if they are required, are generally specified under Plumbing.

The plumbing contractors figuring the job, however, may or may not include all of these. Sometimes they include all but the manholes, or all but the manholes and the covers for the catch basins. These are additional items for the general contractor's estimator to check carefully. Several manholes on a job may alone cost over $2,000.

Water closet and bathroom accessories, such as holders for soap and paper, mirrors, cabinets, etc., are sometimes specified under Plumbing. Regardless of this, many plumbing contractors choose to omit them, especially the cabinets, and may so state in their bids. Even if they do not state this in their bids, there will be a question as to whether these items were included. This will apply especially when their bids read "For all the Plumbing work" instead of "For all the work noted in the Plumbing Section of the specifications."

PLUMBING COSTS

Because all plumbing work must be done by licensed plumbers working for licensed plumbing contractors, the general contractor's estimator will not make a quantity survey for all the plumbing. Instead, he will check the plumbing contractor's bid to see that he has included all fixtures on the plan and provided all the necessary piping to make the fixtures operable. Before including the plumbing contractor's bid price in the estimate summary, the estimator checks to see that all items required by the plans and specifications are included and that they are of the quality specified.

Regular plumbing fixtures cost the general contractor between $200 and $350 each, installed, with the piping and trimmings included. A building with many bathrooms may run between $600 and $800 per bathroom, complete. Small jobs of only a few fixtures cost much more per unit than the same fixtures in a large job. Street sewer and water connections cost several hundred dollars each, with the incidental excavating and replacing of pavements.

Figure 19-1 shows a typical plumbing section for a four-story building. Drawings of this nature are purely diagrammatic and cannot be scaled. This one shows all the plumbing fixtures and the drainage and vent piping.

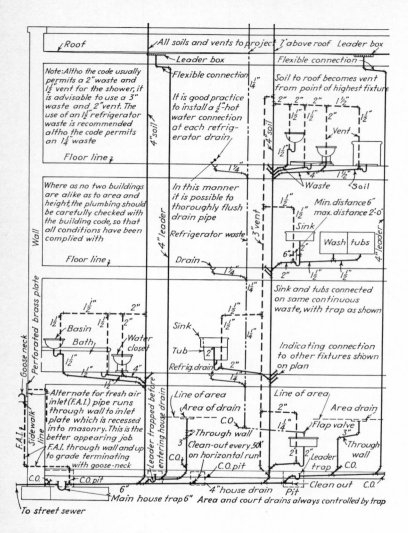

FIGURE 19-1 Plumbing piping.

PLUMBING REQUIREMENTS

Building codes regulate plumbing installations. These codes have been established to safeguard the public against the hazards of poorly designed or poorly installed plumbing. The estimator has no responsibility for the design of the plumbing installation, but he should have some knowledge of plumbing requirements so that he can recognize a deficiency in the plans.

Plumbing systems should be designed to guard against fouling and clogging. Pure water, with sufficient volume and pressure, must be provided to enable the fixtures to function satisfactorily under all normal conditions.

Hot-water lines should be provided with safety devices arranged to relieve hazardous pressures and excessive temperatures.

Standpipe and automatic-sprinkler lines should have water in sufficient volume and pressure to enable them to function satisfactorily.

Acids and other damaging wastes should be chemically treated to neutralize their effect, before being discharged into the plumbing system. Where grease in quantities that would produce pipe stoppage is to be handled, an approved device should be provided for intercepting and separating it from the liquid wastes before it is discharged into the plumbing system.

The drainage system should be designed to provide adequate circulation of air in the pipes so that siphonage or pressure will not cause a loss of trap seal. Each vent line should extend to the outer air and be installed so as to minimize the possibility of clogging, frost closure, and the return of foul air to the building.

Adequate cleanouts should be provided and arranged so that the pipes may be readily cleaned.

The water-supply main for one-family houses is usually of $\frac{3}{4}$- or 1-inch galvanized steel or $\frac{3}{4}$-inch copper. For business buildings it may be 2 inches or larger. Flush-valve toilets require 1-inch branches. Branches to other ordinary fixtures are generally $\frac{1}{2}$-inch pipe or $\frac{3}{8}$-inch copper tubing.

Each fixture or group of fixtures is provided with a shutoff valve for repairs or changes.

Cold-water lines are enclosed in antisweat covering, and hot-water lines in heat-insulation covering.

Toilets and toilet tanks and the higher grades of lavatories are made of vitreous china, which is a clay product baked at high temperatures. Other lavatories, and sinks and bathtubs, are usually of enameled iron or pressed steel. Stainless-steel sinks are also available.

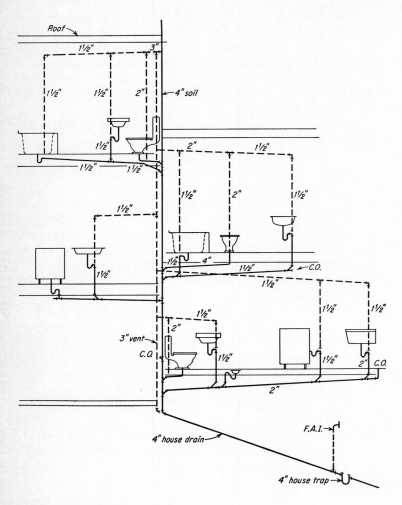

FIGURE 19-2 Plumbing section.

The metal trimmings, such as faucets, drains, and shower fixtures, do not come with the sinks, lavatories, and tubs but are supplied and installed by the plumbing subcontractor. Architects frequently specify that all the fixtures shall be of one manufacture and sometimes also that the trimmings shall be of the same manufacture.

Sinks are often set into kitchen work counters. In these cases the plumbing subcontractor usually furnishes the sink, but someone else sets it into the counter. The plumbers then connect the sink to the plumbing lines and install the faucets.

When fixtures are grouped, a saving in material and labor is effected. If the bathroom in a house adjoins the kitchen, for example, or is over the kitchen, one soil-and-vent stack may serve both rooms, but two stacks would be required if the rooms were far apart. If there are two other bathrooms, or a bathroom and a toilet room, a saving is similarly made if they adjoin each other. In like manner, a minimum of piping is required if the fixtures are placed along one wall of a room.

Figure 19-2 is a plumbing section for the house shown in Chapter 5. When studying this section it should be noted that the fixtures have been arranged to take advantage of one central vent stack. The plumbing specifications for this building can be found in Appendix A.

EXERCISES

1 What does the term mechanical trades generally include?

2 What are some items of temporary work included in the plumbing estimate?

3 What omissions should an estimator look for in a plumbing estimate?

4 What overlaps should an estimator look for in a plumbing estimate?

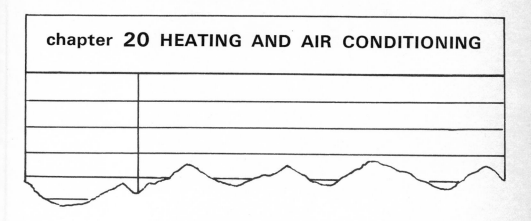

chapter 20 HEATING AND AIR CONDITIONING

INTRODUCTION

Heating systems may employ steam or hot-water boilers as a source of heat piped to radiators. On smaller jobs and on much residential work a hot-air furnace is used to provide heat distributed to the registers.

The heating boiler, mains, risers, branches, radiators, and return lines, together with the incidental valves and supplies, are included in the work of the heating subcontractor. In hot-air heating systems the ducts are also included in this work. Oil burners and fuel-oil tanks are part of the heating work. Heating contractors also install refrigeration systems and special piping and equipment in hospitals, factories, industrial buildings, and processing plants. Some plumbing contractors also do heating work. Air-conditioning and ventilating systems are usually part of the heating work, although some subcontractors handle only air conditioning and are not particularly interested in ordinary heating jobs.

It is the responsibility of the general contractor's estimator to coordinate the estimates of subcontractors in all lines and to see that everything is properly provided for.

Heating systems are usually tested before they are accepted by the architect. Since the testing involves the use of fuel, the estimator must see that the heating contractors figuring the job provide for this, or else he must make an entry here or under General Job Expense to cover the fuel. Likewise, the heating system may be placed in operation before the building is completed, to provide temporary heat. If possible, the estimator should have the heating contractor whose bid he plans to use quote also the cost of furnishing the temporary fuel and the radiators and other material that may be required and of maintaining this temporary heat for the job. If this is not done, he will have to estimate it himself and make an entry under Heating or in the General Job Expense division of the estimate, to cover the cost.

Boiler pits and foundations and other masonwork in connection with heating plants are sometimes specified under Heating. Despite this, the heating contractors seldom include this work. They may state in their bids that they include all the heating work, but unless they have stated plainly that they included all the work noted in the Heating division of the specifications, it would be questionable whether they had in fact included these items in their bids.

Ventilating and air-conditioning systems are often included with the heating work. In such cases, the estimator has to check with the sheet-metal and the electrical estimates to see that all the required work in all three lines is included in the bids that he expects to use in his own summary. Much overlapping can occur. Occasionally, it is found that a few of the items involved are included by two different trades, such as fans in roof ventilators and the motors and controls for various fans.

Architects are often vague regarding mechanical work and do not write clear-cut specifications. Sometimes they mention items under two or more headings in the specifications instead of only one heading. Work is frequently shown on the plans, or is obviously necessary, but is not noted at all in the specifications. Plans seldom show the mechanical lines of work completely, and the use of uniform symbols and other indications is not well established. All this makes it necessary for the estimator to check bids, plans, and specifications carefully to make sure that there are no omissions.

Many new systems of heating, ventilating, and air conditioning are being introduced, and estimators find that great care is required in analyzing and comparing the bids for quality of work and for possible omissions. Some items that may be omitted by the subcontractors include pipe covering, duct covering, toilet-room vent ducts and registers, roof ventilators, kitchen fans, electric heaters, grilles on fresh-air openings, return-air grilles, meters, oil-tank excavating or enclosures, water heaters, hot-water tanks, water-supply mains, boiler and tank water connections, radiator and convector enclosures, thermostats, controls, electrical and gas connections, machinery foundations, cooling-tower supports, and many others.

These items may or may not be provided for in other divisions of the estimate. Water-closet and roof vents may be included in the roofing division. Water heaters or tanks, or both, may be entered under Plumbing. Water connections to heating, ventilating, and air-conditioning equipment may be entered under Plumbing work. The electrical connections to some or all of the equipment may be entered under Electrical work, as may also the thermostats and some of the other control devices. Some of the grilles and enclosures may be entered under Carpentry or under a metal heading. The machine foundations, supports, and hangers may be included in the Concrete, Masonry, or Steel divisions of the estimate.

HEATING SYSTEMS

The fuel used in most heating systems is either oil or gas. However, the type of fuel used has nothing to do with the method by which heat is brought to rooms.

Oil heating systems have an oil-storage tank which is connected to the boiler or furnace by a small pipeline. Gas heating systems have a direct gas connection. Fuel-oil tanks are placed inside the building, usually in the cellar, or are buried in the ground outside. One or two 275-gallon tanks are generally used for indoors. Outside tanks are of 550-gallon capacity and sometimes larger. Building codes and board of fire underwriters' requirements must be complied with in regard to tank sizes and locations.

An electrically operated burner is used in connection with either the oil or gas system, to control the boiler or furnace. The burner is activated by a thermostat, which is a type of electric switch controlled by the temperature of the air where the thermostat is located. It turns the heat on or off to suit the desired degree of temperature at which it is set. The dials on the simplest thermostats are set manually. More elaborate thermostats contain a clock which can be set to accommodate different day and night settings. A still more elaborate one is coupled with an outdoor thermostat, on the theory that cold, windy weather necessitates a higher indoor temperature to keep the building comfortable. Two-zone and multizone heating employs additional thermostats which activate a pump or blower at the boiler or furnace, sending heat only to the zone desired.

Radiators radiate heat; the heated air rises naturally in a room and, as it cools and drops, recirculates around the radiators and is again heated. Radiators are made of cast iron.

Convectors are like radiators, but they are composed of tubes and fins, which have a greater surface than radiators. They heat the air by the force of convection. The cool air enters the lower openings of the convector enclosure, and the construction of the enclosure, which forms a flue, increases the speed of the heated air coming from it. Convectors are usually made of copper or aluminum, which also adds to their efficiency.

Copper tubing is sometimes embedded in floors, and convectors are sometimes installed in baseboard enclosures, in place of radiators or regular convectors.

In the one-pipe system, steam from the boiler flows through the radiators or convectors consecutively and returns to the boiler in the same pipe, the steam flowing in the upper part of the horizontal pipes and the condensate water in the lower part. The stream of return water is very small, about the size of a lead pencil. Larger-than-normal radiators are necessary near the end of the line to offset the drop in the temperature of the steam. A gravity one-pipe steam heating system is the least expensive to install, but it is not the most desirable. It is suitable, however, for small buildings.

In the two-pipe system, steam or hot water from the boiler flows or is pumped through one pipe to branches leading individually to each radiator or convector, and therefore normal-size radiators or convectors are used throughout. It returns to the boiler through another pipe connected with separate branches leading individually from each radiator or convector.

Other systems of heating are also employed. These include various types of hot-air or air-conditioning systems, vacuum-pumped steam systems, and special systems of many varieties.

AIR CONDITIONING

There are many ways of conditioning air. Some only blow the air around or bring in fresh air and therefore merely employ ventilating devices or systems. Others are for summer use to cool and dehumidify the air. More elaborate systems fully condition the air all year by heating in winter and cooling and dehumidifying in summer.

Ventilating mechanically is accomplished by the use of electric fans or blowers for circulating air to the various rooms through a system of duct work. The ventilating system may be combined with the heating and air-conditioning system to provide all-year air conditioning. In some cases this may bring several subcontractors together to complete the job because the installation of fans and duct work may be done by a ventilating contractor, the heating and cooling units by a heating and air-conditioning contractor, and all the electrical work necessary to make the units operable by an electrical contractor. The estimator must therefore be careful to watch for overlaps and omissions when considering the bids of the various subcontractors for ventilating, heating, and air-conditioning work.

On some jobs, such as small apartment buildings, small air-conditioning units are installed for use in summer cooling only. These units are usually installed through the wall and require some rough-in work by the carpenter and an electrical outlet by the electrician. No piping or duct work is required for this type of unit.

All heating and air-conditioning work must be done in compliance with local and state building codes. The estimator is not responsible for the design or the specifications of a heating and ventilating system, but he should be aware of the code requirements so that he can check the bids he will use in his own estimate and avoid some possible shortcomings. Because of the great variety of work encountered in this field, there is a wide range in prices. The estimator would do well to deal with subcontractors who have an established reputation in this field and thereby avoid the pitfall of low bid prices and work poorly done.

EXERCISES

1 Name ten items that may be specified by an architect under Heating work and yet may be omitted by subcontractors bidding on this work.

2 Name several types of heating systems in common use.

3 Outline the procedure you would follow in preparing an estimate for two of the systems named in Exercise 2.

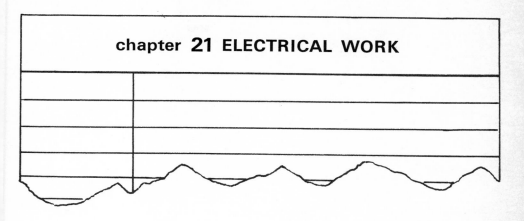

chapter 21 ELECTRICAL WORK

INTRODUCTION

All electric wiring done at the job for lighting, power-supply, and signal purposes comes under the heading of Electrical work. Special machinery, such as elevator machines, pumps, and fans, are installed under other headings, but the electrical connections are made by electricians and the cost for these connections is included under Electrical work. Plain and special lighting outlets and reflectors, also, are always put under this heading, but the lighting fixtures are sometimes given a special heading. Electrical contractors are licensed by the city, and their work also comes under the inspection of the board of fire underwriters organized by the fire insurance companies.

Electrical symbols are shown in Figure 21-1 as they appear on plans.

The electrical work in a building can present a problem to the general contractor's estimator mainly in regard to the machinery, fans, and other such equipment. Concerning the main wiring and the lighting system, it is usually quite well established as to who furnishes what. Motors attached to fans and unit heaters, elevators, oil burners, and other motor-driven equipment are the things that must be watched. Unless these are clearly specified, it is likely that neither the subcontractor furnishing the motor nor the elec-

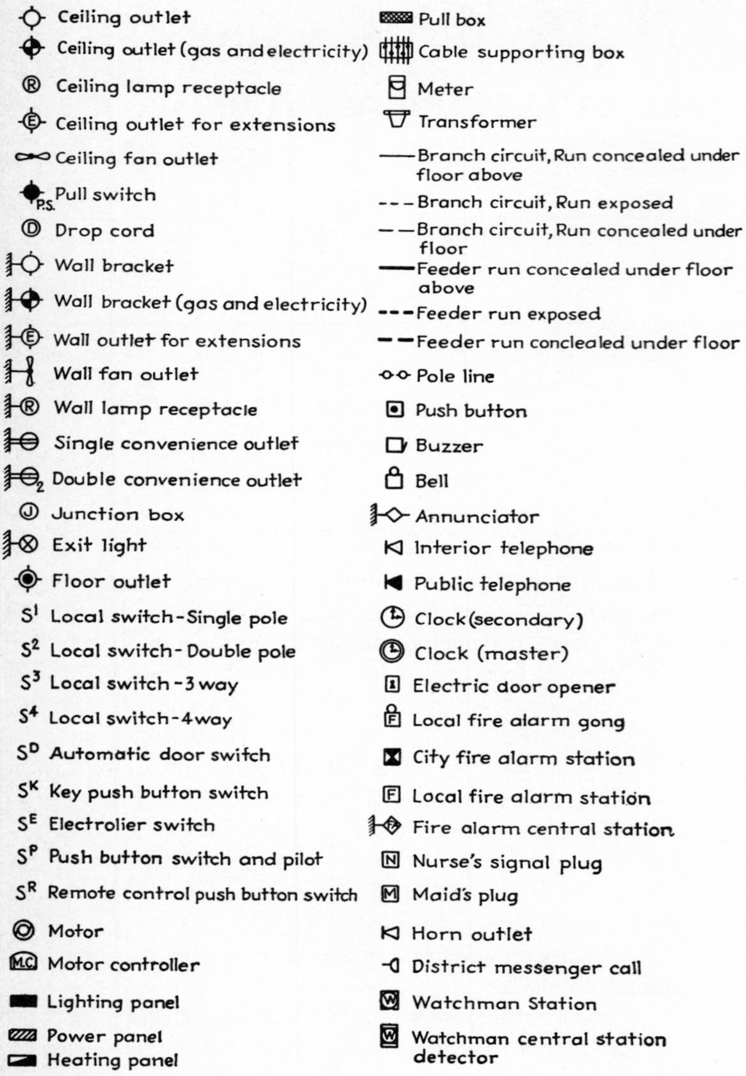

○- Ceiling outlet

⊕ Ceiling outlet (gas and electricity)

® Ceiling lamp receptacle

-Ⓔ Ceiling outlet for extensions

∞ Ceiling fan outlet

◆ Pull switch
P.S.

Ⓓ Drop cord

⊦○ Wall bracket

⊦⊕ Wall bracket (gas and electricity)

⊦Ⓔ Wall outlet for extensions

⊦⦚ Wall fan outlet

⊦® Wall lamp receptacle

⊦○ Single convenience outlet

⊦⊝₂ Double convenience outlet

Ⓙ Junction box

⊦⊗ Exit light

◆ Floor outlet

S¹ Local switch-Single pole

S² Local switch-Double pole

S³ Local switch-3 way

S⁴ Local switch-4 way

Sᴰ Automatic door switch

Sᴷ Key push button switch

Sᴱ Electrolier switch

Sᴾ Push button switch and pilot

Sᴿ Remote control push button switch

◎ Motor

Ⓜ.Ⓒ Motor controller

■ Lighting panel

▨ Power panel

◪ Heating panel

▨ Pull box

▥ Cable supporting box

⊟ Meter

▽ Transformer

—— Branch circuit, Run concealed under floor above

– – – Branch circuit, Run exposed

— — Branch circuit, Run concealed under floor

—— Feeder run concealed under floor above

--- Feeder run exposed

— — Feeder run concealed under floor

○-○ Pole line

◙ Push button

▭ Buzzer

⌂ Bell

⊦◇ Annunciator

◁ Interior telephone

◀ Public telephone

◔ Clock (secondary)

◕ Clock (master)

▣ Electric door opener

⌂ Local fire alarm gong

◪ City fire alarm station

▣ Local fire alarm station

⊦◈ Fire alarm central station

◨ Nurse's signal plug

◧ Maid's plug

◁ Horn outlet

◁ District messenger call

▨ Watchman Station

▨ Watchman central station detector

FIGURE 21-1 Electrical symbols.

trical contractor will have included the control switches and connections at the motors. In preparing the estimate, it is necessary to make sure that one or the other does include the cost of this work. Heavy controls are expensive. Sometimes even the motors are left out, because no one has included them. The sheet-metal contractor, for example, may take in a lot of exhaust fans and omit the motors for them. The electrical contractors may assume that these will come with the fans and so merely include wiring to the motors, even omitting the switches or other forms of controls.

Another item of electrical work that is troublesome is the temporary lighting or power that the job may require. Several of the subcontactors, requiring electric power to operate their equipment on the job, may specify in their bids that they assume the general contractor will furnish them with suitable current connections at proper locations in the building and at their shanties. The general contractor also may require power for equipment and nearly always has to provide temporary lighting in and about the job. Owing partly to regulations of the electrical unions, this temporary electrical service can become an expensive item, sometimes to the extent that a job must employ one or more electricians full time and with considerable overtime, merely to turn switches on and off morning and evening. This matter must be investigated for every job and properly provided for in the estimate. The electrical contractors fight shy of it, and generally the estimator has to use his own judgment in estimating the cost of installation, maintenance, overtime, and current consumption for the entire job requirements.

If the electrical contractor whose bid is to be used states that he includes only the work inside the building, or work extending to a point a few feet outside the building, the requirements of the job must be checked thoroughly, since there may be much outside work, such as poles, transformers, outside lighting, and signal work. Even if the electrical utility company is to do some of the outside work— running the service to the building, furnishing transformers, etc.—it may be left to the general contractor to pay for this service.

Electrical work sometimes involves the construction of a transformer vault, machine foundations, supports for motors and fixtures, etc. Items like these require that the estimator look into the question as to who furnishes them, since they are not electrical work, and although they are specified in the electrical portion of the specifications, the subcontractor who states in his bid that he includes "all the electrical work" may take the stand that because these are not part of electrical work, he does not include them, even though they may have been so designated in the specifications.

Lighting fixtures and other items of electrical equipment made in nonunion shops will almost surely cause trouble with the electricians working on the job. If items of this nature are to be supplied by the owner, it is the general contractor's place to notify him, through a statement in the bid for the job, that it is assumed that any items to be thus furnished will be satisfactory in every way to the union requirements on the job. Some electrical unions insist upon removing all the wiring from lighting fixtures at the job because they were wired by nonunion shopmen or by members of another union, and then rewiring them at the job, all at the expense of somebody, who may be the general contractor.

Some types of lighting fixtures require considerable carpentry work to be done at the job to accommodate them—boxes for recessed lights, etc. This work is usually done by the carpenters on the job, and unless it is actually included in the electrical bids, it should be provided for under the heading Carpentry.

If a sum of money is specified for the purchase of lighting fixtures or any other items on the job, it is the task of the estimator to ascertain just how the money is intended to apply, whether as the list price for such items or as the actual price to be paid out by the subcontractors. Otherwise there may be a dispute when the items are being purchased.

ELECTRICAL COSTS

Electrical work is done by licensed electrical contractors. Therefore the general contractor's estimator will not make a detailed estimate of electrical work, but instead will use an electrical contractor's bid when preparing the job estimate. As with bids from other subcontractors, the estimator must check the electrical bid carefully for omissions and overlaps before including it in the job estimate. The cost of electrical work will vary with the size of the job. Some typical unit costs are given below to familiarize the beginning estimator with some of the categories and variations.

Wiring and outlets cost between $10 and $15 per outlet for lighting work if flexible cable is used and between $15 and $30 per outlet if rigid pipe conduit is used. Ordinary lighting fixtures cost between $3.50 and $18 each, delivered, and about $4 to $8 each for installing. These are the prices that the general contractor is charged by the electrical subcontractor. Switches count as outlets. Letter boxes also come under the heading of Electrical work, since they are commonly installed in connection with the bell system.

An electrical service for a residential job may cost $175 to $250. Wiring for a range may cost an additional $175, and wiring for a clothes dryer may cost $80.

Heavy-duty wiring on commercial jobs is of great variety and has a wide range of prices. Therefore it is difficult to quote average prices. The estimator may need to check bids from several reliable contractors before deciding on which bid to use.

ELECTRICAL REGULATIONS

Electrical work is generally done in accordance with the requirements of the National Board of Fire Underwriters, in addition to the regulations of the local authorities having jurisdiction.

The local electrical utility company also has regulations governing electrical work. The following regulations, from one company, will introduce the student to such requirements.

Service The company has adopted as its standard the three phase, four wire, alternating current system of distribution, at approximately 60 cycles with 120 and 208 volts, in the interest of a standardized, unified and economical system.

The standard service comprises: three phase, four wire, 120/208 volt service; or single phase, two wire, 120 volt service; or three wire, 120/208 volt service, with two conductors and a neutral of the three phase, four wire system.

Three phase, four wire, 265/460 volt service will be designated by the company, subject to the customer's concurrence, for supply to buildings when warranted by the magnitude or location of the load or other physical conditions.

Connections   Electric service will be supplied to each building or premises through a single service lateral, except where, for reasons of company economy, conditions on the company's distribution system, improvements of service conditions, or magnitude of the customer's load, the company elects to install more than one service lateral. The company reserves the right to determine the location of any service lateral.

If the company designates overhead service, the company will install its service conductors from its street system to the first point of attachment on or near the front face of the building or to the first intermediate supporting structure on the customer's property, which, in such case, shall be the point of service termination.

If the company designates underground service, the company will install its service conduit and cables from its street system to the property line or suitable sub-sidewalk space, which, in such case, shall be the point of service termination.

Transformers   Where the company considers transformers and associated equipment reasonably necessary for the adequate supply of service to a customer or a customer's premises, the customer shall provide suitable space and reasonable access thereto. To facilitate access and ventilation, such space shall, wherever practicable, be adjacent to the property line and should be outside the building and immediately below the street grade.

At the request of the customer, the company's transformers and associated equipment may be installed by the customer at one or more points in his building or premises on the same or different levels, provided that the entire service installation within his premises, including the installation of, or connections to, the company's transformers and associated equipment, or replacements thereof, is made at the customer's expense in accordance with the company's specifications.

Construction   Where service is requested for construction purposes and where the facilities installed therefor will not be used for permanent supply, the customer will be required to pay in advance to the company a sum of money, as determined by the company and endorsed upon the agreement for service, which shall be the estimated non-recoverable cost of furnishing and installing all necessary additional facilities of the company and the removal thereof.

Meters   The company will install, upon the request of the customer, as many meters as he shall desire, provided the circuit or circuits connected to each meter are kept separate from all other circuits.

The customer shall furnish, install and maintain all wiring and equipment, including standpipes, conduits, fittings, wires, cables, fuses, end boxes, service switch, meter equipment and meter wiring, beginning with the point of service termination. The customer shall install and connect metering transformers on initial installation and upon subsequent alteration to the main cable or bus circuit.

The company will not supply service until the customer's installation shall have fulfilled the company's requirements and shall have been approved by the authorities having jursidiction over the same. The final connection for making the service alive shall be made only by the company.

RESIDENTIAL WIRING

The electrical service may be either a simple two-wire or a three-wire service. The three-wire service is preferred because it provides the regular voltage for lighting and also double voltage for power requirements.

In the three-wire service three wires enter the building. One is a neutral wire which is connected to one leg of each of the building circuits. The remaining legs are connected to the other two service wires, one-half of the legs being connected to each, thus providing for 110- to 120-volt circuits. Where a 230-volt circuit is required, the neutral wire is not used and one live wire is connected to each leg of the circuit. The 230-volt wiring is used in circuits to motors and heaters that operate at twice the lamp voltage. Most small appliances, however, operate at 110 to 120 volts.

Metallic tubing, or "thin-wall" conduit, is commonly used for good work. It is like rigid pipe conduit but is lightweight and easy to bend and cut. The ends are not threaded but are fastened with clamp-type couplings.

Rigid conduit, or steel "pipe conduit," comes in 10-foot lengths with a coupling screwed on one end. It is cut with a hacksaw, and the cut ends are then threaded to fit the couplings. Both the thin-wall and pipe conduits are empty, and the wires are pulled through them. Pipe conduit is used on very high grade jobs and in certain cases where the applying regulations require its use.

Flexible spiral armored cable, or BX wiring, comes in coils with the wires already contained in it. This is used in ordinary work and for unimportant branch wiring in connection with jobs having pipe conduit or thin-wall conduit.

Outlets are controlled from two locations, when so desired, by the use of two three-way switches. For a greater number of locations, a four-way switch is used at each extra location.

The lighting circuits are employed for lighting and for clocks, radios, small fans, portable lamps, etc.

Appliance circuits are used for hand irons, mixers, refrigerators, and small appliances.

Individual circuits of double voltage are used for ranges, water heaters, clothes dryers, and other equipment requiring heavy-capacity wiring. Several such circuits may be required, especially if electric heating is to be provided or if a workshop with electric machinery is involved.

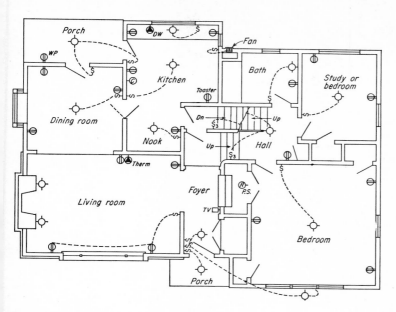

FIGURE 21-2 First-floor electrical plan.

Push buttons are installed at front and back doors to ring bells, buzzers, or chimes located in the hall or kitchen. An electric door opener, operated by a push button on the second floor, is sometimes used.

Conduits and outlet boxes for telephone wires, to one or more locations, are often specified.

Television connections, consisting of nonmetallic outlet boxes located in the attic and in several of the rooms and connected with a suitable transmission line, are provided in modern houses.

EXERCISES

1 Draw ten electrical symbols and name them.

2 What are pipe conduits? Thin-wall conduits?

3 Outline the procedure you would follow in preparing a survey for electrical work.

4 Prepare an estimate of the electrical work for the house shown in Chapter 5, using Figure 21-2 and the specifications in Appendix A.

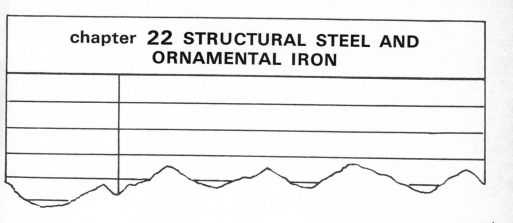

chapter 22 STRUCTURAL STEEL AND ORNAMENTAL IRON

INTRODUCTION

The subcontractors for steelwork include all the steel columns, girders, and beams and the steel plates and connections that go with these items. They also include the heavier types of steel lintels and any special steel framing that may be required for tank and machinery supports and other purposes, in addition to that for the general support of the building. If there are steel trusses, these also would be figured by the steel contractors' estimators.

The subcontractors for ornamental and miscellaneous ironwork include all the steel and iron items called for on the plans and in the specifications, except those put under the Structural Steel heading. Sometimes there is a question as to the heading under which certain items should be entered. Small items of steel, especially plain members or those that do not frame into other steel, are examples. It is part of the general contractor's work of coordinating the trades to see that questionable items are taken care of by one or the other of steel contractors.

Occasionally, one subcontractor will include all the structural steel and the miscellaneous and ornamental iron. This happens especially when there is a considerable amount of ironwork and only a few items of structural steel.

STRUCTURAL STEEL

To compute the cost of the structural steel, the steel estima
tors first list all the pieces of steel shown on the plans
The cross-section type and size, the length, and the weigh
per lineal foot are generally taken. The extensions are made
in tons, and the work is priced on that basis. Some o
the factors considered in making up the estimated cos
are shop drawings, erection drawings, time for delivery
mill or stock material, fabrication, shop painting, freight
trucking, steel members, rivets, welding, bolts, connections
bearing plates, unloading erection equipment, scaffolding
planking, field painting, foremen, insurance, general jol
expense, overhead expense, and profit.

If inspection of the structural steel is called for, eithe
at the steel plant or fabricating shop or at the job, th
expense in connection with this must be considered also
Perhaps the specification makes a lump-sum allowance fo
this purpose or specifies the name of an inspection concer
to do the inspecting. In addition to this element of cost
which may have to be included by the general contractor'
estimator instead of by the steel contractor, other item
require careful consideration. The shop or erection drawing
are sometimes so specified that the general contractor ha
to judge the cost and make a suitable entry in the genera
estimate, instead of having the steel contractors includ
such cost in their estimates to him.

Steel specifications often call for the grouting or bed
ding of the steel members that bear on concrete or masonr)
This work is practically never included by the steel contrac
tors, and the general contractor's estimator must therefor
make sure that the cost is covered in his estimates fo
the concrete or masonry work.

The student should become aware of the fact tha
architects assume no responsibility for the correctness c
shop drawings and schedules sent to them for approva
in any line of work, even if they sign the drawings or schec
ules as meeting with their approval. The approval is alway
understood to cover the general design of the work onl)
and not the correctness of the detail members or measure
ments or the fitting together of the work in the job. To

many contractors rely on the architect's approval of the drawings submitted by themselves or by their subcontractors. This approval does not constitute a thorough check of the drawings. Neither does an architect guarantee that various drawings sent in by subcontractors in different trades coordinate with one another. This all means that the estimator has to consider carefully any cost items of this sort that come to his mind in estimating. He may have to make the drawings himself for some of the subcontractors, or he may have a lot of trouble checking and correcting drawings. It may even be necessary for him to reconsider the type of subcontractors that his firm plans to use on a particular job.

The contractor assumes practically all the responsibility for the job once he has signed the contract. He may pass along a considerable amount of this responsibility to his subcontractors, and of course this is what he should do, because they are the experts and specialists in their own fields of work and may therefore be expected to undertake the responsibilities that their work entails. The estimator must see that subcontracts are so worded that the subcontractors take the whole of their fair share of responsibility. The estimator should also endeavor to have his firm's interests properly covered in the general contract with the owner. Contractors are too prone to sign the contract form that is given them by the architect (and usually double-checked beforehand by the owner or the owner's lawyer) without considering whether changes or additional clauses might not reasonably be requested by himself, the better to protect his own interests.

The steel framework of buildings is made up mainly of H columns, WF beams, channels, and angles. This is highly standardized. Architects and engineers refer to the AISC *Steel Construction Manual* when they design a structure to determine the physical characteristics of standard steel shapes. Steel contractors also use this manual when they prepare drawings, material lists, and schedules.

Structural steelwork usually costs the general contractor between $400 and $500 per ton in place. The cost can vary greatly, depending on the height of the building and the distance the steel must be transported. On monumental structures the cost may run as high as $1,000 per ton in place, or more. About 4 percent for rivets and bolts is added to the total weight of the members listed from the plans, and between 15 and 20 percent is added for connections and other details. Shop drawings may cost $15 to $25 per ton and is part of the cost of steel construction. The shop painting may cost $12 to $15 per ton of steel. Before any steel can be erected the contractor sends a considerable amount of equipment to the job. This may include derricks, cranes, hoisting engines, tackle, scaffold planks, a shanty, and an assortment of small tools. Getting all this to the job, installing it in readiness to start operations, maintaining it in good order while the job is under way, dismantling it, and finally removing it from the job are all necessary elements of cost. Setting up a large derrick alone may cost $200. The labor of unloading and erecting the steel will depend upon the type of building, the accessibility of the work, and the amount of steel involved. Riveting or welding, field painting, and other items of direct job cost require consideration also, and the insurance, general expense, and overhead expense must be considered before adding the profit. The cost of workmen's compensation insurance for erecting structural steel amounts to about 42 percent of the job payroll. Thus, if a small building requires a steel gang for about two weeks and the payroll amounts to $1,600, an amount of $672 must be added to cover this one form of insurance alone.

MISCELLANEOUS IRON

To compute the cost of miscellaneous and ornamental ironwork, the iron subcontractors' estimators list their work much as the general contractor's estimator lists millwork. Some of the items, like stairs, fire escapes, door bucks, lintels, and other commonly used items, have become standardized and require only simple listing of the amounts and sizes. Special ornamental railings, grilles, curved features, and other decorative work, however, require careful study of the plans and specifications and careful analysis of the costs involved. Stairs cost between $900 and $1,200 per story for plain work. Ordinary fire escapes cost between $700 and $1,000 per story. Door bucks, plain grilles, plain window guards, and other simple items of ironwork cost between $40 and $80 each.

The specification division dealing with miscellaneous ironwork is one that demands careful scrutiny by estimators. Architects use this as a division in which they may include many items of a special nature that should have special headings, and also some that are already covered under Masonry, Carpentry, or other headings, besides the ironwork heading.

Subcontract bids may read "For All the Miscellaneous Ironwork" or "For All the Ornamental Ironwork" or other wording that does not mean to include everything that is in the architect's specification division referred to. It is the estimator's task to make a list of possible items that he thinks will need checking. Wirework, bronze and other nonferrous items, safety treads, masonry anchors, flagpoles, metal chimneys, delivery chutes, hoists, awning boxes, steel sash, metal partitions, and fittings of various kinds are some of the items that are often thrown into the iron specifications by the architect or the specification writer. The estimator usually has to pull these items out and make special headings in his estimate for them or include them in other divisions of his estimate.

Generally speaking, the miscellaneous ironwork includes area gratings, covers and frames, coal chutes, door bucks, ladders, sidewalk doors, steel stairs, wheel and corner guards, curb angles, etc.

Ornamental iron includes grilles, balconies, lamp standards, ornamental brackets, ornamental railings, iron canopies, and special iron construction for decorative purposes.

The iron subcontractors usually suit themselves as to which items on a job they will include in their bids. Some submit, along with their bids, a list of the items included. It frequently happens that a few items are left hanging, being covered by neither sub-bids nor material quotations. The general contractor's estimator then has to scout around and get prices on them or price them himself. Loose lintels, intended to be set by the masons, are often omitted both by the steel contractors and by the iron contractors.

Many items of steel and iron are handled and set by the concrete workers or by the masons, and the cost of this handling and setting must be provided for under appropriate headings in the estimate. Anchors, inserts, sockets, safety treads, gratings, door frames, guards, curb angles, bearing plates, and small steel lintels are some of these items.

STEEL JOISTS

Open-web steel joists are used for floor and roof supports. They are generally spaced not more than 24 inches on centers in floors and not more than 30 inches in roofs. The ends of the joists must bear at least 4 inches on masonry walls and at least $2\frac{1}{2}$ inches on steel supports unless the ends butt and are securely fastened by welding, bolting, or riveting. The ends in walls are built into the walls, and every third joist is anchored to the wall with steel anchors. All steel joists must be fastened in place and the permanent bridging installed before any construction loads are placed on them.

Steel joists are manufactured by a number of companies and have become standardized in the height of bearing plate. This feature makes it possible to interchange joists manufactured by different companies. A wide range of depths and types of steel joists is available to carry different floor loads. Some of these joists will span distances up to 65 feet.

The cost of steel joists will vary with the size and type, the span, the number needed, and the distance they must be transported. The in-place cost for open-web steel joists may run from $350 to $500 per ton.

PREENGINEERED STEEL BUILDINGS

There are a number of different types of preengineered steel buildings on the market. These buildings consist of a structural steel frame supported by conventional footings.

This framework is engineered for the building use and size and is sheathed on the walls and roof with any of a number of different-colored steel, galvanized steel, or composition materials.

One of the main advantages in using preengineered steel buildings is the speed with which the building may be erected and enclosed after the foundation work is completed. Early enclosure makes it possible for the mechanical and finishing trades to complete their work earlier than with other types of buildings.

The cost of preengineered steel buildings is determined by the steel fabricator's estimator. Being a specialist in this line of work, he is best equipped to determine what the cost will be for the steel frame and sheathing.

Various features will alter the total cost of the building. However, the general contractor's estimator can check the cost of the frame and sheathing by referring to unit costs from similar previous jobs. The in-place cost for the steel frame, wall sheathing, and roof sheathing may run from $2 to $5 per square foot of floor space.

EXERCISES

1 Make sketches of four typical steel sections. Name them and place dimensions on them.

2 List the items shown on the house plans in Chapter 5 that would be included under the Steel and Iron heading in an estimate.

3 What procedure should an estimator follow in determining what steel items are included in sub-bids?

4 List items of steel which are easily overlooked.

5 How is the in-place cost of structural steel determined?

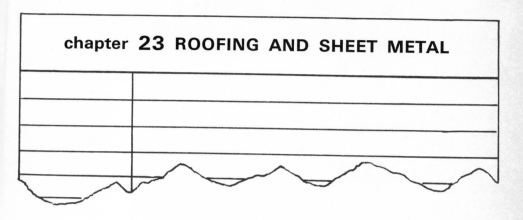

chapter 23 ROOFING AND SHEET METAL

INTRODUCTION

Roofing and sheet-metal flashing may be handled under one subcontract or they may be handled by separate contractors specializing in roofing or sheet-metal work. The work under these headings involves roof coverings, flashings, rain gutters and leaders, heating and ventilating ducts, registers, and miscellaneous sheet-metal work. Roofing contractors also do membrane waterproofing of walls and floors.

ROOFING

Built-up, or composition, roofing (Figure 23-1) consists of several layers of felt and asphalt (or tar). Asphalt is refined from a natural substance found in large deposits in Trinidad and Venezuela and is also refined from petroleum residue. Tar is manufactured from coal and is a by-product of the coke-making process. It has a lower melting point than asphalt and when heated by the sun tends to be self-healing if used on flat or nearly flat roofs. It cannot be used on sloping roofs because it would soften and run off. Tar is often called coal tar pitch.

    The asphalt or tar is applied hot, with mops. On top of the several layers, a surface coating of fine gravel or slag or a layer of smooth or mineral-surfaced roofing is applied. The number of layers and the surface finish are, of course, given in the specifications. Slate roofing is made in shingle form, usually measuring 12 by 16 inches or 14 by 20 inches, and the thickness of commercial grades

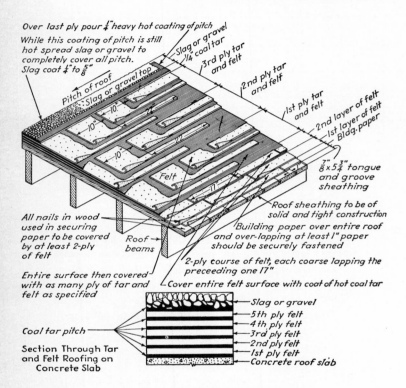

Over last ply pour $\frac{1}{4}$" heavy hot coating of pitch
While this coating of pitch is still hot spread slag or gravel to completely cover all pitch.
Slag coat $\frac{1}{4}$" to $\frac{5}{8}$"
Pitch of roof
Slag or gravel top
Slag or gravel
$\frac{1}{4}$ coal tar
3rd ply tar and felt
2nd ply tar and felt
1st ply tar and felt
2nd layer of felt
1st layer of felt
Bldg. paper
$\frac{7}{8}$" x $5\frac{3}{4}$" tongue and groove sheathing
Felt
Roof sheathing to be of solid and tight construction
All nails in wood used in securing paper to be covered by at least 2-ply of felt
Roof beams
Building paper over entire roof and over-lapping at least 1" paper should be securely fastened
2-ply course of felt, each coarse lapping the preceeding one 17"
Entire surface then covered with as many ply of tar and felt as specified
Cover entire felt surface with coat of hot coal tar
Coal tar pitch
Slag or gravel
5th ply felt
4th ply felt
3rd ply felt
2nd ply felt
1st ply felt
Concrete roof slab
Section Through Tar and Felt Roofing on Concrete Slab

FIGURE 23-1 Built-up roofing. Composition (slag or gravel) roof over concrete is similar to that over wood except for the use of the building paper and untarred felt, which are eliminated. The hot coal tar is applied directly to the concrete and then followed with as many ply as required. The average good roof is 5 ply.

runs between $\frac{3}{16}$ and $\frac{1}{4}$ inch. Other forms of roofing also are used, such as copper, zinc, and asbestos. Asbestos shingles, imitating the appearance of wood shingles, are available. All roofing is measured by the square foot or by the square containing 100 square feet.

Composition roofing costs the general contractor between 25 and 35 cents per square feet. Asbestos, clay tile, slate, and other heavy types of roofing run between $.85 and $1.50 per square foot, depending upon the quality, shapes, colors, and amounts involved. (See Chapter 13 for wood and asphalt strip shingles.)

FLASHINGS

The joints between the roof covering and the adjoining higher walls, chimneys, etc., are sealed with flashings. Strips of copper, galvanized steel or composition sheets, or plastic materials are used for this purpose. The valleys in roofs are similarly flashed. These are measured in lineal feet of each kind, and the material and width are noted.

Reglets formed or cut in the walls for cap flashing are sometimes specified under Roofing, and may not be specified or shown elsewhere. Inasmuch as the roofers will probably not include these in their bids, the estimator must provide for the expense involved under Masonry or some other appropriate heading. If, however, a patented type of reglet is called for, it might be included by the roofers, or, depending on the type, by the masons. No definite general rules can be laid down covering items that may or may not be included in bids from subcontractors. It is essential to realize the importance of taking care in analyzing these bids. Experience along this line is necessary.

Ordinary plastic flashings cost about 35 cents per lineal foot. Galvanized steel slashings cost about 80 cents, and copper flashings about $1.80 per lineal foot.

GUTTERS

Gutters are hung on the fascia at the bottom edge of sloping roofs, or they may be formed by the roof and lined with galvanized steel, aluminum, or copper. Wood and plastic gutters are also available. For estimating purposes a sketch of the gutter, giving its shape and size, is required. The total lineal footage of gutter and the kind of material specified should also be listed. With this information it is possible for the estimator to determine the price for the gutter work.

For stock-pattern gutters hung at the edge of the roof, the cost is determined by multiplying the total lineal footage by the cost per lineal foot of gutter. Additional allowances must be made for hangers, strap braces, and other necessary hardware.

Built-in gutters are a little harder to estimate in that the estimator must use his imagination and judgment in determining all the items necessary to build the gutter. Perhaps the easiest way to determine the amount of flat material needed to make up a gutter is to find the total width of the gutter material by adding up all the dimensions of the cross section and multiplying the sum by the total length. Care must be taken to make allowances for overlaps and corners.

Leaders or conductors are listed by size and shape and are figured by the lineal foot. The number of elbows is listed, with the size, shape, and material. All gutters, elbows, and leaders on a given job should be made of the same material to avoid galvanic reaction between the metals. In preparing an estimate for gutters and leaders an allowance must also be made for miscellaneous hardware.

Metal cornices, which are included under this heading, often require special analysis. Plain cornices of metal are measured in lineal feet, and the full width of the metal is noted, together with a sketch showing the profile.

Copper gutters and leaders cost the general contractor about $1.70 to $3 per lineal foot or more, depending on the type. Galvanized steel gutters and leaders may cost $.70 to $1.50 per lineal foot or more, depending on size, and aluminum gutters and leaders may cost $.80 to $2.50 per lineal foot. Plain cornices of galvanized steel cost about $4.50 per lineal foot for small sizes, and those of copper about $8 per lineal foot. Large and decorated cornices easily cost twice as much or more.

SKYLIGHTS

Skylights, which are of many types, require careful listing as to size, shape, kind of metal, glass, ventilating openings, etc. Galvanized steel skylights cost about $60 apiece for small ones 2 or 3 feet square, $150 apiece for those of about 5 feet square. Copper skylights are much more expensive. A large one, say 8 feet 0 inches by 15 feet 0 inches, with ventilators, might cost $750 to $900. The glass used in skylights is always included with the skylights and is not listed under the regular glass heading.

HEATING AND VENTILATING DUCTS

Ducts may be made from galvanized steel or aluminum. Plain ventilating duct work is listed in lineal feet. The cross-section size is given. All bends and special shapes are carefully counted and described separately. Registers, louvers, and other fittings and supplies are also listed and described separately. Straight duct work in galvanized steel, 12 by 12 inches in cross section, will cost about $3 per lineal foot, and each intersection or bend in it will cost $9 to $12 extra.

WATERPROOFING

Membrane waterproofing is similar to composition roofing work and is done by the roofers. It consists of several layers of felt or burlap, each embedded in hot asphalt or tar, and is applied on foundation walls and in bathrooms, showers, and other locations requiring such protection. This work is measured in square feet, and the cost is generally between 30 and 70 cents per square foot.

EXERCISES

1 List the items of work generally included under Roofing and Sheet Metal, and opposite each one give the unit of measure used and an average price per unit.

2 Make an estimate of all the roofing and sheet-metal work for the plans shown in Chapter 5.

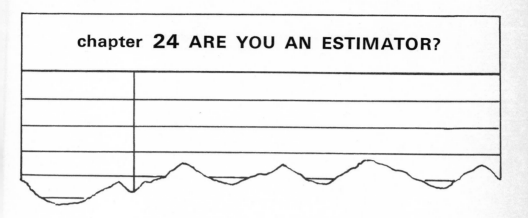

chapter 24 ARE YOU AN ESTIMATOR?

This book was planned as a complete course in the work of the building contractor's estimator. If you have conscientiously studied everything in it, you are at least well on the way toward becoming an estimator. Practical experience is needed, however, as in any other line of work. When a young man completes a course in chemistry or in bookkeeping, he may call himself a chemist or a bookkeeper but he is hardly qualified to take charge of a chemical laboratory or a bookkeeping department. In the same way if you have completed the course outlined in this book, you may call yourself an estimator, but you should not expect to have full charge of preparing complete estimates until you have had considerable practical experience in building work.

This chapter contains a comprehensive examination, which will test your ability in estimating. If you have done the work called for in the book and receive a mark of 70 percent or better in this examination, you may feel confident in embarking on actual estimating work. If your mark is between 80 and 90 percent, you are better than the ordinary assistant in estimating. If you have studied and worked so satisfactorily during the whole course that you earn between 90 and 100 percent in the examination, especially if you receive a mark in this range in each of the two sections of the examination, you need have no hesitancy in calling yourself an estimator. Put it this way: you may classify yourself as a junior assistant in estimating if your final grade is between 70 and 80 percent, as a junior estimator if it is between 80 and 90 percent, and as an estimator if it is between 90 and 100 percent.

Before taking the second part of the examination, get as much practice as possible by borrowing several sets of plans and specifications from architects and builders and going through the entire procedure of making complete and accurate detailed estimates for all of them.

If your mark is over 90 percent in each of the two sections of the examination, take this book with you when you are seeking a position and tell your prospective employer that you know everything in it. Carry along all your work sheets and your notebook for the entire course. If your interviewer is at all fair, he will have to admit that you have a good knowledge of the subject.

Before taking the examination, review all the chapters from the beginning. Chapter 1 calls your attention to the importance of the work of the estimator. It is work that requires patience and a methodical way of doing things. It is not an undertaking for a careless person to attempt. Never vary your way of working in an attempt to please somebody who is looking for speed; you will not be thanked for it if there is a mistake in your work. If at any time your work is not prepared with your usual methodical care, there will be mistakes—always remember that. The estimator is usually the center of activity in a well-organized office, and this means that his work is the important work of the office, the work that means the difference between a profit or a loss on the job! Such work is not always properly valued by employers or by other members of a contracting organization; but the estimator finally learns that his reputation as a careful man is one of his main assets.

Chapters 2 to 4 deal with the people you will meet in building work. They are all interesting, and you will enjoy working with them. One striking characteristic of your work is the constant change that takes place, both in the kind and location of jobs and in the steady flow of different people—architects, engineers, inspectors, superintendents, draftsmen, foremen, subcontractors, material men, and workmen. Here is as great a variety as you could wish for; surely your work will never become monotonous. Learn your work well and really enjoy the company of other trained men, who in turn will enjoy working with you. Learn also to judge men, for you will find that not all are as sincere as you are. Keep your own character and reputation clean throughout all the trials and tribulations you may encounter, for you will learn the truth of the statement made in Chapter 4—that character and reputation of the right sort contribute to your happiness.

Chapters 5 and 6 discuss plans and specifications and the legal side of building work. Plans and specifications have an important legal standing themselves, because they form the portion of the contract that explains just what is to be done. Everything shown on the plans or in the specifications is to be furnished or done by the contractor—the general conditions or the contract itself usually states the matter that way. Advise against signing any contract that you feel is not entirely clear and fair. Be fair in making your own subcontracts and purchase orders, and thus uphold your reputation. Bear in mind that the recommendations given in Chapter 7 for a sort of estimating code are not actually in vogue. Perhaps the time will come when the building industry will develop and use certain standards of bidding that will eliminate some of the abuses of today. In the meantime, we have to make the best of the existing methods. Abide by the law in all things; remember that building codes are only schedules of minimum requirements; try to do better than is called for in these minimum requirements.

Chapters 7 to 9 give a broad view of the preparation of estimates and of the general expense involved in carrying on building operations. Some contractors make up estimates hastily, sometimes without the aid of an estimator trained as you have been. Such estimates can only be termed approximations, and as is stated in Chapter 7, approximate estimates have a bad habit of not being correct and of bringing trouble to those who use them. There is nothing more satisfying to a regular estimator than to see his carefully prepared estimate being used all through the life of a job and serving all purposes well. Picture in your mind, as you estimate, the actual working conditions, especially when you are gauging the unit prices to be applied. Remember to check all the large items and the unit prices you apply to them; they are the ones that will have the greatest effect on the total cost of the job. Do not let others influence your judgment too much. Look into every item thoroughly yourself, so that you can be confident in your own judgment. Keep your estimates and quantity sheets in good order at all times; arrange them so that you or anybody else will be able to find any item quickly and understand each entry. Remember that work that is out of the ordinary in character is always more expensive to build than that with which every workman is familiar. Remember that work to be performed at a great distance from the center of business areas involves particular attention and care in arranging for workmen, deliveries of material, etc., and may require expensive transportation of both men and materials. Winter work usually means a whole list of items of extra expense.

Chapters 10 to 14 give detailed instructions for estimating the work that is usually done by the general contractor's own men. Only regular work has been considered, and you are therefore warned to watch out for unusual work or conditions and to study and analyze them to the best of your ability if you are to estimate on them. Excavating that you do not feel entirely confident in handling should be figured for you by subcontractors. Experienced estimators never hesitate to say that an excavating problem is too much for their firm to handle—if they really think such is the case. Building contractors should not be expected to be experts in difficult excavation or foundation work. Concrete work, likewise, may stump you, especially very complicated formwork. If you attempt to handle any complicated work in any line, measure and list the items with extra care and do not hesitate to put a much higher unit price on such work than you ordinarily would for the same work when it is not complicated. Your high price may prove to be low enough when the job is done, and you will not be thanked for anything less.

Chapters 15 to 23 treat the work usually done by

subcontractors. Unless your firm has had experience in actually doing a number of jobs in these lines, it is always better to rely on dependable subcontractors than to attempt to do, or even to estimate, this work. The mechanical trades, especially, are tricky, and estimators who have thrown in prices on them have often been sorry for having done so. Learn the ways of subcontractors. Learn to judge them. Beware of very young estimators who are sometimes used by subcontractors; they may not have had the training that you have and may lead both you and themselves into trouble. Do not measure plans or give figures for any subcontractors; let them get and be responsible for their own figures. Otherwise, even if they forgive you for unwittingly misleading them, they will always feel they have a moral hold on you and expect you somehow to fix things so they can regain what they lost, or what they say they lost. Be businesslike and perfectly honest with the subcontractors, but do not allow them to develop a personal friendship and then take advantage of such friendship. Be as impersonal as possible, and keep your reputation clean. Be loyal to the firm you work for. Work only for reputable people.

When you take this examination, do so with the knowledge that you will fool nobody more than yourself if you get a high mark without deserving it, by not making it a test that really proves to yourself that you are an estimator. Fail in the test willingly rather than start your career with a stain on your reputation!

The examination is divided into two parts, the first covering Chapters 1 to 9 and the second Chapters 10 to 23. If it is desired, Part 1 may be given immediately after the classwork on Chapters 1 to 9 has been completed.

Students are to do one of the exercises from each of the groups given in the chapters. These are to be selected by the instructor and announced or issued when the examination begins.

In addition to the exercises taken from the chapter groups, the following questions and problems are also to be included. To conserve time, note that in all problems involving the measuring of plans, only the names of the items and their dimensions are required, no time being taken for making any extensions of figures. The numbers in parentheses after some of the questions indicate the number of words used by the average student properly to answer the questions in the time allowed.

The percentages listed for each part of the test are optional with the instructor and can be altered to meet special needs.

EXAMINATION

Part 1

20 questions and problems at 5% each

1–9   These are exercises taken from the lists at the end of Chapters 1 to 9, and will be announced by the instructor.

10   Building estimating requires a working knowledge of all phases of building work. Why? (50 to 75 words)

11   The estimator in a well-organized office is usually the center of activity in the office. Why? (50 to 75 words)

12   Before the work at the job can begin, the estimator makes up the various schedules, etc. What are these, and how are they used? (30 to 50 words)

13   When the job gets under way, the estimator gradually relinquishes hold. How should he turn the work over to the superintendent? (40 to 60 words)

14   The construction of a building involves many kinds of administrative and technical skills. Name ten positions of administrative and technical skill that are found in the actual construction of a building.

15   How does a contractor go about getting plans for new jobs that are to be estimated? (40 to 60 words)

16   What information should a good estimate contain? (50 to 75 words)

17   On a regular building job costing about $200,000 there are usually many items of general job expense. Make a list of these for such a job and show after each the approximate cost that might be involved.

18   Imagine that the job in Problem 17 is actually under way. Make a daily report such as the job superintendent would send to his home office for a day when the job is well organized and about half completed. Include remarks regarding a dispute between the superintendent and the architect's inspector about the quality of some material.

19 Make a diagram and describe the relationship between the men usually concerned with building work, similar to the treatment of this topic in Chapter 2, Construction Relations. (60 to 80 words and diagram)

20 Write a descriptive composition of 100 to 150 words on Plan Reading, using the plans in Figures 5-4 to 5-13 (or plans provided in class) to illustrate the points brought out in your composition.

Part 2

1–15 These are exercises taken from Chapters 10 to 23, and will be announced by the instructor. (15 at 3% each)

16 List every tenth term from the Index, to a total of twenty terms. Every student is to start with a different term. One student starts with the first term in the Index, the next student with the second term, etc., and then each tenth term thereafter. State the meaning and use of each term clearly in twenty to thirty words. Sketches will be accepted in lieu of ten to twenty of the words. (20 terms at 1% each)

17 Make a complete detailed estimate for the plans given in Figures 5-4 to 5-13 (or plans provided in class), omitting the extensions of quantities, to save time, but including roughly approximate totals for the purpose of pricing. Extend and total all money amounts. Use assumed subcontractors' figures for the plumbing, heating, and electrical work only. (35%)

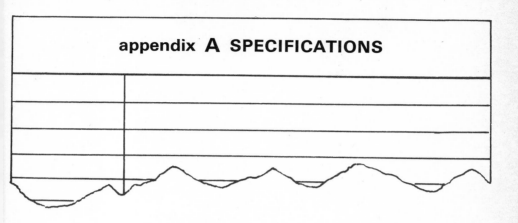

appendix A SPECIFICATIONS

These specifications apply to the plans for the single-family dwelling in Chapter 5. They are included as typical specifications which an estimator would encounter in preparing a construction cost estimate, except that General Conditions and other front matter are omitted.

EXCAVATING

Remove 9 inches of topsoil from the entire width of the property, and for a distance of 60 feet back from the sidewalk, pile this at the rear of the property, and spread it later over the front lawn and terrace and elsewhere as directed by the architect. None of this material is to be removed from the premises.

Excavate for all footings, foundation walls, areas, steps, walks, and driveway, first removing and stacking the topsoil as noted above. Excavate for a sufficient distance from the foundation walls to allow for inspection and to permit the various trades to install their work.

Remove excess subsoil from the premises, and grade and backfill to the finish levels shown on the drawings.

The seeding and landscaping will be done under a separate contract.

CONCRETE FOOTINGS

All footings shall be six-bag-mix concrete with maximum-size crushed-rock or gravel aggregate of $\frac{3}{4}$ inch, poured into substantial forms. All wall footings shall contain three continuous lines of $\frac{5}{8}$-inch-diameter bars held in alignment by $\frac{3}{8}$-inch-diameter bars every 18 inches. The column footings shall each contain four $\frac{5}{8}$-inch-diameter bars in each direction, a total of eight bars in each footing. All bars shall be spaced as directed by the architect.

CONCRETE WORK

All concrete floors, steps, and drives shall be of six-bag-mix, air-entrained concrete with a maximum size of crushed-rock or gravel aggregate manufactured and placed in accordance with PCA recommendations for quality concrete.

MASONWORK

Furnish all labor, materials, and appliances, and perform all operations in connection with the masonry work, complete, in strict accordance with the drawings and as specified herein.

The following items of work are included in this division of the specifications:

Hollow-concrete-block foundations
Concrete fill in certain blocks
Brick piers in garage
Brick on top of block wall at crawl space
Cinder-concrete-block partitions in basement
Brick chimney with terra-cotta flue lining
Firebrick fireplace lining
Cleanout doors, dampers, and chimney cap
Brick hearth and concrete slab under it
Brick veneer on front and left side walls
Brick pedestal for flower box
Brick walls under front porch

Cement windowsills in basement

Setting of bearing plates and anchor bolts

Cutting, patching, and chases

Cleaning and pointing

Mortar and masonry scaffolds

The following work is specified in other sections of the specifications:

Concrete footings

Concrete work—floors and steps

Stonework

The concrete blocks shall be high-pressure and steam-cured and shall conform to the current edition of the ASTM Standard Specifications for Concrete Units, with gravel or crushed-stone aggregate. Provide special blocks for corners and elsewhere as required. Fill with 1:2:4 concrete all the blocks under the chimney and the top course of all the foundation walls. All exposed joints shall be uniform, smooth flush joints.

All exposed brick, both interior and exterior, shall be textured brick. The contractor shall allow the sum of $80 per 1,000 board feet for these bricks, delivered to the job. All other brick shall be sound, well-burned, red common brick. All brick shall be placed in a full bed of unfurrowed mortar, and all points shall be completely filled with mortar.

All mortar shall be 1 part portland cement, 1 part hydrated lime, and 6 parts clean, sharp, well-screened sand. Lehigh, Lone Star, or Brixment masonry cement may be used in lieu of this mixture.

The brick piers shall be well bonded within themselves and to the adjoining block walls.

The 4-inch block partitions in the basement shall be composed of approved cinder-concrete blocks neatly laid up with smooth flush joints.

Terra-cotta flue lining shall be sound and well burned, properly installed, and with a thimble unit for the boiler smoke pipe. The fireplace and the back hearth shall be lined with approved firebrick laid flat. The flue lining and firebrick shall be laid in approved fire-clay mortar.

Provide an approved cast-iron fireplace damper and cast-iron, hinged cleanout door with frame.

The front hearth shall extend the full width as shown on the drawings, on a slab of five-bag-mix concrete over solidly tamped fill. The front hearth and the fireplace chimney breast shall be face brick laid up in a simple pattern as directed by the architect.

The brick veneer and the flower-box pedestal and front-porch walls shall be neatly laid up in Flemish bond with uniform weathered joints. Provide substantial galvanized steel ties as required. Construct rowlock sill course sloped to shed water.

Construct neat, smooth-finished cement sills under the basement windows and a sloping cement cap on the chimney.

Install and build in all anchor bolts, bearing plates, door frames, etc., in masonry. These items will be furnished by others. Build in all girder and beam ends with solid masonry.

Cut and patch masonry and form chases, etc., as required by the work of all trades.

Clean all exposed masonry, both interior and exterior, with muriatic acid and water and repoint joints where required.

STONEWORK

Front Porch Lay 1½-inch-thick bluestone flags, honed finish, on the floor of the front porch. Only large flags shall be used, and they shall be set in cement mortar with tight joints, in pattern as directed by the architect.

Walks Lay standard 1-inch-thick slate flagstone walks as shown on the plans. The flags shall be laid on a bed of compacted sand 1 inch thick. The joints between the flags shall not exceed ¼ inch in width. The flags for the walks shall be one piece in width of the walks and of plain slate color, except those for the front walk, which shall be of colors as selected by the architect.

Driveway Wall   Construct the wall at the driveway, above the grade, 16 inches thick, of selected rough local stone set neatly in random-ashlar formation in cement mortar. The stones shall be properly bonded together, and no small stones shall appear on the exposed surface. Provide three one-piece, $1\frac{1}{2}$-inch-thick copings of bluestone with honed finish on top and all edges.

Front Steps   Construct straight and radial steps as shown on the plans, set solidly in cement mortar, on the rough-concrete steps. The risers shall be of large pieces of rough local stone. The treads shall be of $1\frac{1}{2}$-inch-thick bluestone with honed top and front edge, each tread in one piece and set to project out about $\frac{1}{2}$ inch over the risers. Care shall be taken to make all the steps uniform in height and, as far as practicable, uniform otherwise.

ROUGH CARPENTRY

Materials shall be new, thoroughly seasoned, and protected from the weather until placed in the building. All lumber shall be No. 1 common Douglas fir dressed on four sides for framing. All wall and roof sheathing and subflooring, except the subflooring in the living room and kitchen, shall be 1- by 6-inch No. 2 common shortleaf pine or fir. Subflooring in the living room and kitchen shall be $\frac{3}{4}$-inch-thick fir plywood. The 1- by 6-inch wall sheathing and subflooring shall be laid diagonally, the roof sheathing straight. Construct the subfloor in the vestibule and foyer to accommodate 4 inches of cinder concrete and quarry tile.

Wall and partition studs shall be 2 by 4 inches set 16 inches on centers, in one length where possible, and doubled around openings.

Joists shall be doubled under all partitions running parallel thereto, and doubled or tripled elsewhere as required. Bridging shall be 1 by 3 inches.

Provide all required special framing, blocking, and grounds, etc.

All work shall be done in accordance with the requirements of the building code.

ROOFING AND SHEET METAL

Roofing Felt   Lay 15-pound asphalt roofing felt horizontally on all roof surfaces, with all joints lapped 4 inches, nailed down with copper roofing nails. Lay an extra ply, 36 inches wide, lengthwise, over all ridges and along higher walls, stuck to the first ply with roofing mastic.

Flashings   Flash where required with 16-ounce copper. Install base flashing at all walls and chimney, at least 6 inches high and projecting at least 3 inches on the roofs, and cap flashings turned down not less than 4 inches over the base flashings. Install proper step flashings at the chimney and where vertical surfaces meet sloping roofs. Flash all exterior door and window heads, extending the flashing at least 3 inches above the frames.

Gutters and Leaders   Install heavy molded aluminum gutters, 5 inches wide and 4 inches deep, and corrugated rectangular aluminum leaders, 4 by 3 inches, where indicated on the plans. Provide all necessary heavy-aluminum leader heads, hangers, and straps.

Asphalt Shingles   Lay standard asphalt strip shingles, 235 pounds per square, on all roof surfaces except the two window roofs and the sun deck, color as selected. This work shall be done in strict accord with the recommendations of the shingle manufacturer.

Canvas Roofing   Cover the sun deck with 12-ounces cotton duck, properly laid over a coat of white lead and linseed oil, stretched and tacked at all edges with large-head copper nails $\frac{3}{4}$ inch apart. When the canvas is thoroughly dry, paint it with one coat of lead and oil and two coats of approved gray deck paint.

Copper Roofing   Cover the living-room and dining-room window roofs with 16-ounce soft copper, coated on the back with 15-pound lead per square. Use sheets not larger than 14 by 20 inches and lay with flat lock seams, soldered.

Flower Boxes   Provide flower boxes of 16-gauge copper, with top edges turned and reinforced, in the wooden flower boxes. Provide three boxes in the living-room flower box and one each in the other boxes, a total of five copper boxes.

Dampproofing Apply a full, heavy coat of hot asphalt on the outsid﹐ of all exterior walls, below finish grade.

PLASTERING

Apply expanded metal lath, weighing at least 3 pounds per square yard, to all the wall and ceiling surfaces in the bathrooms and kitchen, and on the walls and soffit in the stairway leading from the kitchen to the basement.

Apply Rocklath on the walls and ceilings in the other rooms, closets, and halls on the first and second floors, except in the storage room. Install strips of expanded metal lath, over the Rocklath, in all vertical and horizontal internal corners and extending at least 3 inches on each of the surfaces. Install galvanized metal corner beads on all external vertical corners throughout, extending the full height of the plaster.

Apply a scratch coat of cement for the tilework in the bathrooms. Apply three coats of lime plaster, with Keene's cement mixed half and half in the finish coat, on all the metal lath elsewhere.

Apply two coats of gypsum plaster on all the Rocklath.

Finish all plaster to a hard, troweled surface.

Apply three coats of cement stucco on the outside of the foundation walls above grade and on the walls in the rear areaway, with smooth, woodfloat finish.

All work shall be done by skilled mechanics and in strict conformity with the building code.

FINISH CARPENTRY

Materials All materials shall be thoroughly seasoned and protected from the weather until placed in the building. All interior trim and doors shall be sandpapered. All tool and erection marks shall be carefully removed from finished surfaces. All workmanship must be perfect. All joints, where possible, shall be tongued and rabbeted together to conceal shrinkage. Exterior wood finish shall be selected stock white pine and all interior finish southern poplar, except where otherwise noted below.

Doors Exterior doors shall be $1\frac{3}{4}$ inches thick of stock design as selected by the architect. The interior door in the garage shall be a flush kalamein door with kalamein frame. All other interior doors shall be white pine $1\frac{3}{8}$ inches thick, of six-panel colonial design, with raised panels. Exterior door frames shall be solid rabbeted $1\frac{1}{8}$-inch-thick white pine. Interior door jambs shall be $\frac{7}{8}$ inch thick. Install hardware as specified under the Hardware heading. Mirrored doors shall have full-length plate-glass mirrors on one side as indicated on the plans.

Windows and Screens Provide a hinged steel window in the basement wall near the boiler, and aluminum louvered frames in the gables. All other windows shall be aluminum of approved good quality with approved hardware and adjusters. The double-hung windows shall have sash balances, locks, handles, and stainless steel weather strips. Provide full-size aluminum insect screens, made by the window manufacturer, on all windows that open.

Exterior Trim Provide all exterior trim required, including $1\frac{1}{8}$- by $2\frac{3}{4}$-inch plain window frames and casings, $1\frac{3}{4}$- by $7\frac{3}{4}$-inch oak windowsills, $1\frac{1}{8}$- by $3\frac{3}{4}$-inch molded door casings, as well as the bay-window and living-room-window woodwork, cornices, cornice returns, rakes, brackets, moldings, overhead door frame, shutters, flower boxes, arbor, and gate, etc., all of substantial construction and as directed by the architect.

Wall Covering Cover all exterior walls, except in the gable areas, with No. 1 red cedar 16-inch shingles set with 10 inches exposed to the weather. Cover all gables with redwood boards $\frac{1}{2}$ by 10 inches, set vertically and 1 inch apart on $\frac{3}{4}$- by 4-inch redwood battens, battens behind the joints. Provide black waterproof building paper, well lapped, behind all siding and casings and wall trim.

Porches Provide front- and rear-porch posts and railings, step and screen at the rear porch, and seat on the front porch, all of white pine substantially constructed. Lay yellow pine or cypress $\frac{3}{4}$- by $2\frac{1}{2}$-inch flooring and nosings on the rear porch and on the sun deck. Provide $\frac{1}{2}$- by $2\frac{1}{2}$-inch tongued and grooved white pine or cypress ceilings in the front and rear porches.

Interior Trim Provide $\frac{3}{4}$- by $3\frac{3}{4}$-inch molded trim around all doors and windows. Provide $1\frac{1}{8}$-inch stools rabbeted over $\frac{3}{4}$- by $3\frac{3}{4}$-inch molded aprons at all window openings. Provide a $\frac{3}{4}$- by $3\frac{3}{4}$-inch molded chair rail in the dining room. Provide a $\frac{3}{4}$- by $5\frac{1}{4}$-inch baseboard, with two moldings, and $\frac{3}{4}$- by $4\frac{3}{4}$-inch cornice mold throughout, except in the basement, bathrooms, and closets. Provide one shelf, a chrome-plated hanger pole, and a $\frac{3}{4}$- by $3\frac{1}{4}$-inch baseboard in all closets, with six shelves in the linen closet. Provide substantial shelves in the basement as indicated on the plans, consisting of three 16-inch shelves under the stairs, a 16-inch workbench, and two 12-inch shelves in the laundry, a 16-inch counter and ten 12-inch shelves in the pantry, and one shelf in the garage. Provide plywood cabinet with two doors, and folding ironing board with cabinet, in the laundry. Construct a cedar closet in the storage room.

Provide prefinished white oak plywood paneling on walls in the vestibule and foyer.

Cabinetwork Provide cabinets in the foyer and vestibule and at the fireplace in the living room, as indicated on the plans, including door trim and trimmed openings, all of oak in high-grade cabinet construction. All the kitchen and dining-nook cabinets, counters, and other fittings will be provided by others under a separate contract.

Stairs The stairs, from basement to second floor, shall have 2- by 12-inch carriages, $1\frac{1}{8}$-inch oak treads, $\frac{7}{8}$-inch white pine risers, $1\frac{1}{8}$-inch square balusters set three to a tread, and $3\frac{1}{4}$- by $3\frac{1}{4}$-inch molded oak newel-posts. Treads and risers shall be mortised together, wedged, and glued. Provide molded oak $2\frac{1}{4}$- by $2\frac{1}{4}$-inch handrails.

Flooring Lay $\frac{3}{4}$-inch-thick Douglas fir plywood flooring, 4-foot sheets in long lengths, in the living room and kitchen, well nailed down at all bearings. Lay clear oak flooring, $\frac{25}{32}$- by $2\frac{1}{4}$-inch face, in the dining room. Lay select oak flooring, $\frac{25}{32}$- by $2\frac{1}{4}$-inch face, in all the other rooms, halls, and closets on the first and second floors, except in the bathrooms. Lay $\frac{1}{2}$-inch-thick plywood in the storage room. Scrape all ridges from the plywood flooring. Scrape all oak flooring and sand it to a smooth surface ready for finishing.

HARDWARE

An allowance of $250 shall be made for hardware. All hardware shall be selected by the owner and charged to the allowance. Any surplus allowance shall be credited to the owner. If hardware costs exceed the $250 allowance, the owner shall be billed the amount of excess based on the contractor's cost.

All hardware shall be installed in a workmanlike manner in strict accordance with the manufacturer's recommendations.

TILEWORK

This work shall be done in strict accord with the recommendations of the Tile Manufacturers Association. The surfaces shall be cleaned and polished and left in perfect condition.

Lay 6- by 6-inch semivitreous unglazed quarry-tile flooring in the entrance vestibule and foyer over 4 inches of cinder concrete.

Install $4\frac{1}{4}$- by $4\frac{1}{4}$-inch semivitreous matte-glazed tile flooring and 42-inch-high wainscoting, including 50-inch-high above the bathtubs, in the two bathrooms. Provide coved base, cap, and corners. The floor border and wainscot base and cap shall be of one color, and the balance of the tile of another color, to be selected by the architect.

Install glass towel bars in chrome-plated brackets, chrome-plated shower-curtain rods and chrome-plated soap dish, and combination tumbler and toothbrush holder in

each bathroom. Provide recessed tile toilet-paper holders
and combination soap holder and grab bars.

GLAZING

Glaze the stationary windows in the living room and dining
room with $\frac{1}{4}$-inch-thick glazing-quality plate glass.

Provide a 34- by 60-inch polished-edge mirror, of sil-
vering quality, $\frac{1}{4}$-inch-thick plate glass with copper-coated
back, on the wall in the entrance vestibule, held in place
where directed by six glass rosettes.

The door mirrors are specified under Finish Carpentry.

PLUMBING

Provide a complete plumbing system, with all material and
workmanship in strict accord with the regulations of all
authorities having jurisdiction. The plumbing subcontractor
shall obtain all the necessary permits and pay all fees.

All materials shall be new, high-grade, and suitable,
and the workmanship shall be best union work.

The work under this section includes street sewer and
water connections, including excavating and backfilling and
street patching, and a complete drainage and water system
in the building.

The house drain and soil line shall be XHCI. All other
waste lines and the vent lines shall be galvanized steel.
All hot- and cold-water lines shall be of copper with soldered
joints, copper fittings, and brass valves and of proper size.
Provide copper $\frac{3}{4}$-inch water service and water meter. Provide $\frac{3}{4}$-inch hose bibs in the garage and outside on the
rear wall. Provide water-supply line to the boiler, complete
with traps and fittings, and connect the hot-water line to
the heater in the boiler. Provide chrome-plated shutoff
valves under all fixtures. Provide black-iron gas lines from
the gas meter to the kitchen range and connect the range.

The kitchen counter, the main bathroom vanity, the
dishwasher, and the clothes washer will be furnished by
others, and the plumbers shall connect the fixtures to the
plumbing system.

The plumbing subcontractor shall furnish a written warranty to the owner covering the materials and workmanship for a period of one year from final acceptance, and shall furnish the owner with all the customary certificates of approval.

Furnish and install the following American Standard fixtures, or Crane fixtures of equal quality and design, of colors selected:

Three water closets, Master one-piece, with Church seats

One lavatory, Comrade, 24 by 20 inches, in second-floor bathroom

One lavatory, Marledge, 20 by 14 inches, in basement

Two bathtubs, Master Pembroke 5-foot 6-inch recess type, with Waldorf Chromard fittings and showers

One kitchen sink, 30 by 21 inches, with Chromard fittings, swinging spout, soap dish, and spray

One lavatory, 24 by 20 inches, for main bathroom vanity, with Chromard Waldorf trim

One laundry tray, Lakeview, 24 by 20 inches

One areaway shower, with Chromard Waldorf trim, and Chromard shutoff valves in adjoining toilet room

One Josam floor drain in areaway, with removable top

HEATING

Provide a complete heating system, with material and workmanship in strict accord with the regulations of all authorities having jurisdiction. The heating subcontractor shall obtain the necessary permits and pay all the fees.

All materials shall be new, high-grade, and suitable, and the workmanship shall be best union work.

The oil-fired boiler shall be an American Standard or equal, having an output of 150,000 Btu, and shall be install in strict accordance with the manufacturer's recommendations.

The heating contractor shall provide a plan of the heating system, showing the location and size of all radiators and convectors, for the architect's approval before work commences. Upon completion of the job, the heating contractor shall furnish a written warranty to the owner covering the materials and workmanship for a period of one year from final acceptance.

ELECTRICAL WORK

Provide a complete electrical system, with all materials and workmanship in strict accord with the recommendations of the National Board of Fire Underwriters and the regulations of all authorities having jurisdiction.

All materials shall be new, high-grade, and suitable, and all work shall be union work.

The work under this section includes the necessary service equipment, feeders, panels, power circuits, lighting circuits, outlets, switches, porcelain pull-chain receptacles, television connection outlets, bell-and-buzzer system, and the installation of the owner's fixtures and equipment requiring electrical connections.

The service equipment shall include a Square-D 120-ampere, three-wire, safety-type service switch connected with three No. 2 service wires.

Install a four-circuit, three-wire panel box in the garage. Run the power wiring, three-wire, from this panel, in steel pipe conduit.

Install a ten-circuit, three-wire panel box in the garage. Run the lighting wiring and the wiring to the minor appliances from this panel, in BX cable, properly distributed.

All wiring, except in the basement and attic, shall be concealed. All exterior wiring and outlets shall be waterproof.

All switches shall be the silent, mercury type. All base and wall receptacles shall be duplex, and the face plates on these and on the switches shall be ivory-finished.

Provide four separate power circuits and connections to serve the clothes washer and dryer in the laundry and the dishwashing machine and toaster outlet in the kitchen.

Provide proper electrical connection to the oil burner and install a thermostat for this in the living room.

Install a kitchen 10-inch exhaust fan, of good make, with aluminum shutters outside, a sheet-metal duct, and a chrome-plated grille on the kitchen side.

Install nonmetallic television outlet boxes in the entrance foyer and in the basement playroom. Run a suitable transmission line from these to the attic, with a slack length of 20 feet in the attic.

Install the electric outlets and wiring shown on the first-floor electrical plan (Figure 21-2).

Install in the basement: 8 ceiling-light outlets, 2 wall-light outlets, 5 wall switches, 6 wall convenience outlets, 1 pull-chain outlet with porcelain lamp receptacle, a flexible-cable convenience outlet in the garage, and three-way switches for the garage and stairway lights.

Install in the second floor and attic: 5 ceiling-light outlets, 1 wall-light outlet, 6 wall switches, 8 base outlets, 1 wall convenience outlet, 1 pull-chain outlet with porcelain lamp receptacle, and a three-way switch for the lower-hall light.

Install the laundry and kitchen equipment and the lighting fixtures. These will be furnished by the owner.

Install a complete signaling system, including transformers, push buttons at the front and kitchen doors, and a combination bell and buzzer in the kitchen and in the second-floor hall.

The electrical subcontractor shall furnish a written warranty to the owner covering the materials and workmanship for a period of one year from final acceptance, and shall furnish the owner with all the customary certificates of approval.

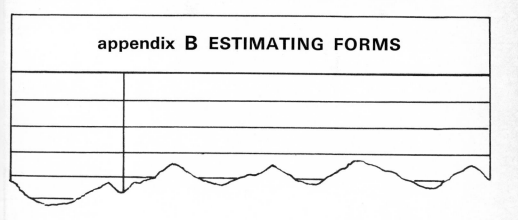

appendix B ESTIMATING FORMS

There are many printed forms available for use in estimating and cost keeping. Some of them are reproduced on the following pages.

The *quantity* sheet contains columns for description, number (of pieces, etc.), dimensions, four columns for extensions, estimated quantity, and unit. A double-width quantity sheet is available for taking quantities on complicated jobs. This sheet has fifteen columns for extensions.

The *recapitulation* form provides a means for pricing the job and is used in conjunction with the quantity sheet. It has columns for item description, quantity, unit, unit material price, total estimated material cost, unit labor price, and total estimated labor cost.

The *estimate recapitulation* form is similar to the recapitulation form but contains additional columns for total unit price and total estimated cost.

The form entitled *general estimate* combines the quantity sheet and recapitulation. It has columns for description of work, number of pieces, dimensions, extensions, total estimated quantity, unit prices, total estimated material cost, and total estimated labor cost. The general estimate form is available in double widths and has additional columns for extensions as well as columns for recapitulating the estimate.

A *summary of estimate* form is available for summarizing the bid. It has columns for estimated material and labor costs, sub-bids, total, and adjustments. These forms are available with classifications printed in or with the classification column left blank.

The *job estimate and cost record* provides a complete record of all costs on one sheet for a residential building. The back of this sheet contains a summary-of-estimate reminder list, as well as space for cost breakdown and other information.

Estimate and cost summary is a sheet which provides a method for comparing estimated cost with actual cost and, finally, profit or loss on each item.

Various methods are used to keep time on the construction job. Two daily time sheets are illustrated here. One sheet is for an individual employee and has space for each job he works on, its description, hours, rate, and amount. The other time sheet is kept for the individual job and is used when a number of employees are working on a single job.

The *labor distribution* form is made out each week for every type of work performed. The occupations are listed along with total hours. These are totaled and summarized to obtain unit costs. The *cost analysis record* on the reverse side is used to convert the total labor hours to time per unit of work. The amount of time per unit of work is valuable information in making future cost estimates because it allows the estimator to apply prevailing wages.

PRACTICAL
Form 516 MFD IN U.S.A.

QUANTITY SHEET

PROJECT _____ ESTIMATOR _____ ESTIMATE NO. _____

LOCATION _____ EXTENSIONS _____ SHEET NO. _____

ARCHITECT
ENGINEER _____ CHECKED _____ DATE _____

CLASSIFICATION _____

DESCRIPTION	NO.	DIMENSIONS								ESTIMATED QUANTITY	UNIT

FRANK R. WALKER CO., PUBLISHERS, CHICAGO

FIGURE B-1 Quantity Sheet. Source: Frank R. Walker Co.,
Chicago.

PRACTICAL
"STANDARDIZED" FORMS FOR CONTRACTORS
Form 517 MFD. IN U. S. A.

RECAPITULATION

PROJECT ESTIMATE NO.
LOCATION SHEET NO.
ARCHITECT ENGINEER DATE
SUMMARY BY PRICES BY CHECKED BY

DESCRIPTION	QUANTITY	UNIT	UNIT PRICE	TOTAL ESTIMATED MATERIAL COST	UNIT PRICE	TOTAL ESTIMATED LABOR COST

FRANK R. WALKER CO., PUBLISHERS, CHICAGO

FIGURE B-2 Recapitulation. Source: Frank R. Walker Co., Chicago.

PRACTICAL STANDARDIZED FORMS FOR CONTRACTORS
FORM 511 MFG. IN U. S. A.

ESTIMATE RECAPITULATION

PROJECT ESTIMATE NO.

LOCATION SHEET NO.

ARCHITECT
ENGINEER DATE

SUMMARY BY PRICES BY CHECKED BY

DESCRIPTION	QUANTITY	UNIT	UNIT PRICE	TOTAL ESTIMATED MATERIAL COST	UNIT PRICE	TOTAL ESTIMATED LABOR COST	UNIT PRICE	TOTAL

FRANK R. WALKER CO., PUBLISHERS, 5030 NO. HARLEM AVE., CHICAGO, ILL. 60656

FIGURE B-3 Estimate Recapitulation. Source: Frank R. Walker Co., Chicago.

PRACTICAL
Form 514 MFD. IN U. S. A.

GENERAL ESTIMATE

BUILDING_____

LOCATION_____

ARCHITECTS_____

SUBJECT_____

ESTIMATE NO._____

SHEET NO._____

ESTIMATOR_____

CHECKER _____

DATE_____

FRANK R. WALKER CO., PUBLISHERS, CHICAGO

DESCRIPTION OF WORK	NO. PIECES	DIMENSIONS		EXTENSIONS	EXTENSIONS	TOTAL ESTIMATED QUANTITY	UNIT PRICE M'T'L	TOTAL ESTIMATED MATERIAL COST	UNIT PRICE LABOR	TOTAL ESTIMATED LABOR COST

FIGURE B-4 General Estimate. Source: Frank R. Walker Co., Chicago.

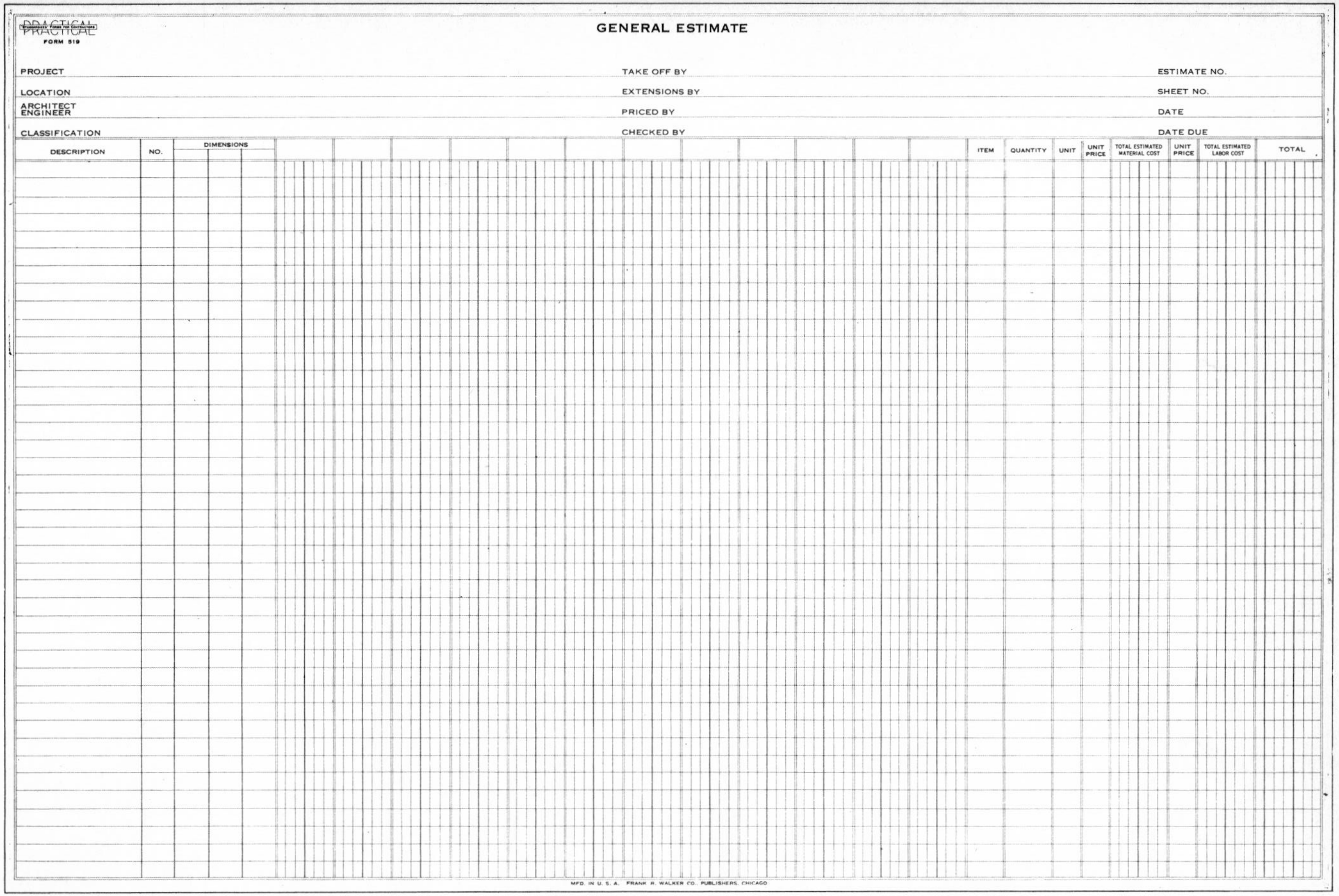
PRACTICAL
FORM 519

GENERAL ESTIMATE

PROJECT
TAKE OFF BY
ESTIMATE NO.
LOCATION
EXTENSIONS BY
SHEET NO.
ARCHITECT ENGINEER
PRICED BY
DATE
CLASSIFICATION
CHECKED BY
DATE DUE

DESCRIPTION	NO.	DIMENSIONS													ITEM	QUANTITY	UNIT	UNIT PRICE	TOTAL ESTIMATED MATERIAL COST	UNIT PRICE	TOTAL ESTIMATED LABOR COST	TOTAL

MFD. IN U. S. A. FRANK R. WALKER CO. PUBLISHERS, CHICAGO

FIGURE B-5 General Estimate (double width). Source: Frank R. Walker Co., Chicago.

PRACTICAL
FORM 115

SUMMARY OF ESTIMATE

BUILDING		LOCATION		ESTIMATE NO.
ARCHITECT		OWNER		DATE
CUBICAL CONTENTS	NO. OF STORIES	COST PER CUBIC FOOT		ESTIMATOR
FLOOR AREA, SQUARE FEET		COST PER SQUARE FOOT		CHECKER

CLASSIFICATION	TOTAL ESTIMATED MATERIAL COST	TOTAL ESTIMATED LABOR COST	TOTAL SUB-BIDS	TOTAL	ADJUSTMENTS
1. GENERAL CONDITIONS AND OVERHEAD EXPENSE					
2. PERMITS, INSURANCE, BONDS AND TAXES					
3. CONSTRUCTION PLANT, TOOLS AND EQUIPMENT					
4. WRECKING AND CLEARING SITE					
5. EXCAVATING AND PUMPING					
6. SHORING AND UNDERPINNING					
7. PILING OR CAISSONS					
8. FOUNDATIONS AND RETAINING WALLS					
9. WATER AND DAMPPROOFING					
10. CEMENT FLOORS, WALKS AND PAVEMENTS					
11. BRICK, TILE AND CONCRETE MASONRY					
12. CAST STONE, CUT STONE OR GRANITE					
13. TERRA COTTA					
14. ARCHITECTURAL CONCRETE					
15. REINFORCED CONCRETE					
16. TILE, GYPSUM OR CONCRETE BLOCK FIRE-PROOFING					
17. ROUGH CARPENTRY					
18. FINISH CARPENTRY					
19. WOOD FLOORS					
20. INSULATION, SOUND DEADENING, ACOUSTICAL TILE					
21. WEATHER STRIPS AND CAULKING					
22. LATHING AND PLASTERING					
23. FIRE DOORS AND WINDOWS					
24. HOLLOW METAL DOORS AND TRIM					
25. STEEL SASH, DOORS, PARTITIONS, SKYLIGHTS					
26. SHEET METAL WORK, SKYLIGHTS, FLASHINGS, ETC.					
27. ROOFING, BUILT-UP, TILE, SLATE, METAL					
28. TILE AND MOSAIC FLOORS, WALLS, STAIRS					
29. ASPHALT, CORK, LINOLEUM AND RUBBER TILE					
30. ART MARBLE AND SCAGLIOLA					
31. MARBLE AND SLATE					
32. GLASS AND GLAZING, STRUCTURAL GLASS					
33. PAINTING AND DECORATING					
34. STRUCTURAL IRON AND STEEL					
35. MISCELLANEOUS IRON AND STEEL					
36. ORNAMENTAL IRON, ALUMINUM, BRONZE, STEEL					
37. ROUGH HARDWARE					
38. FINISH HARDWARE					
39. PLUMBING, SEWERAGE AND GAS-FITTING					
40. VACUUM CLEANING SYSTEM					
41. HEATING AND VENTILATING					
42. AIR CONDITIONING					
43. POWER PLANT EQUIPMENT					
44. ELECTRIC AND POWER WIRING					
45. LIGHTING FIXTURES					
46. ELEVATORS, ESCALATORS, DUMB WAITERS					
47. AUTOMATIC SPRINKLER SYSTEM					
48. MAIL CHUTE					
49.					
50.					
51.					
52.					
53.					
54.					
55. TOTALS					
56.	TOTAL COST				
57.	PROFIT				
58.	SURETY BOND				
59.	AMOUNT OF BID				

MFD. IN U. S. A.

FRANK R. WALKER CO., PUBLISHERS, CHICAGO

FIGURE B-6   Summary of Estimate. Source: Frank R. Walker Co., Chicago.

PRACTICAL FORM 145

| NAME | | | LOCATION | | | | JOB NO. | | | | |

JOB ESTIMATE AND COST RECORD

CLASSIFICATION	CONTRACTOR	ESTIMATE AMOUNT	CONTRACT AMOUNT	CHANGES AMOUNT	PAYMENTS TO SUB-CONTRACTORS							ACTUAL COST
					DATE	AMOUNT	DATE	AMOUNT	DATE	AMOUNT		
1. SURVEY												
2. PLANS AND SPECIFICATIONS												
3. PERMITS												
4. EXCAVATION AND GRADING												
5. FOUNDATIONS												
6. DAMPPROOFING												
7. CEMENT FLOORS AND WALKS												
8. STRUCTURAL STEEL												
9. MISC. AND ORN. METAL												
10. MASONRY												
11. CARPENTER LABOR - ROUGH												
12. LUMBER - ROUGH												
13. CARPENTER LABOR - FINISH												
14. LUMBER - FINISH												
15. DOOR AND WINDOW FRAMES												
16. DOORS AND SASH												
17. DOOR AND WINDOW SCREENS												
18. STORM DOORS AND SASH												
19. GARAGE DOORS												
20. FINISH WOOD FLOORING												
21. WOOD STAIRS												
22. CABINETS												
23. HARDWARE - ROUGH												
24. HARDWARE - FINISH												
25. WEATHERSTRIPPING												
26. CAULKING												
27. SHEET METAL												
28. ROOFING - MATERIAL												
29. ROOFING - LABOR												
30. GLASS AND GLAZING												
31. INSULATION												
32. LATH AND PLASTER												
33. PAINTING AND DECORATING												
34. RESILIENT FLOORING												
35. CERAMIC TILE												
36. SHADES AND BLINDS												
37. BATHROOM ACCESSORIES												
38. MEDICINE CABINETS												
39. PLUMBING												
40. SEWER WORK												
41. HEATING												
42. AIR CONDITIONING												
43. ELECTRICAL WORK												
44. LIGHTING FIXTURES												
45. DRIVEWAY												
46. LANDSCAPING												
47.												
48.												
49.												
50.												
51.												
52.												
53.												
54.												
55.												
56.												
57.												
58.												
59.												
60.												
61.												
62.												
63.												
64.												
65.												
66.												
67.												
68.												
69.												
70.												
71. SUPERVISION												
72. TOOLS AND EQUIPMENT												
73. RUBBISH REMOVAL												
74. INSURANCE												
75. SOCIAL SECURITY TAXES												
76. TOTALS												
77. ESTIMATED BUILDING COST												
78. OVERHEAD AND PROFIT												
79. BUILDING CONTRACT												
80. CHANGES IN CONTRACT												
81. LOT												
82. LEGAL EXPENSES												
83. SALESMAN'S COMMISSION												
84. SELLING PRICE												

PURCHASER	DATE	ACTUAL BLDG. COST
	LOAN EXPENSES
ADDRESS	TEL. NO.	LOT COST
	LEGAL EXPENSES
PRICE	DOWN PAYMENT	SALES EXPENSES
	TOTAL ACTUAL COST
LOAN BY	SELLING PRICE
	PROFIT OR LOSS

CASH RECEIVED

RECEIVED FROM	AMOUNT DUE	DATE	FIRST	DATE	SECOND	DATE	THIRD	DATE	FOURTH	DATE	FIFTH	TOTAL
OWNER												
LOAN CO.												
TOTAL												

MFD. IN U.S.A.

FRANK R. WALKER CO., PUBLISHERS, CHICAGO

FIGURE B-7 Job Estimate and Cost Record. Source: Frank R. Walker Co., Chicago.

PRACTICAL FORM 550

ESTIMATE AND COST SUMMARY

PROJECT — ESTIMATOR — ESTIMATE NO.

LOCATION — EXTENSIONS — SHEET NO.

ARCHITECT ENGINEER — CHECKED — DATE

CLASSIFICATION

CODE	DESCRIPTION	ESTIMATED COST: MATERIAL: UNIT	QUANTITY	UNIT COST	AMOUNT	LABOR: HOURS	AMOUNT	SUB-CONTRACTS OTHER COSTS	TOTAL ESTIMATE	% COM-PLETED	ACTUAL COST: MATERIAL: QUANTITY USED	UNIT COST	AMOUNT	LABOR: HOURS	AMOUNT	SUB-CONTRACTS OTHER COSTS	TOTAL COST	PROFIT OR (LOSS)
	TOTALS																	

COMMENTS

MFD IN U S A FRANK R. WALKER CO. PUBLISHERS, CHICAGO COPYRIGHT 1965

FIGURE B-8 Estimate and Cost Summary. Source: Frank R. Walker Co., Chicago.

DAILY TIME SHEET

EMPLOYEE'S
NUMBER_____

NAME   DATE

NAME OF JOB	DESCRIPTION OF WORK	HOURS	RATE	AMOUNT

TIME AND JOBS CORRECT

REG.		O.T.		TOTALS		
F.I.C.A.		FED. INC. TAX		STATE INC. TAX		

PRACTICAL
STANDARDIZED FORMS FOR CONTRACTORS   FORM P-108   FOREMAN   BALANCE DUE
MFD. IN U.S.A.   FRANK R. WALKER CO., PUBLISHERS, CHICAGO

DAILY TIME SHEET   SHEET NO._____

JOB   DATE   JOB NO.

EMPLOYEE'S NAME	JOB OR DESCRIPTION OF WORK	HOURS	RATE	AMOUNT

PRACTICAL
STANDARDIZED FORMS FOR CONTRACTORS   TIME AND JOBS CORRECT   TOTALS
FORM P-109   FOREMAN
MFD. IN U.S.A.   FRANK R. WALKER CO. PUBLISHERS CHICAGO

FIGURE B-9   Daily Time Sheets. Source: Frank R. Walker
Co., Chicago.

LABOR DISTRIBUTION

'ob____________________ Sheet No.__________

Class of Work Week Ending Job No.

OCCUPATION								HOURS	RATE	AMOUNT
1										
2										
3										
4										
5										
6										
7										
8										
Total										

	Quantity Work in Place	Pay Roll Costs	Labor Average Unit Cost	Average Quantity Per 8 Hour Day	Quantity Work in Place	Pay Roll Costs	Labor Average Unit Cost	Average Quantity Per 8 Hour Day
Previous								
This Week								
Total								

FORM C-105 MFD. IN U. S. A. FRANK R WALKER CO., PUBLISHERS, CHICAGO (Over)

COST ANALYSIS RECORD

TOTAL LABOR HOURS UNIT

	1	2	3	4	5	6	7	8
Previous								
This Week								
Total								

LABOR HOURS PER UNIT UNIT

	1	2	3	4	5	6	7	8
Previous								
This Week								
Total								

REMARKS

PRACTICAL "STANDARDIZED" FORMS FOR CONTRACTORS

FORM C-105 MFD. IN U. S. A. FRANK R. WALKER CO. PUBLISHERS, CHICAGO

FIGURE B-10 Labor Distribution and Cost Analysis Record.
Source: Frank R. Walker Co., Chicago.

SELECTED BIBLIOGRAPHY

CONSTRUCTION

Dalzell, J. Ralph: *Simplified Masonry Planning and Building,* McGraw-Hill Book Company, New York, 1955.
———— and Gilbert Townsend: *Masonry Simplified,* 2d ed., vols. 1 and 2, American Technical Society, Chicago, 1956–1957.

Durbahn, Walter E., and Elmer W. Sundberg: *Fundamentals of Carpentry,* 4th ed., vol. 2, American Technical Society, Chicago, 1969.

Huntington, Whitney C.: *Building Construction,* 3d ed., John Wiley & Sons, Inc., New York, 1963.

Hurd, M. K.: *Formwork for Concrete,* 2d ed., American Concrete Institute, Detroit, 1969.

Merritt, Frederick S. (ed.): *Building Construction Handbook,* 2d ed., McGraw-Hill Book Company, New York, 1965.

Painting and Decorating Craftsman's Manual and Textbook, 4th ed., Painting and Decorating Contractors of America, Inc., Chicago, 1965.

Peurifoy, Robert L.: *Formwork for Concrete Structures,* McGraw-Hill Book Company, New York, 1964.

Ramsey, Charles G., and Harold R. Sleeper: *Architectural Graphic Standards,* 5th ed., John Wiley & Sons, Inc., New York, 1956.

Royer, King: *Desk Book for Construction Superintendents,* Prentice-Hall, Inc., Englewood Cliffs, N.J., 1967.

Voss, Walter C.: *Construction Management and Superintendence,* D. Van Nostrand Company Inc., Princeton, N.J., 1958.

CRITICAL PATH METHOD

Antill, James M., and Ronald W. Woodhead: *Critical Path Methods in Construction Practice,* John Wiley & Sons, Inc., New York, 1965.

Radcliffe, Byron M., et al.: *Critical Path Method,* Cahners Publishing Co., Inc., Chicago, 1957.

Shaffer, L. R., et al.: *The Critical Path Method,* McGraw-Hill Book Company, New York, 1965.

ESTIMATING

Godfrey, Robert S. (ed.): *Building Construction Cost Data,* Robert S. Means Co., Inc., Duxbury, Mass.

Peurifoy, Robert L.: *Estimating Construction Costs,* 2d ed., McGraw-Hill Book Company, New York, 1958.

Pulver, Harry E.: *Construction Estimates and Costs*, 4th ed., McGraw-Hill Book Company, New York, 1969.

Walker, Frank R.: *The Estimator's Reference Book*, 16th ed., Frank R. Walker Publishing Co., Chicago, 1967.

———: *Practical Accounting and Cost Keeping for Contractors*, 6th ed., Frank R. Walker Publishing Co., Chicago, 1968.

Index